KT-483-181

THE HISTORY of the Science FICTION MAGAZINE

03120937 | 813.
509
ASM

By the same author and available from Contemporary Books, Inc:

THE HISTORY OF THE SCIENCE FICTION MAGAZINE: Vol. 1 1926-1935
THE HISTORY OF THE SCIENCE FICTION MAGAZINE: Vol. 2 1936-1945

THE HISTORY of the Science FICTION MAGAZINE

Edited by Michael Ashley
Vol. 3 1946-1955

cbi Contemporary Books, Inc.
Chicago

UNIVERSITY OF WINCHESTER
LIBRARY

Introduction and Appendices, copyright © 1976 by Mike Ashley; used by permission of the author and the author's agent, Cosmos Literary Agency.

All rights reserved

First published in Great Britain in 1976 by
New English Library, London
First published in the United States in 1977 by
Contemporary Books, Inc.
180 North Michigan Avenue, Chicago, Illinois 60601
Printed in the United States of America
Library of Congress Catalog Card Number: 75-323228
International Standard Book Number: 0-8092-7842-1 (cloth)
0-8092-7841-3 (paper)

THE HISTORY OF THE SCIENCE FICTION MAGAZINE, VOL. 3
1946-1955

Introduction and Appendices, copyright © 1976 by Mike Ashley; used by permission of the author and the author's agent, Cosmos Literary Agency.

'Memorial' by Theodore Sturgeon, copyright © 1946 by Street & Smith Publications, Inc for *Astounding Science Fiction*, April 1946. Reprinted by permission of the author's agent, E. J. Carnell Literary Agency.

'The Fires Within' by Arthur C. Clarke, copyright © 1947 by Temple Bar Publishing Co, for *Fantasy*, August 1947. Reprinted by permission of the author and the author's agent, David Higham Associates Ltd.

'Don't Look Now' by Henry Kuttner, copyright © 1948 by Better Publications, Inc. for *Startling Stories*, March 1948. Reprinted by permission of the author's agent, A. D. Peters & Co Ltd.

'Kaleidoscope' by Ray Bradbury, copyright © 1949 by Better Publications, Inc, for *Thrilling Wonder Stories*, October 1949. Reprinted by permission of the author's agent, A. D. Peters & Co Ltd.

'To Serve Man' by Damon Knight, copyright © 1950 by Galaxy Publishing Corporation, for *Galaxy Science Fiction*, November 1950. Reprinted by permission of the author's agent, E. J. Carnell Literary Agency.

'Earthman, Beware!' by Poul Anderson, copyright © 1951 by Fictioneers Inc, for *Super Science Stories*, June 1951. Reprinted by permission of the author's agent, John Farquharson Ltd.

'They Fly so High' by Ross Rocklynne, copyright © 1952 by Ziff-Davis Publishing Co, for *Amazing Stories*, June 1952. Reprinted by arrangement with Forrest J. Ackerman.,

'The Last Day' by Richard Matheson, copyright © 1953 by Ziff-Davis Publishing Co, for *Amazing Stories*, May 1953. Reprinted by permission of the author's agent, A. D. Peters & Co Ltd.

'Hands Off' by Robert Sheckley, copyright © 1954 by Galaxy Publishing Corporation, for *Galaxy Science Fiction*, April 1954. Reprinted by permission of the author's agent A. D. Peters & Co Ltd.

'The Wager' by E. C. Tubb, copyright © 1955 by Nova Publications Ltd, for *Science Fantasy*, November 1955. Reprinted by permission of the author and the author's agent, E. J. Carnell Literary Agency.

Contents

Acknowledgements

While the drafting and compiling of this book has been my own responsibility, including any errors, it would have been a far harder task and a more meagre product had it not been for the invaluable assistance of many people. They include William L. Crawford, John Eggeling, Walter Gillings, Ejler Jakobsson, Sam Moskowitz, Frank Parnell, Hector R. Pessina, Richard S. Shaver, William F. Temple, J. Grant Thiessen, E. C. Tubb, Donald A. Wollheim, and above all Philip Harbottle for his knack for knowing the right things at the right time. To them, and any I may have unintentionally omitted, my sincere thanks.

To Walter Gillings
for his services to British science fiction

Preface

If you have also read Volumes 1 and 2 in this series, then there is little need to tell you my intentions, but I hope you read on all the same so that you may learn something about this volume. And, if you have not seen either of the previous books, then let me just explain.

Firstly, by science fiction magazines I do not mean comics. This is a common mistake, and one of the errors that has led the bona fide science fiction magazine a little nearer its ultimate demise. The science fiction (or sf) magazines, which first appeared in 1926, carried stories, not little cartoons with larger-than-life characters shouting in shorthand. Ten such stories, which reflect science fiction writing of the decade 1946 to 1955, are included in this anthology. They range from Theodore Sturgeon's 'Memorial', written as a direct consequence of the nuclear horrors of Hiroshima, to Richard Matheson's bizarre and compelling 'The Last Day'. Eight other leading authors are represented including Arthur Clarke, Robert Sheckley, Poul Anderson, Henry Kuttner and Damon Knight.

So that the stories can be viewed in perspective, and to give a better understanding of the much-scorned and often overlooked science fiction magazines, I have provided a comprehensive history of them during this decade. It follows on from the previous books though the history here differs in one respect from the others. In this instance I have worked into the body of my introduction valuable contributions from four of the leading personalities involved in the development of British science fiction: Kenneth Bulmer, Gordon Landsborough, Philip Harbottle and the late John Carnell. Each has provided a brief essay on the aspect of British sf with which he was closely associated and so gives a clear insight into the behind-the-scenes intrigue. All four essays appear here in print for the first time.

Also included is new background material behind the notorious Shaver Mystery never previously published. If you think Erich von Daniken has the last word in aliens visiting Earth, wait until you read Shaver's theories. I was in recent contact with Mr Shaver, who scrutinised and verified everything I wrote about him, only a matter of weeks before his death in November 1975.

There is also coverage of the birth of Scientology, and the works of its High Priest, L. Ron Hubbard.

The twists and turns of the evolution of science fiction following World War II is as unpredictable and fascinating as any thriller. That *all* of today's science fiction is dependent upon the development of the magazines and their contributors is proof of their importance. With this book I hope to preserve their memory so that the part they have played in twentieth-century literature will not be forgotten.

Mike Ashley
October 1975

Introduction:
From Bomb to Boom

1—INTO THE NUCLEAR AGE

'. . . You dreamed of life – a fuller life – for the world, but you would have given them, as you have just seen, death!'

'We will control it.'

'All men will have it – the best and the worst . . . and there is no defence.'

'It will free the world –'

'It will destroy it.'

Many of you may recall the above quote. It comes from the short story 'The Power and the Glory' by Charles Willard Diffin, and was reprinted in Volume 1 to represent 1930, the year when it appeared in *Astounding Stories*. Diffin perceptively voiced the fears of many: that the result of man conquering the atom would mean doom for mankind.

Fifteen years after that story was published those fears were no longer hypothetical. For six years the world had been witness to World War II. Then on Monday 6 August 1945, a nuclear bomb was exploded over Hiroshima, followed by a second over Nagasaki three days later. World War II came to an abrupt end – Japan surrendered within a week. The world was thrust into the nuclear age.

Writing in 1949, science fiction author Theodore Sturgeon revealed:

There is good reason to believe that, outside of the top men in the Manhattan District and in the Armed Forces, the only people in the world who fully understood what had happened on 6 August 1945, were the aficionados of science fiction – the fans, the editors and the authors. Hiroshima had a tremendous effect on me. I was familiar with nuclear phenomena; I sold a story in 1940 which dealt with a method of separating Isotope 235 from pure uranium. Years before the Project, and before the War, we had used up the gadgets and gimmicks of atomic power and were writing stories about the philosophical and sociological implications of this terrible new fact of life.[1]

That story of Sturgeon's, along with many like it, had been published in the science fiction magazines and read by the élite group of aficionados referred to above. Before the War, science fiction was scorned by academics as puerile escapism. With the advent of the nuclear age, the general public was suddenly made aware of scientific advances previously accepted as commonplace only by science fiction enthusiasts.

A certain amount of science fiction was appearing in book form, but even most of this had first been published in the science fiction (or sf, to use its most accepted abbreviation) magazines. Developments since the birth of the first, *Amazing Stories* in 1926, have already been traced, and I would advise the reader interested in further background detail to search out Volumes 1 and 2. In its first decade science fiction produced three leading magazines, all in America, where immigrant Hugo Gernsback, from Luxembourg, had first established *Amazing Stories*. When he lost control of this in 1929 he commenced publishing *Science Wonder Stories,* which metamorphosed to *Wonder Stories* in 1930. That same year pulp publisher William Clayton issued *Astounding Stories,* which lasted until 1933. In that year the title was purchased by one of America's foremost pulp publishing companies, Street & Smith. With F. Orlin Tremaine installed as editor, and with a brash new policy for exciting and original stories, *Astounding* was soon the leading publication. It was still at this pinnacle of popularity in 1937 when Tremaine handed over to the legendary John W. Campbell who pushed on to even greater heights. He cultivated talents like Isaac Asimov, Robert Heinlein, Theodore Sturgeon, A. E. van Vogt, L. Ron Hubbard, Fritz Leiber, L. Sprague de

Camp and Lester Del Rey. Nearly all of the major sf published between 1938 and 1945 appeared in its pages, including Asimov's *Foundation* series, Heinlein's 'Future History' stories, and Simak's *City* series.

Gernsback had left the sf field in 1936 and *Wonder Stories,* with a new publisher and a new editor, was now titled *Thrilling Wonder Stories.* It acquired a companion magazine, *Startling Stories,* and both angled their contents towards a more juvenile readership. So too did a revived *Amazing Stories,* also under new editorship, with its headquarters moved to Chicago. The year 1939 saw the start of a boom in science fiction pulp magazines. Many titles came and went but made little lasting impression. The War and subsequent paper and ink restrictions resulted in the death of many sf titles. By the winter of 1945–6 only six science fiction magazines in America survived. They were *Amazing Stories, Astounding SF, Thrilling Wonder, Startling Stories, Famous Fantastic Mysteries* (which relied heavily on nostalgia by reprinting old classics) and *Planet Stories* (which concentrated entirely on interplanetary tales with a very juvenile slant). There were also two borderline publications, *Fantastic Adventures* (a companion to *Amazing*) and *Weird Tales* (the major American weird fiction magazine which had survived since 1923 and featured much science fiction). Just how the advent of the nuclear age would affect these magazines and thereby the course of science fiction over the next ten years is the subject of this volume.

The science fiction fraternity generally looked toward *Astounding* for new trends. Most of the other publications, especially *Amazing* and *Planet,* put their emphasis on escapist adventure. Not so *Astounding,* whose stable of mature authors under the ever-watchful eye of John W. Campbell (1910–71) was continually extending the boundaries of science fiction into new territories. Readers already considered the nuclear bomb subject to be out-of-date. Still fresh in their memories was the episode over 'Deadline', a short, unexceptional story written by Cleve Cartmill and published in the March 1944 issue. The story dealt with an agent's attempts to stop the detonation of a nuclear device. Military Intelligence descended on Campbell and Cartmill charging them with violation of security, but both were able to prove that the story was constructed from information readily available in any public library. Science fiction took one further step up the ladder of respectability.

In fact Campbell was often told by the authorities to restrict the number and content of nuclear stories he published, but he refused. However, by 1946 there was no further need for secrecy: the nuclear bomb was now science fact. So Campbell urged his writers to explore the *consequences* of the nuclear age. The devastation of Hiroshima and Nagasaki had shocked the world. Even the sf fraternity, which had envisaged such results, had never really been prepared for the horrors of reality. And with those horrors fresh in mind the writers launched themselves vigorously into a new spate of atomic-warning stories.

Certainly one of the very earliest to appear in print was Theodore Sturgeon's 'Memorial', published in the April 1946 *Astounding*. Sturgeon called for the establishment of a perpetual memorial to warn future generations of the horrors of a nuclear war. Shortly afterwards he wrote 'Thunder and Roses' (*Astounding,* November 1947), which tells of a United States ravaged by nuclear attack and how one man prevents the firing of retaliatory missiles so that future generations could survive. In a two-sided atomic contest, there could be no survivors.

To some extent the real horror of the Bomb was dampened by the overwhelming relief that the War had ended. Several writers took it upon themselves to shock their readers into realising the full consequences of total nuclear war. The May 1946 *Amazing* featured Rog Phillips's 'Atom War'. In this story the United States is attacked by a mythical country which threatens to bomb major cities. Australia aids America only to be bombed out of existence. Total war follows. It lasts only fifteen hours before the mythical foe is destroyed, but in that time seventy-five million Americans alone are killed. Phillips produced a sequel, 'So Shall Ye Reap!' (*Amazing,* August 1947) which explores the War's after-effects and describes how the radioactive fall-out had produced mutations, in this instance a new race of super-beings.

The mutative effect of atomic radiation became a popular theme in sf immediately after the War. It served as the background to Poul Anderson's first sale, 'Tomorrow's Children' (*Astounding,* March 1947), wherein a team of scientists are hunting down mutants, and its sequel, 'Logic', which develops the consequences further. Henry Kuttner in particular took the theme to heart. 'Way of the Gods' (*Thrilling Wonder,* April

1947), wherein mutants sprout wings and are hunted down and exterminated as freaks, received much acclaim. *Thrilling Wonder* for August 1947 included 'Atomic!', another story by Kuttner, wherein a Final War, lasting three hours, leaves behind hundreds of deadly rings, shunned by the survivors and found to be housing some bizarre forms of sentient life. That same issue contained a second Kuttner story, 'Dark Dawn' under his Keith Hammond alias. In that story radiation has threatened the life of a race of sea-beings.

The July 1947 *Astounding* carried 'The Figure' by Edward Grendon, which despite its brevity (barely 2000 words), creates a tremendous impact. It follows on immediately from the effects of radiation on insect life after the New Mexico and Japanese bombings. Giant insects begin to appear, and when two scientists experimenting with time-probes succeed in retrieving an artifact from the future, they are horrified to discover it is a statue with obvious religious overtones, and that it is the figure of a beetle. It was seven years before Hollywood realised the potential of such stories and made the film *Them!* (1945) – about giant insects that appeared in the Mojave Desert. As usual, sf magazines had been first with the idea.

Within a year or two of Hiroshima, the sf writers had explored the whole area of atomic-warning stories. Indeed the field was saturated, and editors called for cessation, although some such stories would still appear sporadically over the ensuing years. 'Nuclear' science fiction was well under way, and it would soon be seen that, as the Bomb had exploded, within a few years the science fiction field would also explode.

The difference between the leading magazines after the War was fairly evident. *Astounding,* still deftly controlled by John W. Campbell, was superior in quality. Published by Street & Smith Publications of East 42nd Street, New York, it had been the only sf magazine to maintain a monthly schedule throughout the War, having countered the paper restrictions firstly by sacrificing its legendary companion, *Unknown Worlds,* and secondly by changing its format from standard pulp size (7 x 10 in) to digest size ($5\frac{1}{2}$ x 8 in) from November 1943. Being the only digest-sized sf periodical on the stands, which were stacked with other pulp magazines, this format gave it a more distinguished and mature appearance, enhanced all the more by William Timmins's tastefully executed covers.

Meanwhile, *Astounding*'s nearest rival, *Thrilling Wonder*

Stories, was improving with every issue. This, together with *Startling Stories,* was published by Standard Publications of East 40th Street, New York, and the newly acquired editor of both was Samuel Merwin, who was the same age as Campbell. Under the previous editors, Mort Weisinger and Oscar J. Friend, the emphasis had slanted more towards juvenile readership. Their covers had been among the gaudiest, and were the work of Earle K. Bergey. He more than any other artist became associated with the 'Bug-Eyed Monster' stigma: that is, some bizarre, pop-eyed, alien creature bent on absconding with a beautiful, brass-bra'd blonde despite the heroics of her human protector. Merwin strove to raise the status of both magazines, particularly *Thrilling Wonder,* by improving both story quality and presentation. Although limited by the pulp format, he nevertheless began to acquire some improved Bergey covers such as that illustrating Kuttner's 'Way of the Gods'. He purchased fiction by *Astounding's* leading writers, like Murray Leinster, George O. Smith and L. Sprague de Camp, and by 1946–7 science fiction readers no longer considered his magazines juvenile.

A reliable regular was *Famous Fantastic Mysteries* published by All-Fiction Field Inc, a subsidiary of Popular Publications, the largest chain of pulp publishers. It was edited by Mary Gnaedinger, affectionately known as 'The Queen of Science Fiction', from offices in East 42nd Street, just up the road from Campbell's. *Famous Fantastic Mysteries* (called FFM for convenience) was essentially a reprint magazine, using as a storehouse the vast piles of science fiction published in *Argosy* and *All-Story* over the last forty years. In recent months it had changed policy slightly to include reprinting scarce novels which had hitherto had only a minor US book distribution. As a source of 'lost' sf and fantasy by great names like Rider Haggard, William Hope Hodgson, S. Fowler Wright and John Taine, it was indispensable.

Planet Stories was the undoubted home of 'space opera', publishing nothing but interplanetary stories, many of which were straight escapism. It emanated from Fiction House in Eighth Avenue, New York, and was generally managed by Malcolm Reiss, although the bulk of the editorial work in April 1946, as we begin this survey, had just changed hands from Chester Whitehorne to Paul Payne. *Planet* was exceptional in that among its general space adventures could be found some astonishing works. Stories by Ray Bradbury, including many of his *Martian Chronicle* series, plus ingenious tales by Leigh Brackett and Fredric Brown ensured the capture of a ready audience.

At the close of 1945 all of these magazines, except *Astounding,* maintained a regular quarterly schedule. (*Astounding*'s stable-mate, *Doc Savage,* which carried a lead novel concerning that character's bizarre adventures, was also monthly). Most of the magazines took a year or two to re-establish themselves and increase their appearances, but one magazine shot back to a monthly schedule almost overnight, and before the end of 1946 was a circulation leader. That magazine was *Amazing Stories,* and how it did it was the sensation of the decade. To the sf world it brought more shudders than the thought of the atom bomb – it was the Shaver Mystery.

2—A PHENOMENON CALLED SHAVER

The Shaver Mystery, or Shaver Hoax as it was later termed, really started before the end of the War, and was in full gallop by VJ Day. The complete true story has not been told, and this volume includes some revelations never previously in print about this astonishing incident. First let me simply present the facts.

In September 1943, Raymond Palmer, *Amazing*'s editor, received a letter from Richard Sharpe Shaver, who lived in Barto, Pennsylvania. It presented the key to an ancient alphabet which Shaver claimed was the mother tongue of all languages – Mantong. Palmer published the letter in the January 1944 *Amazing* and it brought a healthy response from readers. Palmer struck up correspondence with Shaver, then a welder in a war plant, for he had previously smashed his ankle in a fall on board ship and was consequently unfit to be drafted during the War. Palmer asked Shaver to write for him, and he obliged with a novelette entitled 'Warning to Future Man'. The submission was apparently first seen by *Amazing*'s managing editor, Howard Browne, who took one look at it and threw it into the wastepaper basket, and is quoted as crying, '. . . what a crackpot that guy is!' Palmer, always the seeker after anything sensational, decided to challenge Browne's opinion. Before even *reading* the manuscript he determined to print it and find the readership's opinion of Shaver. 'Warning to Future Man' was set long before the Flood, in the first great civilisation of Earth, which Shaver called Atlan. It was related by Mutan Mion, the last Earthman to leave this planet when the Titans migrated, and involved a battle between two factions, an evil Titan named Zeit, and a good Titan goddess, Vanue. Palmer slightly reworked the story, changed the title to ' "I Remember Lemuria!" ' and surprised *Amazing*'s public with it in March 1945. The result was phenomenal, and the Shaver Mystery began. But Palmer was fortunate in that something happened coincidentally at Ziff-Davis over which he had no control.

Paper restrictions had inevitably led to a scarcity of reading matter, so whatever was put on the stalls sold. Harold G. Strong, the circulation director for Ziff-Davis, decided it was pointless spreading the paper out over four magazines, when two would sell as well. So the kiss of death was given to *Mammoth Detective* and *Mammoth Mystery,* then edited by Howard Browne, and this obviously did not endear Palmer to Browne. Strong then arranged an additional 50,000 copies of *Amazing* to be printed and distributed. These sold out, and by chance Strong's decision coincided with that March 1945 issue. Reaching a greater audience, and one wearied with War, Shaver's fantastic theories struck a responsive chord. *Amazing,* which generally received about forty to fifty letters a month, suddenly received over two and a half thousand! Palmer saw he was on to a winner, and admitted he had no idea why – but why look a gift horse in the mouth? He secured more stories from Shaver, plus associated articles, and everything snowballed. *Amazing*'s circulation continued to rise, and before long other publications became interested.

The slick *Harper's* magazine for September 1946 carried an article, 'Little Superman, What Now?' by William S. Baring-Gould, which derided the whole Shaver Mystery as the mouthings of crackpots. Palmer instantly responded supporting the Mystery. Naturally such publicity was just what he was after: if a book is banned, its sales zoom. So, with the Shaver Mystery, the more its scandal was broadcast, the more *Amazing*'s circulation rose. And it was rumoured that Ziff gave Palmer a substantial raise in salary as a result of the sales figures.

So what was this Mystery? Why did it cause such a sensation? Who was Richard Shaver?

Richard Shaver was born on Tuesday 8 October 1907 in Berwick, Pennsylvania. His father was a pressman – he pressed the first parts for the first steel passenger coach ever made. His mother was an ex-schoolteacher, who wasted no time in giving her five children plenty of pre-school teaching. She was also a notable poet, selling verse to such high-class publications as *Ladies Home Journal* and *Good Housekeeping*. When Shaver was eleven, the family moved to Bloomsburg, where for a while his father owned a restaurant. His formal education over, Shaver filled in a variety of jobs ranging from being foreman in a landscaping company to art instructor.

The Mystery began one evening when he was reading Lord Byron's poem 'Manfred', and came to the line 'By a power to thee unknown, Thou canst never be alone'. Was he really not alone, Shaver thought. Then, somehow, he received visions until suddenly the reception was cut off dead, as if something had deliberately intercepted it.

This incident continued to prey on Shaver's mind. One day, while he was working in Illinois, and whilst thumbing a lift back to Pennsylvania, he was picked up for vagrancy and thrown in gaol. He tried to make contact as before, with the plea, 'Get me out of here.' Shaver takes up the story:

> What happens is a girl comes leading the turnkey, who acts like he is walking in his sleep. He turns the key and lets me go. She leads us both down the hall to the outer door, which he again opens and we both walked out. I followed her with somewhat mixed and numb sensations, for about a mile in the night outside of the town. Then we walked into a hill – a section of the hill closed down behind us very like 'Sesame, close!', and we were in. A lot of stairways and slopes and dim light, and all the time I knew 'she' was just a sort of transparent projection, but you had to get close to see the difference from real.
>
> And so I was in. I spent a day or so talking with them, and they filled me in on the whole complex situation inherited from our misguided forebears who kept the secret so well that today nobody knows anything about their past. Between us we decided something should be done about the situation of ignorance. I was there for only twenty-four hours or so, when I walked out and went on my way. Later I began to write fir tion about it.

In the fiction, Shaver claimed that, many centuries ago, Earth was inhabited by several races, including two super-beings, the Titans and the Atlans. Both were godlike immortals with tremendous civilisations. Over a period, it was discovered the sun was emitting harmful radiation. The super-beings built vast caverns underground in an effort to escape the rays, and established their cities full of mighty machinery miles under the surface. But the harmful radiation still affected them; they aged too quickly and died. Abandoning their mighty civilisation, they left the Earth, and the inferior race of humans that remained found their way into the cave network, and discovered the machinery. They interfered with the unknown power, releasing harmful rays which changed some of them into evil degenerates. This breed Shaver called 'dero' (detrimental robot), as they utilised the machines to emit further harmful rays and so influenced the thoughts of those living on the surface. There was also the race of 'tero', who were good in intent, but it was the 'dero' that caused the major sensation to sf readers.

Shaver maintained that deep under the Earth's surface, in the caverns, 'deros' continued to operate and that the rays were the cause of all the evil intentions in this world. Various rays are used, notably the 'telaug' (telepathic augmentor), one which enables contact between the caves and the surface. (Shaver's means of contact) It is the 'dero' that has given rise to legends such as little people, gremlins, demons and devils. They cause all accidents, wrecks, crashes and other inexplicable disasters. Furthermore, Shaver stated that the Titans have kept watch on Earth and on occasions return, kidnapping people and raiding the caves for equipment. This would account for many mysterious disappearances, and also for the strange unidentified flying object sightings. Shaver's theories thereby provided reasons for just about any 'inexplicable' occurrence.

In his stories, Shaver related many past happenings. After '"I Remember Lemuria!"' came 'Thought Records of Lemuria' (June 1945). The thought records are metallic strips of film on which thoughts are recorded, and so the listener can experience reliving them. These records are played back to Shaver from the caves via the 'telaug'.

The stories were entertaining, although very basically written, and if they had been regarded only as fiction, events may not have snowballed. But the sf fraternity became incensed because critics might be regarding the Shaver sensation as the best science fiction, and viewing all sf in that light. They were further angered because the stories were being boldly presented as fact, with the result that outsiders were viewing all of the sf world as crackpots. Before the end of 1945 there was a 'war' taking place between Palmer and sf fandom.

Did Shaver intend the stories to be presented as fact, or was this a stunt on Palmer's side to boost circulation?

Firstly Shaver is as adamant today as he was then that the basis for all the stories was true. Palmer had initially not known what to believe, but the subsequent influx of thousands of letters from readers supporting Shaver had convinced Palmer of there being some grain of truth in the matter. By late 1946 Palmer admitted there must be a basis for truth; he visited Shaver and heard the strange voices himself. But how does one reconcile the facts when you find an exasperated Palmer writing in 1955: 'Lissen! (sic) I usually plotted Shaver's stories. Much of his 'mystery' is right out of my head.'[2]

Actually, it is possible to trace a parallel between Shaver's Mystery, and H. P. Lovecraft's own fictional Cthulhu Mythos. Lovecraft has the Earth once inhabited by the Ancient Ones, a hostile, supernatural species, who are overpowered and banished by a benign race, the Elder Gods. Ignorant mortals, tampering with the restraints sometimes, open up the way for the Old Ones to come back. Could this have influenced Shaver? It is possible Shaver had never come across Lovecraft's stories, although by the early 1940s most were in book form, and Shaver has admitted to being a voracious reader. Certainly Palmer had read them in their original appearances in *Weird Tales*, and he may well have worked themes into Shaver's submissions. But again Shaver denies any such machinations. He claims all that Palmer did was tone down the sex element in the fiction.

It is fascinating to speculate. Particularly today, in the light of further research by people like Erich von Daniken and Peter Kolosimo. For instance in von Daniken's book, *The Gold of the Gods* (1972), he discusses at length a vast series of underground caverns in South America obviously constructed by an advanced race many hundreds of years ago. Could these be those same caverns left by the Titans? Lack of space forbids too much discussion of the Shaver Mystery, although this is not the last you'll see of it in this volume. I hope it has whetted your appetite to look further into the Shaver writings and decide for yourself just what is the truth behind it all.

The Shaver incident might have alienated fans, but in other ways it helped sf greatly. *Amazing*'s circulation was boosted and both it and *Fantastic Adventures* were soon back on a monthly schedule. The magazines were able to pay top rates, and this thus enabled its publisher to experiment further in the approaching years. Shaver wrote other stories besides his Mystery. Several worthy fantasies appeared in *Fantastic Adventures* as well as historical stories in *Mammoth Adventure*.

Fortunately, Palmer did not devote *Amazing* entirely to Shaver, although there was a special Shaver edition in June 1947, containing four lengthy stories by Shaver plus a complete run-down on the Mystery at that stage. Palmer continued to present other stories by well-known authors. He also helped new figures, notably Rog Phillips, the more familiar pseudonym of writer Roger Phillips Graham (1909-65). Within a year or two of his first story. 'Let Freedom Ring' (*Amazing,* December 1945), he was appearing under some twenty pseudonyms with scores of stories. He could also be found avidly supporting the Shaver Mystery, and discovering a bizarre book, *Oahpse*, purported to be written in 1882 by intelligent beings thousands of years old.

Then there was Chester S. Geier, who first appeared in the December 1942 *Amazing* with 'The Sphere of Sleep', when he was just twenty-one. Geier was apparently stone deaf, but this was by no means detrimental to his writings. He was skilful and had polish, but wasted this on hack-work, though his stories were usually average for *Amazing*. Geier involved himself deeply with the Mystery. He organised the Shaver Mystery Club, and became editor of *The Shaver Mystery Magazine* which serialised Shaver's 'Mandark', a story set at the time of Christ, which even Palmer considered too taboo to publish. Geier collaborated with Shaver on some stories, as he was quicker at assembling the final manuscript. He also completed a fantasy written by Shaver's elder brother, Taylor Victor Shaver, who had died of influenza before finishing it; that story, 'The Strange Disappearance of Guy Sylvester', was finally published in the March 1949 *Amazing*.

Two other newcomers to Palmer's coterie were the Livingston brothers, Berkeley and Herb. Herb, the younger brother by eight years, wrote most of his fiction under the alias H. B. Hickey, and his stories still appear on occasions today, although Berkeley has long since left the sf scene.

Old faithfuls appeared in *Amazing* with less regularity during this period, but a major landmark was the publication, in September 1947, of the complete version of Edmond Hamilton's *The Star Kings*. This 75,000 word novel introduced Hamilton's character, John Gordon, who was summoned from two hundred thousand years in the future to exchange bodies with Zarth Arn, prince of the Mid-Galactic Empire.

The Shaver Mystery reached its height during 1947. Then the management at Ziff-Davis began to listen to complaints that it was unscientific, against all scientific laws. Hitherto they had been content to let Palmer do what he wanted, but after these claims, they looked deeper into what was going on and asked Palmer to soft-pedal it. The Mystery was dropped from the March 1948 issue, but it was far from ended and his fiction continued to appear. This time marked the start of Palmer's separation from *Amazing Stories* and science fiction.

3—BACK IN BRITAIN

Unlike the United States, Britain had no science fiction magazines at the close of World War II. Three publications had existed previously. A rather juvenile weekly, *Scoops,* had appeared briefly in 1934, and was best forgotten. Then Ilford fan, Walter Gillings, succeeded in interesting *World's Work* Publishers to include a science fiction title in their *Master Thriller* series, and *Tales of Wonder* was born in the summer of 1937. After the first trial issue it followed a regular quarterly schedule, and in 1938 its first competitor, *Fantasy,* was published by Newnes, who had been toying with the idea for several years. *Fantasy* only lasted three issues. Because of the War, its editor, T. Stanhope Sprigg who was in the RAF Reserves, was mobilised, and with his departure the magazine died. *Tales of Wonder* became progressively thinner, but survived for sixteen issues before it went under in Spring 1942.

Walter Gillings was in the army, but only for a short while. Suffering from a psychoneurosis he was back in 'civvy street' in 1944 and teamed up with an old friend, Benson Herbert. Herbert had sold several stories to Gernsback's *Wonder Stories* since 1931, including a novel, *The Perfect World,* which in 1936 saw an English hardback edition as *Crisis! – 1992*. He also had a Master of Science degree for radio research. In 1944 he organised Utopian Publications Ltd, with Walter Gillings as director, and they began to issue small, cheaply printed booklets, starting with *Girl in Trouble* by E. Frank Parker. With paper so scarce the situation was the same as in America : any printed matter for sale went instantly, no matter what. Herbert and Gillings had no trouble selling their publications, especially as they often sported nude damsels on the covers, yet there was little new material – it was mostly American reprints. In some cases the collections could be viewed as reprint magazines, in particular *Strange Tales,* which saw two issues in February and March 1946. Containing first class material by writers like Ray Bradbury, Clark Ashton Smith, Robert Bloch, John Beynon (Wyndham) and others, they sold out immediately and are now valuable collectors items.

By 1946, with the War at last just a bad memory, publishers were trying to re-establish themselves, even though paper restrictions were as stringent as ever. Since any printed matter sold, it could be expected that much that was bad would appear as well as anything good. Science fiction suffered in this way. During 1946 the London publishers, Hamilton & Co, produced a handful of large-size, infantile magazines. *Strange Adventures* appeared first and featured three stories by gangster writer, N. Wesley Firth, who knew next to nothing about science fiction. A companion, *Futuristic Stories,* followed and both saw second issues later that year. Then, thankfully, they ceased. Anyone experiencing sf for the first time in those issues can be forgiven for thinking it nothing but puerile rubbish! Hopefully they spotted *New Worlds* first.

Edward John Carnell (1912–71) had at last been lucky. As long ago as 1940 he had been involved in negotiations to pro-duce a professional sf magazine, but it never materialised. Then in January 1946, just out of the army, Carnell met his old friend, Frank Edward Arnold, in London. Arnold had just interested a small-time publisher in bringing out a series of science fiction titles. He took Carnell round to meet him, to-gether with Carnell's prospectus for the still-born *New Worlds*. The publishers were Pendulum Publications, and the man in charge was Stephen Frances, later better known as the original 'Hank Janson'. Frances was most enthusiastic and overcame the problems involved with paper and printing. Carnell had soon assembled the first issue and *New Worlds,* subtitled 'Fiction of the Future', hit the stands in July, priced 2/-. It carried as a lead novelette, 'The Mill of the Gods' by Maurice G. Hugi (1904–47), and the intriguing fantasy, 'The Three Pylons' by William F. Temple, whose classic, 'The 4-Sided Triangle' was included in Volume 2 of this series. The rest of the issue consisted of four stories written by Britain's most prolific sf writer, John Russell Fearn, 'The Blackpool Wonder', who featured prominently in the American fiction scene between 1933 and 1946.

Sales of that first issue proved disastrous: 3000 only out of a print run of 15,000. Carnell felt the fault was partly Pendulum's lassitude, and partly the drab cover illustration by Pendulum artist Robert Wilkin. Carnell himself designed the cover for number two, and the final illustration was the work of Victor Caesari. It was a spaceship scene concocted from two old American magazine covers. On sale in October, the issue was a sell-out, and Pendulum showed some enterprise by removing the Wilkin cover from the unsold first issue and replacing it with the Caesari. Back on the stalls these also sold out, which means that collectors have to beware of which first issue they have. If it features the Caesari cover then it is not *the* first issue.

New Worlds was well and truly off the ground and plans went ahead for number three. Sf enthusiasts were further encouraged when, before Christmas 1946, two more magazines had appeared. Firstly, in October, coincidental with the second *New Worlds,* came a diminutive publication called *Outlands,* 'A Magazine for Adventurous Minds'. Its somewhat pastoral cover, all in blue with an inset river scene, would hardly have caught the eye of the sf fan. What would though would be the boast 'Pre-Natal' by John Russell Fearn spread along the top border. Once again the ubiquitous Fearn was in print, this time nearer to home.

Outlands was edited by Leslie J. Johnson from his home in Liverpool. Johnson, as you may recall from Volume 2, was instrumental in forming the British Interplanetary Society in 1933. He had earlier worked on sf stories with John Russell Fearn and Eric Frank Russell, the high spot of which was the publication of his Russell collaboration, 'Seeker of Tomorrow', in *Astounding* in 1937 (which story was also reprinted in the previous volume). With *Outlands,* he presented a mature magazine with highly readable fantasy fiction by names like Charnock Walsby, George C. Wallis (a real veteran amongst

British writers), and Sydney J. Bounds, whose first sale, 'Strange Portrait' (a kind of latter-day Dorian Gray) appeared here. The issue also contained an obituary to H. G. Wells, who had died on 13 August 1946, just a month before his eightieth birthday. The man who almost single-handedly had popularised science fiction in Britain and had once dreamed of the wonder science could bring, had lived to see the horrors of the atom bomb. His passing firmly brought to a close the days of old and opened the curtains on the nuclear age.

A second issue of *Outlands* was advertised as forthcoming in December, but it never appeared as the main distribution channels refused to handle it. Nevertheless in that same month, devotees would find the first issue of *Fantasy*.

This was not the rebirth of Newnes's pre-War *Fantasy*. Digest-sized, with a very neat presentation, this was the product of Walter Gillings, and was published by Temple Bar Publishing Company in Store Street, London. Gillings had been preparing for the magazine since 1943 and had already collected enough material for nine issues. With *New Worlds* selling well, Temple Bar went ahead with the first *Fantasy* which also sold out. Here again was John Russell Fearn, with the lead story 'Last Conflict', and more notably Arthur C. Clarke with 'Technical Error'.

Arthur C. Clarke had had a couple of science articles published in *Tales of Wonder* before the War. Conscripted into the RAF in 1941 Clarke became involved with the trial experiments for radar and later sold a short article to *Wireless World*, entitled 'Extra-Terrestrial Relays', which postulated three satellites in Earth orbit being used for global television. Seventeen years later Telstar became a reality. When Clarke learned Gillings was requesting material for a new magazine he sent a batch of stories along, several of which Gillings bought. As time passed and *Fantasy* still had not appeared Gillings returned certain stories and suggested that Clarke try selling them to the States. He did. John W. Campbell purchased two for *Astounding:* 'Loophole', which appeared in April 1946, and the now famous 'Rescue Party' (May 1946), wherein aliens explore a vacated Earth hours before the sun goes nova.

A second *Fantasy* appeared in April 1947, leading with Eric Frank Russell's fascinating story, 'Relic', which tells of the landing on Earth of an ancient spaceship and the subsequent explorations of its robot occupant. Clarke was also present with a short story, 'Castaway', under the pen-name Charles Willis. He used another pen-name, E. G. O'Brien, for his story 'The Fires Within', which is included in this volume, and was originally published in the third *Fantasy* of August 1947 – the last issue. Although each had been a sell-out it was discontinued because the paper restrictions forced its publishers to concentrate on more lucrative publications.

The science fiction public was also at a loss to account for *New Worlds*. Where was it? The first two issues had appeared in quick succession, yet now, a year later, nothing else had been seen. Finally, at the end of October 1947 number three limped to the stalls. Pendulum had run into financial problems and were now in receivership, yet even though issue three sold out immediately, there was no respite. It included a lead short novel, 'Dragon's Teeth', by John K. Aiken, plus 'Fantasia Dementia', Maurice Hugi's last story, for he died early in 1947 aged only forty-three. Arthur Clarke's alias, Charles Willis, was again present with 'Inheritance'. This brief story, which told of a son living out the future his father had foreseen, was also bought by John W. Campbell for *Astounding*. Now that magazine boasted a no-reprint policy, and the appearance of 'Inheritance' in September 1948 marks the *only* occasion that *Astounding* printed a story which had seen previous publication! Clarke was under way with an auspicious start.

As a result of the publishing setback, science fiction in Britain was bleak by Christmas 1947, even though, ironically, British editions of American magazines continued. Two haphazardly compiled reprint issues of *Amazing Stories* had appeared during the winter of 1946–7. A fairly regular *Astounding* had been on the market since 1939, as had *Astounding's* erstwhile companion, *Unknown*. This was the work of Britain's most methodical distributor, Atlas Publishing Co, who trimmed down the number of stories in the British edition and thus kept it going long after its mother edition had folded. When eventually Atlas ran out of stories after forty-one issues, they began a much-needed British edition of *Thrilling Wonder*. So even with no *Fantasy* or *New Worlds,* fans unable to acquire the original American editions could satiate their appetites somewhat with abbreviated anglicised versions.

4—THE BOOM BEGINS

The United States found itself back to normal before Great
Britain. Concurrent with the temporary slump in Britain,
ripples began to show on the American science fiction sea.
Already *Amazing* was back on a monthly schedule, and by the
end of 1946 all other publications were appearing alternate
months, bar *Planet Stories,* which had always been a quarterly.

Then in February 1947 a brand new magazine appeared on
the stands, the first new American sf periodical since *Uncanny
Stories* had come and gone with one issue in April 1941. The
title was *Fantasy Reader,* though so closely linked is its name
with that of the publishers, Avon Books of West 57th Street,
New York, that it is usually referred to as *Avon Fantasy
Reader.* One could argue that it was more of a regular paperback anthology, which is what editor Donald Wollheim called
it in his introduction to number one, but over its lifetime it was
accepted as a magazine. It was unusual since it was digest-sized,
printed with a laminated cover, and priced at thirty-five cents.
Hitherto the dearest sf magazines, *Astounding* and *Amazing,*
had only been twenty-five cents, with others as low as fifteen!
That *Fantasy Reader* sold was evidence of a hungry readership.

Donald Wollheim was the ideal editor for such a project.
He had already achieved much in the popularisation of sf in
his guise as editor of the first ever paperback science fiction
anthology. *The Pocket Book of Science Fiction* had been
published in May 1943 by Pocket Books Inc, of New York,
and was a huge success. It had included ten stories ranging
from Stephen Vincent Benet's 'By The Waters of Babylon' from
the *Saturday Evening Post,* to 'A Martian Odyssey' by Stanley
G. Weinbaum from *Wonder Stories.* The sf magazines were
well represented, half of the stories having originated therein,
three in *Astounding.*

In 1946 Wollheim was working for A. A. Wyn's 'Ace' pulp
magazines, but he wrote to Avon Books to see if they were
interested in adding a fantasy title to their present series of
mystery and western imprints. The editor, Herbert Williams,
was most enthusiastic, and contracted Wollheim to compile a
Fantasy Reader. There was no set periodicity; once the
previous issue had broken even, the next was published.
Fantasy Reader's success was such that Wollheim accepted an

invitation to join Avon's staff. Shortly thereafter Williams resigned and Wollheim became editor of the entire Avon range.

For *Fantasy Reader* he exercised that same expertise of choice as he had with his anthologies. The first led with Murray Leinster's classic of space station intrigue, 'The Power Planet', from the June 1931 *Amazing*. Also present were William Hope Hodgson, A. Merritt, H. G. Wells, August Derleth, Clark Ashton Smith, H. Russell Wakefield and Lord Dunsany; a stellar cast, with fiction ranging from hard science to bizarre ghosts. By the end of the first year, after four publications, Wollheim had managed to reprint a superb cross-section of all the top names and acknowledged classics in the fields of science fiction, fantasy and horror, and *Fantasy Reader* was already becoming a much sought-after magazine.

By the summer of 1947 it had two rivals, whose competitive values were minimal, but they marked a difference. Hitherto sf magazines had emanated from either New York or Chicago, but these came from the American West Coast.

The Vortex was a very high-class, professional-looking magazine. It was joint-edited from San Francisco by two fans, Gordon M. Kull and George R. Cowie, who issued and distributed this speciality *free*! A leaflet enclosed requested that if any reader felt so inclined a donation of twenty cents would be gratefully received. Eighty digest pages carried some five stories, plus a poem and articles. Fiction was split between fantasy and sf, though none of the names was well known. (They may have been pseudonyms of the editors) Each glossy page carried a coloured whorl as the symbol of *The Vortex,* and the cost of this project must have been suicidal. For that reason alone it is not surprising that *The Vortex* was not seen again. Such was the maniacal devotion of fans.

Nearly four hundred miles south of San Francisco lies Los Angeles, the home of fan William L. Crawford, whose name you may recall from the first volume in connection with his own semi-professional magazines *Marvel Tales* and *Unusual Stories.* Now he was back with *Fantasy Book,* a large-size magazine, with 40 pages selling for twenty-five cents. Crawford, who was born in September 1911, had been quite active in sf fandom during the thirties, but faded from the field with the War. He reappeared in 1945 with the publication of a booklet, *The Garden of Fear,* collecting together five stories from the pages of *Marvel Tales,* including the title story by Robert E.

Howard, and 'Celephais' by H. P. Lovecraft. The booklet sold well and, having secured a distributor, Crawford decided to take advantage of the situation and issue a magazine. Alas, before the first issue of *Fantasy Book* was ready, the distributor ceased business, and Crawford was left high and dry. Consequently, with a print run of only 1,000 copies, few ever reached news-stands outside California, and most were sold by subscription and through specialist dealers.

Crawford was able to utilise the stories he had acquired for *Marvel Tales*. For instance, the first issue led with 'People of the Crater' by Andrew North. North was the pen name of best-selling woman writer, Andre Norton, who had delivered the original manuscript to Crawford back in the early 1930s, along with a sequel, 'Garan of Yu-Lac'. The manuscript was lost, but rewritten. 'People of the Crater' at last saw print in this first *Fantasy Book*. 'Garan of Yu-Lac' had to wait until 1969 to see a printing, and even then incomplete! Such are the perils of sf writing and editing.

It would be an exaggeration to say *Fantasy Book* was a neat magazine. It was clumsy in appearance and rather shoddy in presentation, but in that first issue were Robert Bloch, and A. E. van Vogt with his unpronounceable 'The Cataaaaa', plus four other stories. Interior artwork was sparse but well executed, and included the work of Charles McNutt who was later to become better known as the writer Charles Beaumont.

With its second issue, still large-sized, *Fantasy Book*'s presentation declined, although the fiction was readable, particularly A. E. van Vogt's classic, 'The Ship of Darkness', which began with a time journey to AD 3 million and the discovery of a mysterious dark ship. Collectors should be interested to know that this issue also had two different covers, depending on the printing. A special book paper edition, bearing a rather dreadful cover by Lora Crozetti, was priced at thirty-five cents and is more generally available. A lesser-circulated news-stand edition, priced at only twenty-five cents, carried a far better cover by Roy Hunt. But that issue was printed on poor quality pulp paper and is now rather rare.

Determined to publish regularly, Crawford ambitiously commenced a serial in the second *Fantasy Book:* 'The Machine-God Laughs' by British writer Festus Pragnell. Its minor plot involving a super robot and Chinese agents was barely sufficient to support reader interest through its three instalments over ten months.

With its third issue *Fantasy Book* became digest-sized, but the cover and interior art, mostly by Crozetti, were appalling. Still printed on pulp paper nothing was done to elevate its shabby appearance. However, by number four Crawford wisely abandoned interior illustrations and reprinted a pleasant Neil Austin sketch for the cover, which had originally accompanied 'The People of the Crater' in the first issue. Presentation improved steadily thereafter reaching a high spot with the sixth in January 1950. A smaller digest size, with a cover by Jack Gaughan, his professional magazine début, this ran to 112 pages and featured a novelette, 'Scanners Live in Vain', which marked the start of the stunning career of Cordwainer Smith. A harsh story, it relates the grim existence of the Scanners, whose lives are devoted to the safety of mankind. The story left an indelible impression on the minds of the readers, all the more so when the enigmatic Cordwainer Smith did not reappear in magazines until 1955. Smith was the pen-name of American professor of Asiatic politics and military advisor, Paul M. Linebarger (1913–66). He had an MA and a PhD and could speak Chinese, German, French and Spanish and read Russian, Portuguese and Dutch. How such a personality could appear in a small circulation science fiction magazine with a story that has since passed into legend is added emphasis of the many surprises and intrigues of the sf world.

There was another new publication in January 1948: *The Arkham Sampler* from Arkham House publishers in Wisconsin. Arkham House was originally established in 1939 by August Derleth and Donald Wandrei to perpetuate the works of H. P. Lovecraft. By 1947 the venture was a fair success and the *Sampler,* edited by Derleth, was produced as a regular quarterly journal to cover the news of Arkham House, and to print and reprint weird and scientific fiction. It was here that Lovecraft's fantasy classic, 'The Dream-Quest of Unknown Kadath', saw light. *The Arkham Sampler* is best remembered today as the home of many invaluable book reviews and editorial comment, with articles by Lovecraft, Moskowitz, Bloch and many others. On the fiction side one would find van Vogt, John Beynon Harris and Ray Bradbury amongst others. After eight quarterly issues, sales were such that Derleth folded the *Sampler,* and it now fetches extremely high prices.

Since *Fantasy Reader* and *Arkham Sampler* basically included reprints, and *The Vortex* and *Fantasy Book* had only a small circulation, they can hardly be considered critical when evaluating the start of the second boom of sf magazines. Their existence is evidence that a market existed, but they are not of foremost importance. The giants at Street & Smith, Ziff-Davis, Standard and Popular were the powerful ones and any move on their behalf would divine the resurgence of a drive for sf publications.

Ziff-Davis had started to show this when the unprecedented Shaver rumpus helped first *Amazing* and then *Fantastic Adventures* to resume monthly appearances. Not only that but the enterprising management repeated their wartime ploy, binding together sets of three consecutive monthly issues and selling them as Quarterlies, beginning in the winter of 1947–8. Such practice continued until 1951.

But it was at Popular that the first real sign of the boom was seen. Before the War, Popular had published a clutch of science fiction titles, all of which went into suspension because of paper restrictions except for *Famous Fantastic Mysteries* (FFM). Now, as restrictions were lifted, the kiss of life was given to *FFM*'s companion *Fantastic Novels*. This emphasised the popularity of *FFM*, since during the War it had more or less duplicated for *Novels* by reprinting full-length works. The rebirth of *Fantastic Novels* would thus seem superfluous, but it was welcomed with open arms. Once again the slant was put on the old-style *Argosy/All-Story* scientific romances, whilst *FFM* continued reprinting from hardbacks.

The first reborn *Fantastic Novels*, with Mary Gnaedinger again in control, appeared in March 1948, and led with Merritt's 'The Ship of Ishtar'. This had previously been serialised in *Argosy* in 1924, and in 1938 had won a readers' poll conducted by *Argosy* as the most popular story it had ever published. Yet a hardcover edition in 1926 had scarcely sold. To the new post-War generation of readers therefore this was a lost classic, well worthy of revival. Of course, it was comparatively easy for *Fantastic Novels* to succeed. Reviving a magazine with a set policy already familiar to readers was not as difficult or risky as launching a new project. Readers who supported *FFM* would be likely to buy its companion, and with that confidence Popular established *Fantastic Novels* on a bi-monthly schedule, alternating with *FFM*. Once again A. Merritt was the foundation on which to build. One could not help feeling however that the Merritt saleability might be pushed too far, especially when in December 1949 Popular launched the *A. Merritt's Fantasy Magazine,* leading with Merritt's *Creep, Shadow!,* his own last novel published in 1934. *Merritt's Fantasy* lasted only five issues, but it was not just a surfeit of Merritt that led to its demise. Those other reasons however I shall leave till later.

With *Fantastic Novels* back on the straight and narrow, Popular looked to another of its suspended titles, and decided to revive *Super Science Stories.* This had originally been the brainchild of Frederik Pohl, when he had approached Rogers Terrill of Popular in 1939 to try interesting them in a science fiction magazine. *Super Science* and its companion *Astonishing Stories* had proved highly successful, and were only wound up when paper restrictions and Pohl's departure to the War effort left them high and dry. Pohl had not returned to Popular. After the War he set himself up as a literary agent and was proving moderately successful. Instead, the associate publisher at Popular, Alden H. Norton, went after Ejler Jakobssen, the man who had filled in on *Super Science Stories'* final issues. Jakobssen was a Finn who had been born in December 1911 and came to the United States in 1926. He took up pulp writing during the thirties and in 1943 joined Popular. By 1948 he was a department head, which included control of *FFM.* In the summer of 1948 Jakobssen was on holiday. He recalls: 'I was five miles from the nearest phone, floating on my back in a hot lake, on an unbearably hot day, when a boy on a bicycle showed on shore and shouted, "Call your office." I followed him the requisite five miles to a farmhouse, called, and Al Norton told me that *Super Science Stories* had been revived and added to my department.'

The magazine reappeared in January 1949 and carried as its lead novelette 'The Black Sun Rises' by Henry Kuttner. This story had been submitted to *Super Science Stories* in its earlier days, but when that magazine had ceased, it was printed in the Canadian edition of *Super Science* that had begun in August 1942. That edition had continued to appear every other month throughout the War for twenty-one issues until its demise in December 1945. When the new *Super Science* was born it too was initially printed in Canada.

Super Science Stories has tended to be overlooked by collectors. Yet for its period it was a highly competent magazine and carried a plethora of readable and enjoyable stories by all the major authors. Ray Bradbury was regularly featured with stories that included his classics 'I, Mars', which deals with the bizarre state of a man alone on the Red Planet, and 'Changeling', wherein a man has several android duplicates of himself made to satisfy his lovers. Arthur C. Clarke appeared in its pages with his Möbius-style puzzle 'The Wall of Darkness'. Poul Anderson, rapidly making a name for himself, contributed several stories including 'Earthman, Beware!' which is reprinted in this volume. And it was the first magazine to print a story by Chad Oliver, when 'The Land of Lost Content' appeared in November 1950. It was also a major market for leading detective/mystery writer, John D. MacDonald, who had nineteen stories under his own name and two pseudonyms in the magazine's fifteen issues.

Super Science Stories catered for the science fiction fans by including a 'Fandom's Corner' column conducted by leading fan James V. Taurasi, reviewing fannish publications and activities, and Frederik Pohl regularly provided 'The Science Fictioneer' book review column. For many issues Ejler Jakobssen was assisted in the editing by Damon Knight. Jakobssen chose and bought the stories, while Knight built up the issues. The two experimented with the magazine and encouraged writers to venture into new directions. Almost overlooked, it was in fact *Super Science Stories* that acted as the necessary link between *Astounding* and the new breed of magazines to follow. It provided that needed refresher course wherein authors had a chance to rethink their style and approach in preparation for what was to come.

The proximity of Canada to the United States would imply the existence of a reasonable audience for science fiction. But this does not seem to be the case. Certainly native writers are few and far between in Canada, and an original indigenous magazine a rarity. Canadian editions of American magazines existed, such as the *Super Science Stories* just cited. That, along with similar versions of *Science Fiction, Weird Tales* and *Uncanny Tales*, consisted usually of reprints plus a smattering of new stories from American authors. It was thus a very rare sight indeed when in March 1949 a totally original Canadian magazine appeared – and what's more in French, catering for that third of the population.

Les Adventures Futuristes came from Montreal in Quebec,

where approximately eighty per cent of the population are French-speaking. It is surprising that such a publication had not appeared before, and even more surprising that when it did finally come, it was twice monthly. *Les Adventures Futuristes* consisted primarily of adventures centred around two super-heroes, and involved such bizarre creations as a spherical man and talking plants. After its sixth issue it slowed to a monthly schedule, and then abruptly vanished after its tenth in September 1949. The magazine is extremely scarce today and in the science fiction annals is remembered as a fascinating novelty.

A year or two afterwards another native Canadian magazine just broke the surface. *Brief Fantastic Tales* was about the smallest of all magazines, being about $5\frac{1}{2}$ x $3\frac{1}{2}$in with 64 pages, and carrying just four stories. It emanated from Studio Publications in Toronto, Ontario and cost just ten cents. It was never seen again.

An event happened in 1949 that was a precursor of things to come, had anyone the foresight to predict. Super-heroes had been an integral part of science fiction for over two decades. During the 1930s many new publications had been built around such a creation, usually with a lead novel devoted to his adventures. Undoubtedly the most famous in the pulp magazine field was *Doc Savage*. The first number had appeared in March 1933 from Street & Smith and had maintained regular monthly sales through the War. Many of the lead stories, almost all of which were written by Lester Dent (1904-59) have since re-appeared in American paperbacks, and there is a current British edition also. With around 180 adventures in all, there's quite some reading in store for those interested. A Doc Savage film by sf movie maestro George Pal, was also released in 1975. Briefly, Doc Savage had a fabulous combination of scientific skill, mental wizardry and physical prowess, and he made it his business to help people out of bizarre perils. *Doc Savage* was considered one of the backbone publications of the pulp magazines, yet to the disbelief of many, in 1947 *Doc Savage* began to miss months, went quarterly, and then folded with the Summer 1949 issue. The last of the great character magazines had gone.

And the major contribution to its demise was the astonishing mushrooming of the comic-book industry. The comic heroes, in particular Superman and Batman, had been an offshoot of science fiction just before the War, and many sf writers and artists worked for them. Mortimer Weisinger, editor of *Thrilling Wonder* from 1936 to 1941, left the magazine to become editor of *Superman* and later of the whole chain of associated comics. By 1949 it was these super-heroes with their 'easy to follow' pictures and 'bubbles' that caught the heart of the younger reader and the young-at-heart. The reading of an entire novel was stodgy in comparison. With their growth there was a comparable decline in the sales of pulp magazines, particularly the hero pulps.

The end of *Doc Savage* left a void that the comics readily filled. But, as if a final fling were necessary, Popular Publications decided to step into the breach with an updated hero, Captain Zero. Here was a man rendered invisible by an atomic explosion, but he had some anti-hero qualities in that he was clumsy, nearsighted and forgetful! Popular commissioned G. T. Fleming-Roberts, a stalwart pulp writer who had appeared regularly in most of the mystery/terror magazines since the 1930s, to write the full-length lead novels, starting with 'City of Deadly Sleep' in November 1949. Fleming-Roberts brought a much needed strain of humour to the pulp hero, but it fell on stony ground. *Captain Zero* never caught on, and after three issues it became as invisible as its hero.

Nevertheless, Popular's president, Henry Steeger, should be congratulated. With *Fantastic Novels*, *Super Science Stories* and *Captain Zero* the publishers had been adventurous and taken a chance. *Captain Zero* was a gamble that had failed. But the other two publications were flourishing, and this, plus the success of the established sf magazines, signalled the green light for the future.

Late Summer 1949 was very much the eve of the storm. By that time next year nearly one dozen new magazines would have appeared, two of which were destined to make history. Before plunging in at the deep end therefore, it seems a suitable time to look at some of the new authors who had made their début in the sf magazines in the three years following the War, and also at some of the more renowned stories that had appeared.

I have already mentioned Arthur C. Clarke and Poul Anderson, two of the major names just after the War. Another was William Tenn, pen-name of London-born American, Philip Klass, who also made his début in *Astounding*, which was maintaining its impressive record for culturing embryo talent.

'Alexander the Bait' (May 1946) was written just three months after the end of World War II when Tenn was working as a technical editor for the Army Air Force. The story uses this background as a basis for a concerted effort to reach the moon. He followed it with 'Child's Play' (March 1947) which starts with the delivery of a Christmas present from AD 2153 to a modern-day man, with chilling consequences.

April 1947 *Astounding* presented H. Beam Piper's first sale, 'Time and Time Again', about a chemist who finds his inner conscience back thirty years in the past occupying his own teenage body but with all his future memory. This came as a consequence of a pain-killing drug he was administered after being wounded during World War III. That story was voted into first place in the readers' poll, ousting the giant of the period, A. E. van Vogt, with his novelette, 'Home of the Gods'. Piper's career was successfully launched, and he secured his popularity with his second story, 'He Walked Around the Horses' (April 1948), which opened with the historical disappearance of Englishman, Benjamin Bathurst, in Prussia in 1809. Piper postulated that Bathurst had vanished into a parallel world, and the tale follows on from that. It has since become recognised as a minor classic.

A much revered name within the sf field, despite very rare appearances, is that of T. L. Sherred, who appeared in the May 1947 *Astounding* with a time-travel gem, 'E For Effort'. The story involves a pair of scientists who make a fortune producing historical films of 3D recordings of history. It too is cited as a minor classic, as is the work by female writer, Wilmar Shiras: 'In Hiding' (*Astounding*, November 1948) which tells of the problems of a psychiatrist confronted with a supranormal ten-year-old child. Wilmar Shrias was one of a number of female writers who were beginning to make an impression in sf. There were only a few before, the leading names being C. L. Moore (Mrs Henry Kuttner), Leigh Brackett (Mrs Edmond Hamilton) and Leslie F. Stone. Then the June 1948 *Astounding* carried 'That Only a Mother' by Judith Merril. This story, about a mutated child prodigy that the mother regards as perfectly normal, is one of the most frightening of sf stories. Another woman writer who made her début at this time, was Katherine MacLean, whose 'Defense Mechanism' also appeared in *Astounding* (October 1949).

Britons were also making a mark in America, aside from

Arthur C. Clarke. London-born Peter Phillips produced a highly original story, 'Dreams Are Sacred' (*Astounding*, September 1948), where a psychologist projects himself into the mind of his patient in order to cure him. The February 1949 *Astounding* saw the name Christopher Youd in print for the first time with 'Christmas Tree', a poignant tale of Christmas spent away from Earth. C. S. Youd was the real name of the writer soon to become internationally famous with books like *Death of Grass*: John Christopher, who was to rival Arthur C. Clarke for a period as Britain's major sf writer. He had sold a short story to Walter Gillings in 1946 for *Fantasy*, but that tale, 'Monster', was not published until 1950. Pre-War leading British writers were also making a come-back after settling down to 'civvy street'. Eric Frank Russell had supplied an incredible serial, *Dreadful Sanctuary*, that appeared in *Astounding* during 1948. It begins with the failure of any moon rockets to leave Earth with success, and goes on to the revelation that Earth is in fact an insane asylum of the Galaxy! If ever Russell's talent and skill neded a showcase, this was it. He had already received countless accolades for his 1946 short novel, 'Metamorphosite', which traced the change in mankind over a millenium in the future, and he was cementing his own special highway which would lead him into the 1950s as one of the most respected of sf writers.

John Wyndham had also made a return to the fold; writing as John Beynon he produced 'Adaptation' (*Astounding*, July 1949) about a baby girl specially conditioned for alien survival.

That same issue of *Astounding* contained the first sf work by American writer, James H. Schmitz. Schmitz had first been published in *Unknown Worlds* in 1943 with a fantasy, but 'Agent of Vega' was his bombshell entry into science fiction. The story was full of action and splendour, involving the vast Vegan Confederation and the intrigue centred upon its super police force and their agents. 'The Witches of Karres', three young girls with formidable psi powers, followed this in the December *Astounding*.

July 1949 also marked the début of Kris Neville with 'The Hand From the Stars' in *Super Science Stories* and the first appearance of the by-line Cyril Kornbluth with 'The Only Thing We Learn' in *Startling Stories*. As detailed in the last volume, Kornbluth had written and sold scores of stories, while still in his teens, to many magazines in the early forties, but they had appeared under a host of pseudonyms. Most of those names are now forgotten, but Kornbluth passed into legend after his death in 1958 when only thirty-five.

Probably the most notable new author to be first published outside *Astounding* was Jack Vance; 'The World-Thinker' had appeared in the Summer 1945 *Thrilling Wonder*. He remained a mainstay of the Standard magazines over the next seven years, creating memorable planetary adventures, particularly his Magnus Ridolph series. As now, many of these early pieces had elements of fantasy in their backgrounds. For instance, 'The World-Thinker' includes action on the planet of Laoome, the World-Thinker. In one scene Laoome loses control of his creations with bizarre results, including the sun turning into a giant slug and crawling down from the sky to become impaled on huge pylons that have sprouted from the ground!

Lack of space here disallows more than a passing mention of the work of established writers of this period. There was the continuing expertise of the Kuttner husband and wife team, writing primarily as Lewis Padgett. They had two serials in *Astounding* during 1947, 'Tomorrow and Tomorrow', a downbeat story set in the future, and 'Fury' (as Lawrence O'Donnell), a tremendous adventure set on a turbulent Venus. Jack Williamson, a big name in sf since 1928, was writing better than ever. His long story, 'The Equalizer' (*Astounding*, March 1947) concerned an invention that could transmute any element, and was followed by his oft-reprinted robot classic, 'With Folded Hands . . .' in July. That story, about robots that overrun the Earth with their hyper-philanthropic desire to help mankind, is today considered the definitive tale of its kind. Williamson produced a novel-length sequel, '. . . And Searching Mind', which was serialised in *Astounding* during 1948.

The indefatigable E. E. Smith was around with *Children of the Lens*, serialised in *Astounding* (surprised?) from November 1947, during which period Isaac Asimov continued to supply further stories in both his Foundation and robot series. A. E. van Vogt was present with the long-awaited sequel to 'World of Null-A', 'The Players of Null-A', which began in *Astounding* for October 1948. However, his climactic story in the Weapon Shop series, 'The Weapon Shops of Isher', appeared in the February 1949 *Thrilling Wonder,* which serves to remind us of that magazine's increase in quality, and the drive by its editor to make it a fitting rival for *Astounding*. By the close of 1949 it could almost be said that each of the major magazines was at its best, although die-hards will still look back on *Astounding* of the early 1940s as The Golden Age.

It was also increasingly apparent that science fiction as a literature was becoming more accepted by the general public, although it still had a long way to go to lose the stigma associated with gaudy pulp adventure magazines and their covers. Science fiction was being regularly collected in hard-cover anthologies, notably by editors Donald Wollheim and Groff Conklin, and a major landmark was the establishment of an annual series of the year's best science fiction – a device still popular today. This was the work of collectors Thaddeus E. Dikty and Everett F. Bleiler. Bleiler had just made his name among sf enthusiasts for his tremendous bibliographic work, *The Checklist of Fantastic Literature* (1948), listing over 5000 works of fantasy and science fiction. Then in September 1949 appeared their jointly edited *The Best Science Fiction Stories: 1949* from Frederick Fell publishers of New York. It included twelve stories, ten of which originally appeared in the sf magazines. They ranged from Ray Bradbury's 'Mars is Heaven!' (*Planet Stories*) to Fredric Brown's 'Knock' (*Thrilling Wonder*). To summarise, six were from *Astounding*, three *Thrilling Wonder*, one *Planet*, and two from outside the field. In August 1950 a second annual appeared with thirteen stories from 1949. *Astounding* and *Thrilling Wonder* had three stories each, plus one from each of *Startling, Planet* and *Fantastic Adventures*. Of the three remaining stories, two came from the same issue of the *Saturday Evening Post*!

The *Saturday Evening Post* was one of the leading periodicals in the 1940s, a general 'slick' magazine. For it to be publishing sf *by science fiction pulp writers* was a definite pointer of things to come. The *Post* had published sf before, but by main-stream writers who had an occasional flight of fancy, which, because of their status was viewed as respectable. Names like Stephen Vincent Benet, Gerald Kersh, Aldous Huxley, all had contributed such tales. This was acceptable. Murray Leinster, writing under his real name of Will F. Jenkins, was equally acceptable. Jenkins was a respected writer of westerns, somehow a more highly regarded genre, and had won prizes and awards for his short stories, including one from the prestigious *Liberty* magazine. But Robert A. Heinlein? Here was a name straight from the sf pulps. Heinlein had taken the advice of Murray

Leinster. He recalls: 'Several years ago Will F. Jenkins said to me, "I'll let you in on a secret, Bob. *Any* story – science fiction or otherwise – if it is well written, can be sold to the slicks." '[3] Heinlein had proved himself a number one writer with the sf audience. Why not try with a general audience? He did – and immediately met with success. 'The Green Hills of Earth' appeared in *The Saturday Evening Post* for 8 February 1947, and told of the sacrifice made by a blind poet Rhysling to save a spaceship. In quick succession thereafter he made sales to *Argosy*, *Town and Country*, and *The American Legion Magazine*.

Hot on his heels was Ray Bradbury, who had placed a short fantasy, 'The Invisible Boy', with *Mademoiselle* in 1945. He was soon selling both fantasies and non-fantasies to a whole host of slick magazines. Then he succeeded in placing such science fiction as his Martian Chronicle stories, 'Dwellers in Silence', to the Canadian *MacLean's* (15 September 1948) and 'The Silent Towns' to *Charm* (March 1949). Canadian slick markets were quite receptive to science fiction; John Russell Fearn had been regularly selling sf novels to the Toronto *Star Weekly* since 'The Golden Amazon' in April 1945.

Now magazines like the *Saturday Evening Post* and *Collier's*, which, starting from 6 January 1951 would carry John Wyndham's *The Revolt of the Triffids*, were looking at science fiction in a new light. It was almost solely the result of the approaching nuclear age, that had stirred readers' interest in science and mankind's future, which had ushered in this new-found respectability in science fiction. That, combined with the new generation of sf writers who had perfected the writing of science *fiction* as opposed to the fictionalised scientific treatises prevalent in the 1920s, or the many preposterous juvenile adventures of before the War. Leinster and Heinlein had opened the doors, and Bradbury demolished the wall. Thereafter writers knew that by polishing their style they could sell to the far more lucrative slick markets. And they could sell fairly basic sf. There was nothing exceptional to the sf reader in any of Heinlein's *Post* stories – in fact they were rather mundane. It was his skilled approach that the editors were after.

Where did this leave the pulps? Suddenly their leading writers had opened up a market that the pulps could not hope to match in terms of financial reward or prestige. But the hard truth was that even though the slicks would now look at science fiction, it still had to be fairly down-to-earth. Anything too experimental or daring would instantly be rejected, even though to the sf fraternity it was unexceptional. The pulps still supplied their specialist service. The obvious next step was to kill the pulp image. Thus, along came the dignified *Magazine of Fantasy and Science Fiction*.

5—LET BATTLE COMMENCE

The first issue of *Magazine of Fantasy*, as it was initially entitled, was dated Fall 1949. It was published by the Fantasy House imprint of Mercury Press, under the guiding hand of Lawrence Spivak, (today a noted radio and television producer) who was also responsible for the prestige publication *American Mercury*, and the famed *Ellery Queen's Mystery Magazine*. For thirty-five cents the reader bought 128 digest-sized pages. The cover, depicting a young lady being chased by a green monster, was a photograph. Photographic covers were a rarity on sf magazines, though both Palmer and Campbell had experimented with them. *Magazine of Fantasy's* cover was the work of Bill Stone and was highly effective.

The lead story was Cleve Cartmill's 'Bells on His Toes', but the one that attracted the most interest was Theodore Sturgeon's entertaining 'The Hurkle Is a Happy Beast', which editors Bleiler and Dikty would later include in their *Year's Best* selection. The magazine was a choice blend of original stories and reprints. Four reprints in the first issue varied from Guy Endore's 'Men of Iron' to Perceval Landon's noted ghost story 'Thurnley Abbey'. In fact the bias of the first issue was towards fantasy. It was with the second issue (Winter/Spring 1950) that the title lengthened to *The Magazine of Fantasy and Science Fiction* (usually abbreviated to *F & SF*) and sf featured more prominently.

From the outset, *F & SF* demanded quality writing. The fictional range of the magazine was limitless, including any kind of fantasy from hard-core sf to spooks. The only stipulation was that the story be masterfully told and exceedingly well written. One might have thought that it was not too much to ask for a well-written story, but many leading authors found it difficult to sell to *F & SF* because of the editors' strictness.

The two editors who handled *F & SF* were Anthony Boucher

and J. Francis McComas. 'Mick' McComas entered publishing in 1941, when he was thirty-one. He became associated with Raymond J. Healy in 1946 when they jointly edited the 997-page sf anthology, *Adventures in Time and Space,* still considered one of the milestones of sf publishing. Boucher's real name was William Anthony Parker White, but a story under that name in the January 1927 *Weird Tales,* was probably not his work. Boucher, born in Oakland, California in August 1911, was then only fifteen. He kept the Boucher alias for his fantasy and sf, using H. H. Holmes for mysteries. He had a considerable number of brilliant fantasies in *Unknown* in the early 1940s, and he made a name for himself in sf with his time-travel story 'The Barrier' (*Astounding,* September 1942). Between them, the two editors had a thorough working knowledge of the whole range of fantasy, and more importantly had not been restricted to the pulps.

F & SF had a delayed impact because of its early sporadic appearances, and because it was easily overlooked in the welter of magazines that were then being launched. But once the writers realised the potential of *F & SF,* they geared themselves to it. Such an alteration in course had happened once before. In the 1930s many writers were happy to sacrifice the fiction for the science, then in 1938 Campbell firmly dictated his policy for stories that stressed the effects of the science rather than the science itself. Now Boucher and McComas were emphasising the literary angle. It was inevitable, but had been a long time in coming. One needs to realise that it had taken a world war and a nightmare Bomb to do it!

Many sf readers may have completely avoided the first issue of *Magazine of Fantasy.* But just one month later they were able to witness the continuation of a legend with the appearance of *Other Worlds Science Stories.*

Dated November 1949, the first issue of *Other Worlds* was very impressive. Digest-sized, its thirty-five cent cover price purchased 160 pages. Of course *Astounding* was the same length but its paper was of better quality. *Other Worlds* consisted of heavy pulp stock that made the issue half-an-inch thick which happily gave the impression of value for money.

Malcolm Smith's beautiful cover illustrated 'The Fall of Lemuria' by Richard S. Shaver. Yes, that name again. How come Shaver was writing for another magazine? Come to that, what about the magazine's hitherto unknown editor, Robert

N. Webster, who in his editorial was boasting twenty-six years of experience in the sf world. Fans would have scratched their heads, Robert who?

It would be the same sf fans who would first learn the secret. Attendees at the World Science Fiction Convention held at Cincinnati over the period 3-5 September 1949 would hear Ray Palmer tell how he had resigned from Ziff-Davis to establish his own publishing company. He described his plans for *Other Worlds* and even went as far as acquiring a local fan, Beatrice Mahaffey, as assistant editor. Just twenty-one years old, this was the first ever convention she had attended, and little did she realise what was in store!

Raymond A. Palmer, born 1 August 1910 in Milwaukee, had been hit by a van when he was seven which broke his back. The resultant spinal curvature gave Palmer a dwarfish appearance, but he overcame any lack in height with imagination and energy. Since his contact with Shaver, Palmer had shown more and more interest in the occult. It is feasible that subconsciously Palmer was willing to accept the 'deros' as the direct cause of his tragic accident (and subsequent ones), and he could channel his hate in their direction rather than against humanity. Certainly it was a way out. Palmer became active in anything and everything bizarre. Besides publicising the Shaver mystery in *Amazing,* he began to champion the cause of flying saucers, which were receiving increased publicity after the War. Palmer involved himself with fire equipment salesman Kenneth Arnold who, on 24 June 1947, whilst flying his own aircraft over Mount Baker in Washington, had sighted a chain of nine mysterious saucer-shaped objects. Investigating, he became embroiled in a fantastic series of events that led eventually to a dead-end.

Palmer showed interest in these facts, and Shaver supported them as further evidence for his own theories. When at the same time *Amazing's* publishers requested that Palmer soft-pedal the Shaver Mystery, he was ready for a break. Even though still employed by Ziff-Davis, and still nominally editor of *Amazing (Fantastic Adventures* was now completely edited by William Hamling), Palmer went through the various plans necessary to establish his own concern, Clark Publishing Company, in Evanston, a suburb of Chicago. In the spring of 1948 he launched the first issue of a new magazine, *Fate,* devoted to the occult. Since the name Palmer continued to be featured on *Amazing's* masthead, he concocted the alias, Robert N.

Webster. *Fate,* initially quarterly, soon increased in frequency and eventually became a standard occult publication. In fact it still appears, though Palmer is no longer connected. There was a regular British reprint edition from 1954, and the title still remains although now the US and UK editions have no connections.

Palmer was moving out of *Amazing.* The Shaver Mystery had created friction between himself and sf fandom, and he often derided fans, antagonising them even more, calling them 'the lunatic fringe'. Naturally, such comment did not endear him to fandom, and finally Palmer decided to make amends. Starting in the March 1948 *Amazing* he inaugurated 'The Club House' column to review fan publications and activity. Run by Rog Phillips, who made himself a great friend of fans, it was welcomed with open arms and was later admitted to be the leading fan column of the professional magazines. With the Shaver Mystery out of *Amazing,* most fans buried the hatchet.

And then it was back in *Other Worlds.* 'Webster's' editorial was typical Palmer, and only a complete newcomer to sf would not recognise it. 'Webster' praised the Palmer *Amazing,* lauded Shaver. He put forward the idea that *Other Worlds* would be a montage of the types of fiction published in *Astounding, Amazing* and *Thrilling Wonder,* plus an *Other Worlds* special. But he hastily added that he hoped his readers would suggest their own ideas for the magazine's ultimate policy.

Other Worlds proved successful. Letters published in the second issue praised it, and even included one from Theodore Sturgeon.

Palmer's name eventually disappeared from the masthead at Ziff-Davis after the December 1949 issue, and then it appeared on *Other Worlds.* He was succeeded at Ziff-Davis by Howard Browne. Born in April 1908, Browne had previously been an assistant editor on the magazines, but had left in 1947 to write full-time in Hollywood. Returning to take over *Amazing* and *Fantastic Adventures,* he hurriedly states his intentions to install some literate fiction back in the magazines' pages, and not to cater to any occult fringe. He threw out some $7000 worth of purchased Shaver material, and talked the publishers into making the magazines digest-sized, raising the rates and buying stories from quality writers. Ziff-Davis agreed, and Browne began work. Alas, the entry of the United States into the Korean War brought about restrictions on extra expenditure, and Browne was forced to shelve his plans and suffer for a few more years – and, suffer is the right word. Browne was essentially a mystery writer and has gone into print as saying, 'Actually, science fiction bored the beJesus out of me . . .'[4] Nevertheless his drive for sanity had its effect, and he produced a highly readable pair of magazines.

Meanwhile, Ray Palmer was not content to have just the one sf magazine. With *Fate* and *Other Worlds* successfully launched he began plans for a third, to be called *Imagination*. Beatrice Mahaffey officially became managing editor of *Other Worlds* with its March 1950 issue, although Palmer still had most influence. Then suddenly the accident-prone Palmer had another calamity, and by 4 June 1950 was paralysed from the waist down. Doctors were sure it was permanent, but Palmer was a fighter. He just would not lie down, and over the ensuing year began to show signs of a miraculous recovery.

Bea Mahaffey therefore was suddenly alone, in complete control of *Other Worlds*, and still inexperienced. She accepted the challenge without a qualm and is to be praised, for she succeeded admirably. An assistant, Marge Budwig Saunder, was employed to do the first reading and much of the donkey work. Mahaffey in turn appealed to the agents and writers and was able to acquire work from major authors. Consequently, early in its lifetime *Other Worlds* was able to escape being tarnished without stigmata attacked it. Here one would find Theodore Sturgeon, Eric Frank Russell, Lester Del Rey, William F. Temple, Poul Anderson, Fredric Brown, Robert Bloch, Gordon Dickson . . . all helping to make *Other Worlds* a neat and highly readable magazine. But naturally, Palmer was not entirely out of the picture. The October 1951 publication saw his serialised contribution, 'I Flew in a Flying Saucer', credited to both Ray Palmer and a mysterious Captain A.V.G. The story was supposed to be fiction based on fact. Ray Palmer was off on his tricks again . . .

And what of *Imagination*? Was this shelved after Palmer's accident? The first two issues had already been assembled, and it reached the stands in October 1950. Identical in format to *Other Worlds*, it was subtitled 'Stories of Science and Fantasy' and was intended to be the fantasy sister magazine, such as *Fantastic Adventures* had been to *Amazing*. Boasting an evocative Hannes Bok cover, its lead novelette was Chester Geier's 'The Soul Stealers', and other contributors were Willard Hawkins, Kris Neville, Rog Phillips and Edward Ludwig (his first appearance). It also met with success. But since Palmer was paralysed and Bea Mahaffey fully occupied with *Other Worlds*, *Imagination*'s future seemed dicey.

It so happened that another publishing house was just being established in Evanston – Greenleaf Publishing Company. The man behind it was none other than William Lawrence Hamling. Hamling was born in Chicago in June 1921 and became an sf fan in his early teens. He attended the large Lane Technical High School in Chicago, and became editor of its 10,000-copy circulation magazine, *Lane Tech Prep*, into which he inserted sf. He collaborated on a story with schoolfriend Mark Reinsberg, which they sold to *Amazing* in 1938, but Hamling did not immediately follow it up. In 1940 however he began editing a highly professional-looking fanzine, *Stardust*, which lasted for five numbers from March to November, and included several stories by leading authors. Hamling was called upon by Palmer to help on *Fantastic Adventures* in 1946, when Palmer had some domestic problems, and he proved so efficient that he entered the employ of Ziff-Davis, and in January 1948 became managing editor of both publications, effectively taking over while Palmer established his own company. When Browne succeeded to *Amazing* plans were afoot to move the editorial offices from Chicago back to New York. Hamling did not want to move, so in 1950, he left and formed his own publishing house. Thereupon Palmer handed him *Imagination*, and Hamling assumed full control with its third (February 1951) issue. The whole affair worked out so smoothly one could have thought it it had been choreographed as long ago as 1946!

Popular Publications had tested the waters of the sf magazine market and found it favourable. Palmer had jumped in the deep end and surfaced successfully. It was too early to tell with *F & SF* but it was certainly afloat. Now it was Standard's time to venture into deeper waters.

Standard decided to play safe. A popular feature of *Startling Stories* was its Classic 'Hall of Fame' Reprint section. *Famous Fantastic Mysteries* from Popular was mostly reprint, and that was a success. Avon's *Fantasy Reader* was also reliant on reprints, and that was now eleven issues old and still going. So Standard plumped to start their own reprint magazine – in fact two, one a quarterly, and one an annual. Like other Standard titles, they were pulp-sized. *Fantastic Story Quarterly*

appeared first in the spring of 1950, featuring as lead novel
Edmond Hamilton's 'Hidden World' from the Fall 1929 *Science
Wonder Quarterly*. It also included a short story, 'Trespass',
which marked the début of Gordon R. Dickson, one of today's
most respected sf writers. *Wonder Story Annual* followed in
Summer 1950, a hefty 196-page pulp featuring several novelettes
plus a lead novel, *The Onslaught from Rigel,* by Fletcher Pratt
from the Winter 1932 *Wonder Stories Quarterly*.

Both the *Quarterly* and the *Annual* proved an instant success.
Together with previous publications they gave substance to the
revitalisation of science fiction, and other publishers decided it
was time to rejoin the market.

First to follow suit was Louis Silberkleit of Columbia
Publications. Before the War he had published *Science Fiction,
Future Fiction* and *Science Fiction Quarterly* all of which had
been fairly successful. Charles D. Hornig had been their initial
editor, but then Robert Lowndes had taken over. When those
magazines were folded during the War, Lowndes stayed on at
Columbia as editorial director in charge of most of the pulps.
But when May 1950 saw the return of *Future combined with
Science Fiction Stories,* Lowndes was again at the helm.

The appearance of *Future* was the real clincher that science
fiction was about to undergo a boom. It was also the first
'spanner in the works'. Hitherto the magazines had each had
their own identity and had trespassed little. Ranging from
Astounding as the leader in *science* fiction, down through
Thrilling Wonder, Amazing (with its potboiler image still) to
Planet with its space opera and *F & SF* with its all-round aspect,
every publication had its own territory clearly marked out.

But now it was becoming a tight squeeze. Where could
Future fit in the framework? It had no independent policy, and
unlike *Other Worlds,* did not pretend to be a hybrid of all
magazines. Because of this, and its miniscule budget, *Future*
had no option but to be an average of most magazines, containing both the best and worst by the mainstay sf writers. It had
no regular stable of its own, nor much possibility of acquiring
one. Lowndes, like any other editor, saw new material by
aspiring authors but, with the sf market expanding, those
authors were as likely to go elsewhere. It was rapidly changing
from an editor's market to a writer's.

So Lowndes could do little more than aspire after the best.
But he did have one advantage: he was very much the personal

editor. He liked the contact between editor and reader, whereas Campbell remained aloof. Even though Lowndes had broken from sf fandom during the 1940s, the encouraging response to the reborn *Future* rekindled his old verve, and soon *Future* became *the* personal magazine. One felt one knew the editor, and had known him all one's life. That's how Lowndes liked it, and he reciprocated any feedback between reader and writer. Consequently he encouraged writers, since they knew they would have a response to their fiction. Lowndes was also able to rely on his many old friends in science fiction who had since begun to make a name for themselves: James Blish, Frederik Pohl, Damon Knight and so on. However, it was clear the quality was being spread thinner. For instance the first issue included writers George O. Smith, Lester Del Rey, James Blish and Murray Leinster, all of whom were as much associated with *Astounding, Super Science* and *Thrilling Wonder.* The fight for survival was thus beginning, and every magazine would soon be out for itself.

Future was the first of the magazines to have a personality but no policy. It retained the old pulp size, but with only 114 pages, it was able to sell for fifteen cents, the cheapest of the publications. Obviously that helped secure an audience, but without doubt it would need a vastly expanded sf readership to sustain any further magazines.

As if from thin air that audience materialised. New publications came on to the market, but from the outset their future was not always clear. May 1950 for instance, besides the return of *Future,* also saw number one of *Fantasy Fiction,* a digest-sized magazine edited and published by Curtis Mitchell from East 67th Street, New York. Its cover, depicting an alluring female and a skull, was a photograph, again the work of Bill Stone. The magazine looked a carbon copy of *F & SF,* especially as it also ran both new and reprint fiction. The only difference was that Mitchell included 'true-weird' stories like 'The Moose That Talked'! But *F & SF* had acquired its loyal readership by then. *Fantasy Fiction* stumbled; the second, retitled *Fantasy Stories,* appeared in November 1950, but thereafter was never seen. Since only the month before *A. Merritt's Fantasy* had folded it seemed that *science* fiction was now winning over fantasy. Fantasy, in fact, was becoming a dirty word, commercially speaking.

In July 1950 a new magazine came out under Wollheim's

editorship from Avon Books. But it was a pulp, not digest. Called *Out of This World Adventures,* it was a blatant copy of *Planet Stories,* slanted towards the comic market since it included a full colour comic-strip section. This was the idea of publisher Joseph Meyers, who had an offer from a printer to do some pulps for him at a very advantageous price. He suggested binding excess comic pages into the middle and making a 'bargain' package. Although the comic art was well illustrated by such as John Giunta, and moderately well plotted by writers like John Michel and Gardner Fox, it brought howls of horror from old time fans. Meyers however was subject to whims, and the printer found him unreliable. The offer was dropped, and *Out of This World Adventures* vanished after a second issue in December. March 1951 however saw the birth of another pulp, *Ten Story Fantasy* (somewhat of a misnomer as it carried thirteen stories). Wollheim made a fine selection of stories here, and there was no comic section. Then again Meyers changed his mind, and after only the one publication the magazine folded. Today, *Ten Story Fantasy* is chiefly remembered as marking the first appearance of Arthur C. Clarke's story 'Sentinel of Eternity', which later formed the basis of the spectacular film *2001: A Space Odyssey.* How many would have thought that such a film had its origins in a single-issue, almost forgotten pulp magazine?

Wollheim tells me that Meyers frequently had these whims. Earlier in 1949 he had toyed with the idea of an sf pulp and Wollheim had collected and purchased the necessary stories. Then he changed his mind and the magazine never appeared. But Wollheim simply published those stories in book form as the paperback anthology, *The Girl with the Hungry Eyes and Other Stories.* That book, one of the first all-original sf anthologies, is thus a magazine in book's clothing. As a paperback it received glowing reviews, is remembered with much respect, and has become quite a collector's item. Would the same have happened if it had appeared as a pulp? The chances are it would have been overlooked and now be forgotten by all but the die-hard collectors, just like *Ten Story Fantasy.* Such is the justice of the magazine world!

Meyers did not return to the pulp idea. Instead, Wollheim succeeded in putting out a new digest, reprint magazine, *Avon Science Fiction Reader,* which was much more welcome.

By late 1950 the perceptive reader and editor could learn

a lesson from what was happening in the sf world. Remember, sf magazine publishing was expanding. Already by the summer of 1950 there were some twenty publications where four years earlier there had been just eight. Were these being supported solely by the same loyal sf fans? They accounted for some of the readership, but not all. New readers were being attracted to the magazines by curiosity, and many had discovered sf in the recent anthologies and the slick magazines. Therefore they were more drawn to those magazines which presented a wholesome and mature outlook, which the pulps just could not. No, the pulps were by and large being supported by the old-guard loyal sf fan, and the younger readers discovering it for the first time. The digest magazines were being supported by those same readers *plus* those won over from other media. Quite obviously the battle was in action between pulp and digest, a battle that would reach its height in the very near future.

6—SCIENCE OR SANITY?

In 1950 there was still no doubt that *Astounding* was leading in quality, and one of its most respected names was L. Ron Hubbard. Born Lafayette Ronald Hubbard in Tilden, Nebraska in 1911, he was already a regular writer of adventure fiction for pulps like *Argosy* when in 1938 he made his first appearance in *Astounding* with 'The Dangerous Dimension', a humorous tale of a professor who could wish himself between dimensions. With his ability to weave a fascinating story to imaginative extremes Hubbard became a top entertainer in *Unknown*. At the same time he wrote some top-rank sf for *Astounding,* most notably 'Final Blackout', serialised during 1940, which traced the rise to power of 'the Lieutenant' in a world ravaged by perpetual war. Appearing at the time when the War in Europe was reaching the end of its first year, although it had originally been supposed to end in a matter of weeks, it struck home to many of its readers, and the resultant controversy catapulted Hubbard's name into the first rank. Following the War, under the transparent pseudonym of Rene Lafayette, Hubbard produced an immensely entertaining series starting with 'Ole Doc Methuselah' (*Astounding,* October 1947). Ole Doc, who was over seven hundred years old, was a Soldier of Light, who travelled around the Universe dispensing his medical services.

and somehow becoming involved in planetary politics even though he shouldn't. The seven stories of the series that ended with 'Ole Mother Methuselah' in the January 1950 publication all proved highly popular.

The issues of February and March 1950 kept Hubbard's name alive with his controversial serial, 'To the Stars', depicting the sacrifices man must make in order to explore space. It was thus with mounting interest that fans awaited the May 1950 *Astounding,* as Campbell had announced it would feature a major article by Hubbard heralding a totally new science – dianetics. In conjunction with the publication of the article, Hermitage House of New York brought out a hardcover book by Hubbard, *Dianetics: The Modern Science of Mental Health.*

The article and the book caused an explosion in the sf fraternity. What was dianetics? Was it a science?

Hubbard postulated that the mind is essentially divided. The Analytical Mind is that part which is fully aware, which stores and records everyday events and thoughts – the part with which you are thinking about this now. But there is also a Reactive Mind which continues to store information even when the Analytical Mind is uppermost concerned with some major event. If that Reactive Mind enters into problems which should be solved by the Analyitical Mind then very likely the wrong solution would be planned, disastrous to the person. This is analogous to a computer having two memory banks, one of which it is not aware, but which nevertheless feeds back information. Hubbards claims that through hypnosis false memory banks, which could cause harm, can be erased with the result that the person is a Clear – one who is perfectly sane, who can think clearly in solving a problem without the necessity of relying on some previous solution which would probably be the wrong one.

Hubbard maintained that his method would cure all mental diseases. Was there ever such a claim as that!? Campbell was convinced Hubbard was on to something. A most revealing aspect of this was recently revealed by sf writer, Alfred Bester, in his contribution, 'My Affair with Science Fiction', to *Hell's Cartographers* (1975) edited by Brian Aldiss and Harry Harrison. He recalls a conversation he had with Campbell after the editor had received Hubbard's dianetics article and was rushing it into print. Campbell's comments linked together were as follows:

You don't know it, you can't have any way of knowing it, but Freud is finished . . . Psychiatry, as we know it, is dead . . . Freud has been destroyed by one of the greatest discoveries of our time . . . dianetics . . . It was discovered by L. Ron Hubbard, and he will win the Nobel Peace Prize for it.[5]

Campbell championed the cause, and soon Hubbard was able to establish his Dianetics Foundation. Patients flocked to him and the staff he had built up around him. That staff included top sf writer, A. E. van Vogt, who became an 'auditor': one who listens to the patient as he pours out his past life under hypnosis, thereby clearing his memory banks. When one recalls that many of van Vogt's novels, especially *Slan,* had dealt with super-minds, it was inevitable that he should be attracted by the lure of dianetics. Another writer ensnared by the 'science' was Katherine MacLean. Now, devoted to dianetics, Hubbard, van Vogt and to some extent MacLean completely abandoned science fiction, which was a disastrous loss.

The medical profession was quick to attack Hubbard's 'science' and ridiculed it as abject quackery. Over the next few years the whole enterprise was subject to schisms and secessions. Ironically, the first 'clear' was supposed to be Hubbard's second wife, Sara. But in 1951 she sued him for divorce on the grounds that he was insane!

Campbell finally disavowed dianetics in 1951, and the sf world was able to settle down again. But in its various incarnations dianetics flourished and Hubbard rapidly became rich as a result. Rumour had it that Hubbard, following his discharge from the navy in 1946 (through psychological disability), professed his dissatisfaction with pulp writing, and planned a get-rich-quick campaign. Was dianetics this plan? If so, then it worked. By the mid-1950s when dianetics was running into several legal tangles Hubbard moved to Arizona proposing his new doctrine, an offshoot of dianetics – Scientology. He established a Foundation in Britain. The organisation grew into a religion, the Church of Scientology. Then in 1963 Hubbard reputedly *sold out* his interest for a huge sum of money and retired to his fleet of five yachts cruising the Mediterranean. Today Scientology, banned in Britain, still flourishes. How many realise it was the brainchild of one of pulp's major sf writers?

During 1950 when dianetics took the sf world by storm, it was clear that many sf purists were highly sceptical of Hubbard's theories. What's more, didn't the whole episode seem reminiscent of something from which the sf world was still reeling – Shaverism? In the same way that Shaver's theories had taken over *Amazing* and with it Ray Palmer, so too had *Astounding* and Campbell been overcome with dianetics. Here was something else that appealed to the lunatic fringe – and suddenly, very suddenly, *Astounding's* loyal readers teetered. For a moment *Astounding* was no longer the impregnable bastion that it had been for the last fifteen years. And at the very moment that it was at its most vulnerable, along came *Galaxy*.

The first issue of *Galaxy Science Fiction* was dated October 1950, the same month that *Astounding* carried a further Hubbard article on dianetics, 'The Analytical Mind'. *Galaxy* was digest-sized, neatly printed on fairly good grade paper, and its 160 pages sold for twenty-five cents. Its first issue boasted most of Campbell's stable of major authors, leading with the first part of a three-part serial, *Time Quarry* by Clifford Simak, a fascinating novel involving formless beings who claim to control all the living intelligences of the Universe. Also present were Isaac Asimov, Fritz Leiber, Theodore Sturgeon and Richard Matheson. The sales potential of the names alone was sufficient to guarantee a large audience, and when the stories met their anticipated quality, *Galaxy's* future was assured.

Galaxy was published by World Editions, Inc, of West 40th Street, New York, and edited by the agoraphobic Horace L. Gold. He did much of the work from his home, aided by his wife Evelyn. Gold was a much respected writer. Born in Montreal, Canada in April 1914, he was raised in New York and the New England area. When still in his 'teens he sold a science fiction story to F. Orlin Tremaine, then editor of *Astounding Stories* and it appeared in the October 1934 issue under the alias, Clyde Crane Campbell. Later, using his real name, Gold's 'A Matter of Form' was used by John W. Campbell as an example of the experimental 'nova' stories he wanted to publish. The story tells of a man who has a mind switch with a collie dog, and it appeared in the December 1938 *Astounding*. Gold contributed some excellent stories to *Unknown,* and later worked on the staff at Standard Magazines, so all this experience, and his later involvement with two detective magazines that he created, stood him in good stead with *Galaxy*.

Other writers listened to Gold when he suggested ideas. He proved to be a Spartan taskmaster, ruthless in his determination to extract the best from his writers. But that policy brought him respect and it ultimately paid. Sf writer and researcher L. Sprague de Camp wrote of him in 1953:

> Gold is a zealously hardworking perfectionist. He sets an extremely high standard of literary excellence for his writers, who often complain of the amount of rewriting and revision required of them.[6]

Like Boucher and McComas and *F & SF,* Gold was after a literate magazine that would appeal to those readers coming into sf from the slicks and books, as much as to the followers of *Astounding* or *Thrilling Wonder.* It was mere coincidence that it arrived at the time *Astounding* was vulnerable, and certainly *Galaxy* would have scored a hit regardless of the environment. Gold went to great lengths to emphasise that *Galaxy* was the readers' magazine. His editorial to the second issue asked a host of questions to sound out readers' opinions. He also stated:

> We have challenged writers to present themes that could not be sold elsewhere . . . themes that are too adult, too profound or revolutionary in concept for other magazines to risk publishing.[7]

Quite some boast, and one which it is hard to assess that *Galaxy* maintained. As we shall see later, sf was undergoing a great maturing process and without a doubt *Galaxy* was instrumental in that change. In that second issue was a short story by Damon Knight, 'To Serve Man', which was certainly highly original for the sf of that period. That story is included in this collection.

Galaxy also carried a competition to attract readers. In no more than two hundred words the entrant had to give his own theory on flying saucers. By the end of 1950 it was an all-out drive to capture readers and to have the edge on all the other sf magazines. But most important was to convince the publishers that it was a paying proposition.

That fact is reflected in the fate of *Worlds Beyond,* another digest magazine, first issue dated December 1950. It came from Hillman Periodicals, with an editorial address in Fifth Avenue, New York. The editor was Damon Knight, on holiday from Popular Publications, and itching to edit his own magazine. *Worlds Beyond* ran to 128 pages, sold for twenty-five cents, but it lacked the bold presentation of *Galaxy,* and featured a rather drab cover by Paul Calle. The fiction was excellent. Knight showed discernment in choosing both new and reprint material, unearthing a lost story by Philip Wylie, 'An Epistle to the Thessalonians', as well as giving William Temple's fascinating story about the lunar origin of cats, 'The Smile of the Sphinx', an American airing. It had first seen publication twelve years earlier in the British *Tales of Wonder.* Despite an enthusiastic reception, initial sales were poor, and the publishers brought down the axe. As a second and third issue had already been prepared they appeared and, even though sales were healthier and the magazine was undoubtedly good value, Hillman was adamant: *Worlds Beyond* had died. Yet reading those three today it is hard to find a bad story. The magazine has been riffled by anthologists for tales like William Tenn's 'Null-P', Poul Anderson's 'The Acolytes' and H. B. Hickey's 'Like a Bird, Like a Fish'. Space was given to promote Jack Vance's *The Dying Earth* novel that Hillman's had just published by including an excerpt about Liane the Wayfarer called 'The Loom of Darkness'.

But alas, Hillman was convinced *Worlds Beyond* would be no money spinner and it disappeared for ever.

The closing months of 1950, and the opening of 1951 found the sf world in something of a dilemma. The digest magazines were doing well – *F & SF, Other Worlds* and *Galaxy* primarily, although failures like *Fantasy Fiction* and *Worlds Beyond* might indicate the opposite. *Astounding* had been digest for seven years and was thus no indication of trends. But equally the pulp magazines were suffering no casualties. *Thrilling Wonder, Startling, Amazing* and *Planet* were all faring well. But then mid-1951 suddenly saw the folding, once again, of *Super Science Stories* and *Fantastic Novels.* Popular had decided that the pulp magazine was soon to be an extinct animal and that paperbacks were becoming the vogue. They pulled out before the crunch came. But they did keep *Famous*

Fantastic Mysteries alive for a while, proving its popularity, but that too eventually succumbed to their axe, finishing in June 1953. The magazine that had brought life back to the old classics, and that had provided its readers with some of the most beautiful black-and-white illustrations from the pens of Virgil Finlay and Lawrence Stevens passed into legend.

Yet at the same time that Popular withdrew their pulps, other pulps increased in regularity. In the autumn of 1950, for the first time in its life, *Planet Stories* went from a quarterly to a bi-monthly schedule. The same publishers introduced a new thick pulp magazine, *2 Complete Science Adventure Books,* which packed together two full-length novels, either new or reprint, into one magazine for just twenty-five cents. Since the first issue (Winter 1950) led with Isaac Asimov's new novel, *Pebble in the Sky,* it could not fail to attract an audience. It succeeded more than was ever imagined, and being on only a tri-annual basis, each issue was eagerly awaited. It was also a fitting rival to *Galaxy's* digest companion, *Galaxy Science Fiction Novel,* which had begun at that same time with Eric Frank Russell's classic, *Sinister Barrier.* Pulp vs digest was most definitely on!

The success of *Planet Stories* proved however there was still a huge audience for fast action space opera, despite the otherwise maturing of sf in *Astounding* and *Galaxy.* Still generally managed by Malcolm Reiss, *Planet* had recently, since its Summer 1950 issue, been edited by Jerome Bixby. While he only stayed with the magazine for a year, it owed much to him because of his initial drive for the stories to be well written. This became *Planet's* forte against any imitators. The stories were excellently narrated, particularly those from the adept pens of Leigh Brackett, Poul Anderson and Gordon Dickson. Poul Anderson's 'Duel on Syrtis' (March 1951) for instance, which follows the intriguing to-and-fro action as an Earthman tracks an alien on Mars, is as captivating and enjoyable a story as one would find in any of the contemporary publications.

Shortly after *Planet* went bi-monthly, *Startling* for the first time in its life became monthly, showing it was now more popular than *Thrilling Wonder.* And Standard's reprint magazine, *Fantastic Story Quarterly,* had proved so popular that it now appeared every other month, and became *Fantastic Story Magazine.*

So just what was the situation: pro-pulp or pro-digest?

Highly revealing was the case of *Marvel Science Stories.* In the pre-War boom, *Marvel* had been the most controversial magazine on the market. It was the sf companion to Red Circle's *Mystery Tales* and *Uncanny Tales* which emphasised the sexual and sadistic elements of terror. The publishers had tried to liven up science fiction by the inclusion of sexy passages. It proved abhorrent to the sf purists, but it sold well to the bulk of the pulp magazine readership, and was part of the reason for the 1939 boom. It had folded in 1941 and was now almost forgotten. Its reappearance in November 1950 therefore raised some eyebrows. Robert Erisman was still overall editor, but the man who did the donkey work was a young Daniel Keyes, who ten years later would win the Hugo award for his profoundly effective tale 'Flowers for Algernon'. Keyes, just twenty-three years old, was a perceptive and talented young man who exercised much taste at *Marvel,* and with each successive issue, the standard rose surprisingly. The first two were pulp-sized, but the third in May 1951 was digest-sized. Despite containing readable fiction by Mack Reynolds, Jack Vance, Richard Matheson and Arthur Clarke, sales did not improve. Two more digest issues appeared in August and November 1951 and then for a while nothing. Readers surmised *Marvel* had once again sunk beneath the waves. But then in May 1952 a further issue appeared – but *pulp*-sized. Almost certainly, Stadium Publishers could not agree over *Marvel's* format, or whether pulp or digest had the most sales potential.

What was the solution? *Marvel's* May 1952 pulp issue went a long way to answering it. *Marvel* was never seen again.

7—BRAVE NEW WORLDS

Meanwhile, what was happening in England, where paper rationing and other wartime restrictions were still enforced? My colleague, Phil Harbottle, who has acted as research consultant throughout this history, has made a special study of the British sf scene of the early fifties, which has always fascinated him. His own period of editorship with the sf magazine, *Vision of Tomorrow,* enabled him to meet and get to know many leading personalities of the period. 'When I wasn't pumping them for new stories,' Phil wryly recalls, 'I was pumping them for information about their old ones!'

The fruit of this research is contained in a vast amount of correspondence with those leading authors, editors and fans. Many of the letters are, in effect, personalised histories and definitive essays on the development of the British sf magazines. Such authentic documents deserve to be published as a book, and Phil hopes so to incorporate them when he has completed his researches. Meanwhile he has kindly made them available to me, and within the body of the following chapter I am privileged to be able to present a number of first-hand accounts of the histories of the British sf magazines.

Aldous Huxley's classic 1932 novel of a controlled future Earth, *Brave New World*, saw a new hardback edition in England in 1948. It was small consolation to the science fiction fans, whose own brave *New Worlds* had vanished after three issues the previous year. Editor John Carnell, however, had a lot more fight in him, and was determined to find a publisher. In printing the following extract from John Carnell's own account of the rebirth of *New Worlds,* I seek to pay deserved tribute to this greatest of British editors:

The winter period of 1947-48 following the end of Pendulum Publications was a sad one, at least for myself, enlivened only by the regular weekly meetings of authors and fans at the White Horse Tavern in Fetter Lane. Wartime import restrictions were still in force and the only American sf magazines which found their way in were those arranged privately by mutual exchange. The British reprint editions did a great deal to reduce the gap but they were mere shadows of the parent magazines.

By the spring, however, optimism was once again on the upsurge, promoted largely by the one-day Whitsun SF Convention held at the White Horse and presided over by Walter Gillings. At that meeting I was able to inform the delegates that a scheme was being pursued with a view to forming our own publishing company for which they would have the chance of purchasing shares. The idea was started quite innocently at a typical Thursday gathering during the never-ending argument about shortsighted publishers, when a nameless voice asked, 'Why not start our own company? We could publish our own magazines.' The idea had been heard before, but not by Frank Cooper, a retired RAF Officer who had put some of his gratuity into a bookshop in Stoke

Newington, with a popular sf section. He had recently joined the regulars at the pub and took up the idea by volunteering to obtain all the necessary information on floating a company.

In fact it was entirely due to his fine efforts that the company prospectus was finally drafted, approved, and sent to a list of some 400 names acquired from various sources. Shares were offered at £1 each, with a minimum of five to be purchased. Nearly fifty enthusiasts subscribed an initial capital of just over £600, which was thought to be sufficient to launch the company. Frank's solicitor handled the formation details, Walter Gillings' wife, Madge, thought up the name Nova Publications Ltd, and by the end of the year the dream was moving into reality.

The first six working directors (spare-time, unpaid), were John B. (Wyndham) Harris, Chairman; G. Ken Chapman, Treasurer; Frank C. Cooper, Secretary; Walter Gillings, Advertising; Eric C. Williams, Subscriptions; and myself, John Carnell, Editorial. A top-class printing house convenient to Stoke Newington was located, paper was coming off the ration, and the blockmakers were glad to welcome a new account. By the spring of 1949, the new company was in business, and *New Worlds* 4 was planned as a trial issue, demy format ($8\frac{1}{2}$ x $5\frac{1}{2}$ in), 96 pages selling at 1/6d, with quarterly publication ultimately in mind. That issue went on sale in June, with a traditional bullet-shaped spaceship in a braking orbit near the Moon, painted by 'Dennis', with interior artwork by White, a young art student who was lodging at our home at the time. The contents were exactly as planned for the defunct Pendulum edition. The issue also featured a lively article by Arthur Clarke titled 'The Shape of Ships to Come', in which he postulated the possibility of dumb-bell shaped spaceships for extra-planetary voyages – used seventeen years later in the epic film *2001*.

To economise, Nova did its own distribution, no mean feat for a group of amateurs, but Frank Cooper and his manager, Leslie Flood, proved to be capable of this monumental task and by July we were confident that we could plan ahead for regular quarterly publication. In fact issue five was published in September, and number six, dated Spring 1950, in January of that year. While number five was at press, I had been one of the guests of honour at the Seventh World SF Convention held in Cincinatti, going on a partially assisted passage originated by Forrest Ackerman, and backed by donations from both sides of the Atlantic. I was completely over-whelmed by the generosity of a host of American publishers, authors and fans toward the first UK representative to make contact in the USA. I returned full of ideas and useful contacts.

New Worlds could not really be mistaken for its American counterparts. Its dimensions, format and policy echoed *Astounding,* but there remained an eminently British atmos-phere about it. The covers were more subdued, thus appealing to the average reader, rather than the more juvenile element of the bookstall browsers who were attracted by the brash action covers of the 1940s pulps. It is almost certain that with *New Worlds,* as *Astounding,* the average age of its readers was older than that of the pulp magazines. The stories also reflected a British flavour, with more of that sense for the unhurried, reserved life that had been our heritage, rather than the American frontier existence. Much American space opera was accused of being interplanetary wild west. This was not the British approach although some authors imitated it. *New Worlds* was now reaching a large sf audience in Britain, one formerly starved of indigenous material.

Since the demise of *Fantasy,* Walter Gillings had been privately publishing his highly professional-looking *Fantasy Review,* packed with news, reviews and information about the genre. After its fifteenth number he retitled it *Science-Fantasy Review,* and three more issues appeared until Spring 1950. By then, the next part of the Nova plan was put into operation, to produce a sister magazine for *New Worlds*: *Science-Fantasy,* under the editorship of Gillings. Its first issue, incorporating *Science-Fantasy Review,* appeared in the summer of 1950. It was a smaller digest size than *New Worlds,* and its 96 pages also cost 1/6d. Lead story was 'The Belt' by J. M. Walsh. Walsh (1897-1952) was a prominent character in the British sf world, having sold a feature novel, *Vandals of the World* to Gernsback's *Wonder Stories Quarterly* in 1931. The lack of a British market meant that Walsh had to concentrate on mysteries and thrillers in order to earn a living, but wrote sf whenever he could. 'The Belt', which tells how an errant piece of space flotsam knocks the Moon from its orbit causing it to break up and form a ring around the Earth, was written in a highly professional style and set a good standard for the magazine. When I say that this story was followed by Arthur C. Clarke's 'Time's Arrow', it emphasises the quality that *Science-Fantasy* had from the word 'go'. It was, in fact, drawing on the best of the unpublished stories which Gillings had previously garnered for the Temple Bar *Fantasy*.

Since Gillings was as much a scholar and collector of sf as an editor and reader, *Science-Fantasy* included a fine brew of articles and reviews. One such piece, 'The Jinn in the Test-Tube', by Herbert Hughes (né Gillings) explored the views of those outside sf to the current boom in the USA, and in particular the comments of that late, much respected professor, Dr Jacob Bronowski, who christened sf 'the folklore of the atomic age'.

A second *Science-Fantasy* appeared in January 1951 and included Arthur C. Clarke's much reprinted 'History Lesson'. That story had previously been published in the May 1949 *Startling Stories,* which showed that Clarke was getting as much mileage out of his fiction as the boom would allow. Because of the expanding sf markets in both Britain and America, authors could at last sell their stories more than once and receive more adequate remuneration for their efforts.

A whole year elapsed before the third *Science-Fantasy* appeared, dated Winter 1951-2. Now 2/- in price, it was a larger digest size, compatible with *New Worlds,* and it was not edited by Walter Gillings, although he did supply the editorial. It had been decided at Nova Publications that it was uneconomic to have two editors, and it was voted that Carnell should edit both magazines – the decision being swayed somewhat by the fact that the make-up of the existing *Science-Fantasy* was more costly than *New Worlds*. Gillings also lost control of *Science-Fantasy Review* which disappeared from the magazine's pages in favour of an all fiction line-up. This, coupled with a domestic tragedy, caused Gillings, the man who had been the chief driving force for the establishment of an sf magazine in Britain since 1934, to withdraw into the background. In fact he would not take an active part in the professional sf scene for nearly twenty years. Happily he is now back in the fold, and maybe the day will come when once again he will be editing a science fiction magazine.

Science-Fantasy continued to appear spasmodically as the

poor sister of *New Worlds*, its appearances often delayed because, Carnell claimed, there was insufficient good material. *Science-Fantasy* never was to attain the popularity of *New Worlds*, although it was of a generally superior literary standard.

By the start of 1951, with the Nova magazines the backbone of British sf, other publications were appearing, which proved that sf was selling. Unfortunately these were not the comparatively mature and intelligent magazines as *New Worlds* or *Science-Fantasy*. Publishers were exploiting the sf audience starved of their favourite reading material. Several 'mushroom' publishers appeared and began to issue cheaply printed, low quality sf paperbacks written by people with little or no background knowledge of science fiction. They were guilty of raping the genre and producing an offspring that was weak, puerile and unwholesome. Some publishers managed to acquire the services of experienced sf writers and thus issued some reasonable novels, but sadly by that time most of them were all tarred with the same brush, and paperback sf in Britain was derided as utter rubbish.

One of the most guilty publishers was John Spencer & Co, of Shepherds Bush, in London. In the summer of 1950 they issued a spate of magazines – not just one, but *four*, all in similar digest format to the paperback novels, but carrying custom-built, hackneyed short stories. The first to emerge was *Futuristic Science Stories,* featuring 'Nightmare Planet' by Norman Lazenby, the same Norman Lazenby who had appeared in *Fantasy* and *New Worlds*. Alas many writers had succumbed to the temptation of earning money fast by writing for the market. This was not detrimental to Lazenby, who was capable of writing good sf, but taking time over the fiction did not put bread on his table. He eventually drifted into the writing of gangster fiction. At this time paperback publishers paid extremely poor prices anyway, and so the more fiction turned out hurriedly and sold, the better. Actually, by Spencer magazine standards, Lazenby's 'Nightmare Planet' was bearable. So was J. Austin Jackson's 'Worlds of Fear'. Jackson had been published in *Fantasy* three years earlier and this story may well have been a carry-over. But as the publications appeared and the small residue of well-written fiction by better writers was exhausted, the quality rapidly plummeted. In quick succession came *Worlds of Fantasy, Wonders of the Spaceways,* and *Tales of Tomorrow*. A stable of names became associated with the magazines: Hamilton Donne, Frank Kneller, D. R. Mencet, none of whom could produce anything exceptional. Lazenby soon reached his all-time low in the second *Futuristic* with 'Plasma Men Bring Death', set on a miniature planet Earth, called Earthkin, which is invaded by the ruthless outlaw Arturo Korlin and his Plasma Men! That same issue carried the appalling 'Vultures of the Void' by Clifford Wallacem telling of the space heroics of Captain Starlight and his chum, Tubby Masters. These stories were every bit as awful as they sound!

British sf readers may have been starved of their favourite material, but this was *not* what they wanted. Furthermore, it was damaging to the sf scene, giving a totally wrong impression and creating a dustbin atmosphere. Fortunately, a publishing recession during 1951 kept the Spencer magazines off the market, but they returned in 1952 with even more meaningless gibberish than before. It is difficult to find much in their favour. But they did provide a market for writers to earn some money hack-writing while concentrating in the meantime on better quality fiction. It also provided a training ground where writers could practise their skills. In this way E. C. Tubb, Britain's most prolific writer during the 1950s, sold a few stories as 'Charles Grey', while writing good quality material for *New Worlds*. Similarly, Lan Wright, one of the Nova reliables, made his first sale, 'Heritage', to Spencer's. This was a moderately readable story about space war tactics, and it appeared in *Futuristic Science Stories* number 6, early in 1952.

The sales of the Spencer magazines were sufficient to maintain them through to 1954, and just over fifty individual issues appeared. Obviously, therefore, they did attract an audience which hopefully later graduated to the adult magazines. Certainly, the major publication that served as an apprenticeship for the budding teenager was not a magazine, but a comic – *Eagle*.

During the late 1940s British opposition mounted to the growing cult of American 'horror comics' which many feared were having an adverse affect on their children's psychology. The gruesome details depicted in certain publications horrified parents. It resulted in a Horror Comics Bill being passed through Parliament in 1955, stopping the import of American comics into Britain. This might have left a void, had it not been that a suitable alternative existed. The enterprising Reverend Marcus Morris had proposed to Hulton publishers a comic magazine that children could read, one with a religious and educational slant. Hulton agreed, and Morris went ahead to prepare *Eagle* which was issued amongst great publicity on 14 April 1950. The lead character was the famous Dan Dare. Morris had originally envisaged this as the Reverend Dan Dare, but thankfully Hulton modified it along more conventional lines. The Dan Dare strip was drawn and plotted by ex-RAF artist, Frank Hampson, who had acquired a special technique of clean-line realism which revolutionised comic strip art. Printed on high-quality paper, *Eagle* had a superb professional appearance, and its advance publicity was such that parents were readily buying it for their children. Its success was noted by John Carnell in his editorial to the Summer 1950 *New Worlds*, which said in part:

> . . . it gave me a very warm feeling to know this national juvenile weekly is selling out everywhere. Edited by a clergyman, who devised and designed it prior to submitting it to Hulton Press, it carries a strip-cartoon adventure on Venus, and regular science fiction stories with a strong juvenile appeal. Not without a little pride, author Clarke informs me that he has sold a story to the *Eagle*.[8]

If ever any juvenile publication served to recruit new readers to the adult sf magazines it was the *Eagle*. This was due in no small terms to Hampson's thorough knowledge of sf, and the remarkable inspiration shown in his artwork.

Hulton realized the potential of sf with the appeal of Dan Dare, and actually called on various members of the London circle for consultation. William F. Temple recalls with much bitterness how he was approached to edit a *Dan Dare Annual*. Temple spent considerable time commissioning stories and articles from all the leading writers plus working on a full Dan Dare short novel himself. But Hulton's plans went awry, through no fault of Temple who had met the publisher's initial requirements to the full. Everything then went wrong, and when the final *Dan Dare's Spacebook* appeared it was no longer the work of Temple and was a mere shadow of its original conception. Temple was able to rework his novel into his later 'Martin Magnus' series.

Similar disaster struck Herbert J. Campbell, one of the London sf fraternity. He was commissioned by Hulton to edit a new sf magazine. He prepared four pilot issues, only to discover that Hulton's had again changed their minds in favour of a girl's companion to *Eagle*, naturally called *Girl*.

Fortunately, the experience and contacts Campbell had made on his abortive editorial work were not lost, for he became technical editor on a new venture from Hamilton & Co, publishers in Goldhawk Road, London. The man in charge of Hamilton's editorial policy was Gordon H. Landsborough. Not a familiar name to sf fans, he was none the less a highly influential figure in the shaping of British sf expression. With Panther Books (Hamilton's) and later Four Square Books, Landsborough was instrumental in publishing a better grade of sf material in Britain. Today a respected and successful publisher in his own right, Landsborough vividly recalls his early associations with Hamilton's – and the creation of what was to become a major British sf magazine, *Authentic Science Fiction*:

Within a few weeks of being given control of Hamilton's lists, in 1949, I had made changes. I discarded the old hacks and instead recruited newspaper journalists as writers, who were being attracted by the rather better rate of pay. I'm not sure how I recruited sf writers. I think they came in response to advertisments in the then *World's Press News*. A mixed bag, but at least they were an improvement on the gangster writers who had been detailed to 'do something on science fiction'. When I read the so-called sf works which had occasionally appeared on Hamilton's list, I got the shudders. Such rubbish held the seeds of self-destruction.

My opinions were sometimes explosively expressed. The publisher took it in good humour and just said, 'All right, get better stories.' It was then that I was allowed to offer £1 a 1,000 words for good sf, though I had to try and get as much as possible at lower rates!

It seemed to me that with such a mass of rubbish competing for counter space, we had to do something distinctive in order to create reader loyalty. So, having now settled a programme of two sf titles a month, I put a strip across the cover and called them *Science Fiction Fortnightly*. These first stories were very much of a mixed bag – but I argued that the caption wouldn't hurt sales and in time might begin to assist them. Then my publisher came up with an idea. He said he would like to produce a monthly sf magazine.

I was not overjoyed. I'd been a periodical publisher and knew that the editorial work involved was ten times as great as producing a short novel. I had more than enough work on my plate for one man. Besides, where was I to find good-standard authors to fill each issue, with only £1 a 1,000 words to offer? When I insisted on increasing the rate, the publisher winced and changed the subject. Finally we compromised. We would produce a 'magazine' in conventional paperback format, but it would consist of one 35,000 word novel with a short editorial feature, and the odd short story as a filler. *Science Fiction Fortnightly* died, and *Authentic Science Fiction* was born. The title was the publisher's. I was never keen on it, but was never one to argue over trifles: at least it would carry a note of identification and would attract readers for our better-than-average stories.

Authentic became Hamilton's biggest steady seller. Within two years it was selling 20,000 copies at 2/-, compared with about 13,000 for other products selling at 1/6d.

It was only some time afterwards that I learned why Hamilton's had been anxious to start an sf magazine. A London publisher, Atlas, was having great success with the British reprint edition of *Astounding,* which seemed to me well ahead of anything we had in the UK. Rumour had it *Astounding* was selling 40,000 copies a month, and Hamilton's wanted to get in on the act.

Hamilton's agreed to employ artists with some pretensions to sf knowledge, and they were a decided improvement on some previous gaudy and uninspired horrors. Until *Authentic,* no one had ever commented favourably on our covers, so as compliments began to flow in I realised we were progressing. Previously Hamilton's had paid a mere nine guineas for a cover, *and* it had to be hand lettered for title, author and front cover blurb into the bargain. Now payment went up to fifteen guineas, and the lettering was done independently.

The *Authentic* series had been launched in the first week of January 1951. The first novel had the horrendous title of *Mushroom Men from Mars* by Lee Stanton. It was followed

two weeks later by *Reconnoitre Krellig II* by Jon J. Deegan.
This novel introduced readers to the 'Old Growler', a dodder-
ing old spaceship and its motley crew. Their unpretentious,
straight action space adventures were so popular that further
Deegan 'Old Growler' novels appeared, cementing the acceptance of the *Authentic* series. The title metamorphosed from
Science Fiction Fortnightly to *Science Fiction Monthly* with
issue nine in May 1951, and finally *Authentic SF* in September
1951. By October 1952 the lead novel had been augmented by
a serial, starting with Sydney J. Bounds's 'Frontier Legion'. By
January 1953 it was looking more like a magazine, with articles
and short stories. By that time Gordon Landsborough, who
had edited the series under the alias, L. G. Holmes, had left
Hamilton's and Herbert J. Campbell was in control.

Landsborough takes up the story again:

A new breed of author was being attracted to the Hamilton
stable. Bert Campbell, with his black beard and excellent
manuscripts, John Brunner floated through my office, Bryan
Berry, S. Fowler Wright, Ken Bulmer, Syd Bounds and many
more. Scientologist L. Ron Hubbard wrote for us. So did
E. C. Tubb and Bill Temple. Two other names I remember
are Roy Sheldon and Jon J. Deegan. I invented both these
names pre-*Authentic*. Apart from a few well-known writers
like John Russell Fearn this type of publisher always insisted
on employing a pen-name for their authors. Deliberately
they used several writers to that pen-name so that it could
not belong to any one writer. It was a way of controlling an
author who could never achieve fame under a pseudonym,
then go to another publisher taking the name with him.

The trouble was that in spite of the improved rates of pay,
it was still not enough to maintain the enthusiasm of good
writers. But I had pushed my publisher as far as he would
go. He stuck at £1 a 1,000 words. You don't build literary
empires on a quid a thou'!

Meanwhile *Authentic* continued to build up strength. But
all was not well. I had been promised full editorial control
of Hamilton's list. And one of the first things I had done
was to turn off the tap of the unpleasant sexo-sadistic
American gangster novels. There were still some in the pipe-
line and these I let through reluctantly. But I did not want
to handle any more.

So I was shaken one day when the publisher came to me and said that he wanted to maintain his list of American gangster stories after all. There was still a profitable market for them. I gave thought to the situation. These sadistic books were wearisome where they were not nauseating; the writing was so abysmal I disliked having to edit them. So I resigned.

The publisher was upset, but paid me a handsome tribute. He asked me to stay on for three motnhs and arrange for a successor. In fact, I took on two editors for Hamilton's, one to handle the westerns and 'sophisticateds', the other a very good editor for my enthusiasm, *Authentic*. That man was Herbert J. Campbell.

Bert was exactly the man for the job – or rather, he was too good for it. He had been writing sf novels for me since before the launching of *Authentic*, and he was a man who impressed me. He was a scientist first, and a fiction writer (though a good one) second. Whilst he had literary taste, he also had a scientific background, which inevitably meant the acceptance of sound stories only. Bert was rarely satisfied and nothing was really ever up to the standard of his requirement. Which is the hallmark of a good editor. He edited reluctantly, incapable of blaspheming at the worst of intellectual atrocities, as I did. Bert should have had the good fortune to be invited to edit for a major company. Notwithstanding, he made considerable improvement to *Authentic* during his term as editor. Some years after I left Hamilton's I ran into Bert, and it was clear he'd had enough of the publishing world. He was actively studying to begin a career in scientific research. In this he was eventually successful, and we lost him for sf writing. Today he is a respected senior scientist, the author of several important books on brain research and a happy man in the consequence.

It is more than likely that Campbell was the man behind the Jon J. Deegan alias. Certainly, British sf owes much to his tireless efforts and I'm glad to be able to afford him just credit in this history.

By 1952 *Authentic* was firmly established and was equal in popularity to *New Worlds*. Though there was yet another competitor on this scene, this time from Glasgow in Scotland. The magazine was *Nebula,* and one of its leading contributors was later to be Kenneth Bulmer. Bulmer was a great admirer of *Nebula,* and at this point I hand over to him:

When in the autumn of 1952 a new sf magazine appeared on the bookstalls of Britain, few readers could have foreseen that it would become what many fans regard as the best loved British sf magazine. Rumours and news of Nebula's impending début had been rife for many months before it actually appeared, so that the first issue could contain a letter section with congratulatory letters from leading fan personalities of the day. This was to be a strong feature of *Nebula,* a continuous involvement with fandom and its generous catering to fannish affairs.

The lead story was 'Robots Never Weep' by E. R. James, a Yorkshire postman. A long story, it filled no less than 103 of the 120 pages. The size was the same as *New Worlds* which contained only 96 pages, but *Nebula's* type-size was larger. At the time when *Nebula* burst on the scene, *New Worlds* had published its seventeenth issue and was already established in the format it had used to such good purpose, and was publishing material that would make the names of many British writers. *Authentic* was still in its small size publishing the stuff that would not improve until Bert Campbell, assuming full editorship, took a better grip on the magazine's policy. The new magazine was very welcome.

No giant publishing corporation nor combination of enthusiastic fans lay behind this venture, nor was it a cynical opportunistic publication by purely commercial publishers, printed by what the trade term 'Kipper Box Printers'. Instead, it was the brainchild of a young Scottish fan who loved sf to such an extent that he plunged all his slender resources into his own professional magazine. Peter Hamilton, plagued by recurring ill-health that at times brought him perilously close to death, had just been discharged from a nursing home when *Nebula* was born. Appearing at a time when the bookstalls were flooded with garish trash masquerading as science fiction, *Nebula* at once became a quality production and formed the third limb of responsible British sf development – *Nebula, New Worlds,* and *Authentic.*

During the proceedings of the 1953 sf convention held at the Bonnington Hotel in London, and despite the unexpected attendance of L. Ron Hubbard, Peter Hamilton made a

decided impact with his quiet good humour and obvious
dedication to sf. As a teetotaller Hamilton was duly bemused
when the convention committee succumbed en bloc to write
another scarlet page in sf history.

Continuously, Peter Hamilton worked at increasing the
quality of his magazine in every department, engaging very
often in intimate dialogues with his readers, urging them to
co-operate in the development of *Nebula*. His editorials were
invariably lively and honest with a genuine feeling of communication between editor and reader. Noted fan, Walter
Willis, wrote a regular fan column, and Forrest J. Ackerman
provided a regular film news column.

Many currently prominent sf writers had early stories –
often their first – published in *Nebula* over the years. Brian
Aldiss, for example, had his first story accepted by Peter
Hamilton. Robert Silverberg was another, as was Bob Shaw.
Fans struggling for authorship were always helped by Peter.
As Brian Aldiss says: 'He was a sympathetic editor to a
beginner. He was also a patient editor.' But of the better
known writers of the time nearly all were pleased to have
material in *Nebula*. And that included Bert Campbell of
Authentic!

The most prolific and popular author was E. C. Tubb who
managed the not inconsiderable feat of appearing consecu-
tively from numbers two to eleven, and who consistently
won the Best Author Award. Other prolific contributors
included William F. Temple, Brian Aldiss, Philip High, Eric
Frank Russell and myself. Other familiar names included
Harlan Ellison, John Rackham, John Kippax, Dan Morgan,
James White, Arthur Sellings and the evergreen Sydney
Bounds.

John Newman wrote many fine scientific articles, and, as
one half of Kenneth Johns, provided comprehensive coverage
of current scientific topics in the popular inside front cover
feature which presented photographic items unique at that
time.

The covers of *Nebula* were painted by many different
artists, including those well known in the field, like Quinn
and Rattigan, Clothier and Hunter, and also the cover artist
Peter was proud to claim he discovered – the late, greatly
lamented Ken McIntyre. Starting from issue ten a back cover
black-and-white illustration was run, mostly drawn by Arthur

Thomson. This gave a tremendously individual flavour to the magazine and added a dignity no amount of back cover advertisements could hope to equal.

Although *Nebula* often looked amateurish in format, this did create a sense of friendship, and as Peter paid his contributors a tidy sum more than other professional magazines, *Nebula,* despite its name, was never nebulous.

Perhaps something of what *Nebula* meant can best be summed up in Ted Tubb's perceptive words: '. . . many authors came to regard *Nebula* as not just another market, but as something with which they could have a peculiar emotional affinity . . . Authors wrote for *Nebula* with financial reward taking but secondary place, the desire of submitting a good story being of primary importance . . . the editor was always willing to experiment and print stories which other magazines may have found unacceptable. The end result was a form of gestalt in which the writers and contributors felt as if *Nebula* was 'their' magazine, and all that became a happy, well integrated family.'

Clearly therefore, even by the close of 1953, *Nebula* had become a prestige publication and helped place British sf firmly on the world map. For *world* map it was. Sf was no longer restricted to the United States and Britain. It was flourishing world-wide. So before returning to the USA and the height of the boom, there is no better time to look briefly at how sf magazine publishing was growing abroad.

8—GLOBAL DELUGE

One British reprint magazine that appeared in 1951 was not from American sources. *Amazing Science Stories,* a large-size magazine from Manchester, carried stories reprinted from *Thrills Incorporated* – an Australian magazine.

Australia had had its fair share of authors, notably Alan Connell, who sold some very entertaining stories to Gernsback's *Wonder Stories* in the early 1930s. It did not have its own indigenous sf magazine until *Thrills Inc* appeared in March 1950, its 50 pulp-size pages selling for 9d. It came from a publishers in Sydney and attracted work from local writers who, not knowing much about sf, blatantly copied their stories straight from US magazines. Local fans soon exposed this, with the result that while the magazine continued to use some (now acknowledged) US reprints, more original Australian sf appeared. Its fiction was predominantly juvenile however, and scarcely established itself. Norma K. Hemming was probably its most accomplished writer, and she was actually born in Ilford, Essex. She emigrated to Australia in 1949, and her fiction was to be found in every one of the last seven issues of *Thrills Inc*. She also appeared in the Nova magazines during the 1950s. Sadly, she died in July 1960, aged only thirty-two.

Thrills Inc collapsed in June 1952 after twenty-three issues, and subsequent Australian publications consisted primarily of American reprints with the occasional original Australian story. Leading Australian fans, Vol Molesworth and Graham Stone, did most of the donkey-work for these publications, but they were a far cry from a truly independent, original Australian magazine.

The Australians had the advantage that they could read American sf in its native language. Not so other foreign countries who were reliant on translations. Nevertheless, as the sf boom reverberated around the world, these translations appeared with more and more frequency.

Argentina, for instance, had had a sporadic pulp, *Narraciones Terrorificas* (*Terror Tales*), since 1939 which lasted until 1950, with seventy-two issues in all. Then came *Hombres De Futuro* which saw three pulp issues of fiction reprinted from *Thrilling Wonder*. But most important was *Mas Alla* which appeared on a monthly schedule in June 1953 from a Buenos Aires publisher. Initially featuring reprints it later contained much work by South American authors and was the mainstay sf publication on that continent during the 1950s.

The Swedish magazine, *Veckans Adventyr* (*Adventures of the Week*), had by 1946 biased its contents away from sf towards westerns and sports stories. This weekly periodical had started life in October 1940 as *Jules Verne Magasinet*. It folded in February 1947 after three hundred and thirty-one issues. Sweden would not again have a major sf magazine until March 1954 when the brothers Kurt and Karl-Gustaf Kindberg of Jönköping published their own magazine, *Häpna* (*Be Astounded*), under the editorship of Kjell Ekström. A monthly, digest-sized magazine in initially relied heavily on reprints, but later nurtured Swedish talent, like Bjorn Nyberg, known chiefly today through his connections with L. Sprague de Camp and the *Conan* stories of Robert E. Howard, *Häpna* was responsible for starting Swedish sf fandom and is thus considered very important in that country.

For the Netherlands to have a native sf magazine so soon after the War is a great surprise. Leading fan, Ben Abbas, in his own one-man effort, succeeded in delivering the first of *Fantasie en Wetenschap* in December 1948. This digest-sized monthly had four issues until problems made it impossible to continue, but the magazine, which contained Dutch material, stands as a monument to the efforts of the Dutch in those stricken days. Four years later another Dutch sf magazine appeared, *Planeet*, which reprinted from British sources, like the 'Old Growler' series. But there was only one issue however.

Mexico had a spate of sf magazines in this period, nearly all of which featured pirated translations from US sources, for which the writers were never paid. First came *Los Cuentos Fantasticos* which started with startling rapidity, having three numbers in July 1948 alone. But it appeared less regularly thereafter and folded after number forty-four in May 1953. Two years later *Enigmas* appeared, also with US reprints, and proved equally popular.

The first Italian language sf magazine came out in April 1952 – *Scienza Fantastica,* which had seven reprint issues. When that folded, Italy's greatest publishers, Mondadori, produced a fortnightly magazine, *Urania,* featuring reprinted US and British novels. *Urania* was a big success and sales soon reached 50,000 copies each issue, becoming the major Mediterranean publication.

France was notably absent from the sf scene for a long time, apart from *Conquetes,* which barely saw two issues before the War, and *V*, which hardly survived one after the War. But in October 1953, a French edition of *F & SF* appeared called *Fiction,* under the guiding hand of Maurice Renault. This leaned heavily at first on its mother publication, but in later years it was regularly publishing fiction by French and Belgian authors, most notably Charles Henneberg and Gerard Klein.

Germany is today regarded as the home of *Perry Rhodan,* which came to fruition in the early 1960s. Hitherto, apart from an enigmatic publication *Kapitän Mors* which existed before World War I, sf magazine publishing in Germany was barren until 1953, even though Germany had been responsible for the brilliant silent sf film, *Metropolis* (1926). It was through the efforts of Walter Ernsting that three magazines were born. *Utopia-Kleinband* was the more juvenile, styled after a single character featuring a lead novel about the adventures of Jim Parker in space! *Utopia-Grossband* featured mostly reprints, and it was not until *Utopia-Sonderband* appeared in December 1955 that the first adult sf magazine appeared in Germany, with both new and reprint material.

Even Japan had a magazine. In 1950 a few reprint numbers of *Amazing* had appeared, then in 1954 a single issue *Seiun* was published featuring four reprints and three native stories.

Without a doubt, science fiction now had a world-wide audience, but it was to America that they looked for trends. Only Britain had any quantity of native writers who could possibly dictate trends, and they were not yet at that stage. But with America undergoing a phenomenal boom in 1953 all eyes were centred on that scene to see what was going on.

9—ASPHYXIATION

The growing number of sf publications was evidence of a lucrative market in the US. With a public far more receptive to science fiction as a result of advances in science since the War. If ever a time was ripe for expansion, it was now.

This was also reflected in the growth of science fiction films. Two were particularly influential at this time: *Destination Moon* (1950), based on a story by Robert Heinlein and produced by George Pal, which attempted to show in authentic detail the first manned trip to the moon; and *The Day the Earth Stood Still* (1951), based on Harry Bate's excellent story 'Farewell to the Master' from a 1940 *Astounding*. In this film an ambassador of peace arrives from another world to make Earth aware of the perils of its nuclear weaponry. Both films were a huge success and helped stir up public interest in science fiction.

The snowball began to roll.

Science Fiction Quarterly revived in May 1951 under the editorship of Robert Lowndes. It was another pulp, and whilst featuring readable stories carried nothing outstanding apart from L. Sprague de Camp's 'Rogue Princess' (February 1952), a merry time-travel romp. During 1952, *Future combined with*

Science Fiction Stories at last shortened its name to simply *Future Science Fiction,* and in November, Lowndes added another pulp to his sf retinue, *Dynamic SF.* It contained a few good stories, Lester Del Rey's 'I Am Tomorrow' and Poul Anderson's 'The Chapter Ends' in particular, but *Dynamic* remained an average publication, only surviving six issues to close in January 1954. By that time Columbia had had their own thoughts about pulp magazines, of which more later.

A new publisher entered the field in March 1952, the Quinn publishing chain of Kingston, New York, with *If, Worlds of Science Fiction.* As its first editor, Quinn acquired the services of Paul W. Fairman.

Fairman was a name closely associated with the Ziff-Davis magazines. He had first been published in the February 1950 *Amazing* with 'No Teeth For the Tiger' and soon became one of their standard writers contributing under his own name and house pseudonyms, notably Ivar Jorgensen. Two of his stories ('The Cosmic Frame' from *Amazing,* and 'Deadly City' from *If*) were subsequently adapted into films (*Invasion of the Saucer Man* (1955) and *Target-Earth* (1954) resepectively). Fairman's associations with Ziff-Davis were obvious from *If*'s first issues. Apart from fiction by Howard Browne, Ray Palmer, Richard Shaver, Rog Phillips and Milton Lesser, Fairman also began a series called 'Personalities in Science Fiction' which led in the May 1952 *If* about Ray Palmer. Palmer instantly answered it in the June 1952 *Other Worlds,* setting certain facts straight.

After editing three issues, Fairman left *If* to join Ziff-Davis as an associate editor, leaving Quinn to edit *If* alone until he acquired the services of Larry Shaw from the May 1953 issue.

Whilst *If* cannot claim to have published any classics in its early years it certainly did not publish any poor fiction. The September 1953 issue, for instance, carried James Blish's 'A Case of Conscience', an early example of religion in science fiction, with a priest landing on a planet that knew no original sin. Arthur C. Clarke's 'Jupiter V', about the discovery of a statue on Jupiter's innermost satellite, also first appeared in *If,* in May 1953. The best description of *If* is that it 'consistently entertained'.

Magazines were now appearing with agonising rapidity. *Space Science Fiction* was launched in May 1952, edited by Lester Del Rey. Del Rey had learned through his agent that a new sf magazine was in the works and the publisher needed new novelettes, but had no idea about the field. The publisher was John Raymond, then better known for his 'girlie' magazines. The current boom in sf though had prompted Raymond's distributor to suggest entering the scene. Del Rey visited the offices and Raymond proceeded to pick his brains about science fiction. He finally suggested that Del Rey edit the magazine, and although Del Rey was not keen on the idea, his wife and several sf agents talked him into it. Del Rey takes up the story: 'I put together the first issue in a hurry out of what was at hand. My work included all buying, dummying the magazine, all proof-reading, and frequent trips to the printers. I found that it took about three days of actual work per issue.'

Despite the haste, number one of *Space SF* was first-class, with an impressive cover by Paul Orban, and carrying Del Rey's own lead novel 'Pursuit', which tells of a chase involving a host of psi powers. Henry Kuttner was in print again with his hilarious 'The Ego Machine', plus Isaac Asimov with 'Youth'. *Space* was digest-sized with 160 pages for thirty-five cents.

Del Rey proved to be an excellent editor. The second *Space SF* included a Robert E. Howard Conan adventure, 'The God in the Bowl', completed by L. Sprague de Camp. This was the first of many new Conan tales to appear. Del Rey also supplied a grim, realistic novel of Martian settlements, *Police Your Planet,* serialised in *Space* during 1953 under the alias, Erik Van Lhin.

Raymond then learned another distributor wanted an sf magazine, so he suggested Del Rey edit a second title of less quality with the emphasis on action. Thus was born *Science Fiction Adventures,* which came out in November 1952. This was the first of four magazines to bear that name. Del Rey is listed as both publisher (under his real name of Ramon Alvarez) and editor (under his Philip St. John alias). The magazine aimed at younger readers than *Space,* but the fiction was far from 'written down'. On the contrary, some very harsh, mature pieces appeared, such as Chad Oliver's 'The Fires of Forever' which led the first issue, and involves a search to save Earth from extinction. Besides its good fiction *SF Adventures* also carried a book review column by Damon Knight, 'The Dissecting Table' (the name he had used on his own column in *Worlds Beyond* three years earlier). Knight opened his review by warn-

ing readers that they might find some of his comments unpleasant and pugnacious, but he intended to say what he meant.
Over the years this insistence earned Knight such a reputation
as a book reviewer that in 1956 his reviews were edited into a
book, *In Search of Wonder*, and he won a special Hugo Award
that year as the best sf critic.

Incidentally, book reviews were becoming an essential part
of the sf magazine line-up. In October 1951 *Astounding*
employed P. Schuyler Miller as resident reviewer in 'The
Reference Library', a column he wrote regularly thereafter till
his death in 1974. Miller was very much the dean of sf book
reviewers, and he also received a special Hugo for his services
in 1963.

In March 1953 appeared Del Rey's third magazine, *Fantasy
Magazine*, featuring another Conan tale completed by de Camp,
'The Black Stranger'. From the second number it became
Fantasy Fiction, the slight change coming because Ziff-Davis
had threatened a law-suit on the duplication of their title
Fantastic. *Fantasy Fiction* featured some splendid Hannes Bok
covers and superb quality contents, and the magazine now
ranks as a fantasy collector's must. Unfortunately, it only
lasted four issues.

For some months plans had been afoot for a fourth magazine, *Rocket Stories*. It finally appeared in April 1953 with the
editor credited as Wade Kaempfert. *Rocket* was a digest-sized
imitation of *Planet Stories* containing several well-written and
mature stories such as John Jakes's 'Jackrogue Second' in the
first issue, about a man brought back to life only to face bitter
opposition from everyone he meets.

By mid-1953 Del Rey was at loggerheads with Raymond over
the hopeless situation at the offices. Recently Del Rey told
me the whole story:

Everything was always confused at Raymond Publications.
The magazines were scheduled by Raymond's whim. (As
when he informed me suddenly they were to be monthlies –
and never quite got around to living up to that.) He'd call
me up, or wait until I came in to pick up manuscripts, then
announce that *Space* (or whatever) was due, and I should
bring in copy the next day. (Incidentally, I had full authority
for what was bought; John W. Campbell called Raymond
and convinced him that an editor had to have a free hand.

John did favours like that.) Anyhow, that meant I got in touch with agents, collected stories, looked through the manuscripts, and made up an issue before the next day – mostly, that's exactly how it went. We paid only after publication, so I never even tried to buy an inventory; I would have some submissions I liked, but to get my lead stories, I either called agents for stories I knew about, or in desperation wrote one myself (often overnight). It was a miserable way to run a magazine.

The magazines made money. Despite what has been said about fantasy being unsuitable for the market that magazine sold about 70,000 copies an issue, *SF Adventures* slightly less (but more than *Galaxy*). Since I broke even at 45,000 copies we were really making excellent returns on the magazines. (*Space* and *Rocket* had more distribution trouble, but they also showed a profit). But instead of putting the money back into the magazines Raymond used it all for god-knows-what, expansion of his office, wild schemes . . . There was never any money available, except the advance made by the distributor after the magazines were printed.

I made a proposal to him for upgrading the magazines, paying better and more quickly, and for a decent return for myself. I proved how few extra copies must be sold to justify that, and I told him I'd be forced to resign otherwise. He agreed. And nothing came of it. Then one day I walked into the office intending to raise hell (and maybe resign) because I'd discovered some authors had not been paid. He wasn't there, but his art director told me Raymond had new plans – maximum payment on all magazines to be 1c a word, no more illustrations except those by the art director, and pages cut to 144. I left word that I had quit and went home. I stayed quit.

Raymond informed everyone that I'd been fired, and his lawyer threatened to sue me for 'slander and libel' because I'd returned the manuscripts to authors, stating that the new rate was in effect. My reply convinced the lawyer to tell Raymond to lay off and stop spreading stories about me.

Raymond hired a new editor, Harry Harrison. Harrison refused to handle *Fantasy Fiction*, so Raymond hired Fletcher Pratt who assembled one issue but refused to deliver it until the authors were paid. They weren't, and Raymond dropped the magazine. The others continued under Harrison for a while longer but Raymond tired of the whole field and he promptly folded the remaining titles. Last to go was *SF Adventures* in May 1954, which had reached a high spot with the serialisation of Cyril Kornbluth's novel about a spy in a future world of crooked governments, *The Syndic*.

Del Rey's magazines are fondly remembered as harbingers of good fiction, and stand as a fine example of what a knowledgeable editor can achieve against the aggravating wall of ignorance displayed by most publishers towards science fiction. *Space SF* was the first magazine to publish a story by Algis Budrys, 'Walk to the World' in November 1952. In retrospect, the passing of these magazines was a great loss to the sf world.

By 1952, *Amazing* had almost discarded the stigma of the Shaver period. For some unaccountable reason Browne tried to replace its esoteric appeal with something more 'respectable'. 'Master of the Universe', a so-called history of the future from 1975 to 2575 revealed in a manuscript found off the coast of Spain, was supposedly the answer. The whole episode, which was serialised in *Amazing* from April to November 1952 was thoroughly boring.

However, Browne was given the go-ahead again to try his slick approach, which materialised in March 1952 with the publication of *Fantastic,* dated Summer. *Fantastic* was digest-sized, 160 pages and sold for thirty-five cents. It had a full six-colour cover by Barye Phillips, plus the reproduction of a work of art on the back cover, plus coloured interior artwork. Stories included Ray Bradbury's vignette 'The Smile', Isaac Asimov's 'What If', Walter Miller's absorbing 'Six and Ten are Johnny' and more remarkably 'Professor Bingo's Snuff' by Raymond Chandler. Sales were reportedly so phenomenal that *Fantastic* was rapidly rescheduled from quarterly to bi-monthly. The publishers now saw the future of the pulps was unpromising and went ahead to change *Amazing Stories* to a digest with the April/May 1953 issue. The price increased accordingly to thirty-five cents, and to be on the safe side, *Amazing*'s schedule was staggered to bi-monthly alternating with *Fantastic*. With the May 1953 issue *Fantastic Adventures* was combined with *Fantastic*.

The first new digest *Amazing* aimed again at a slick audience. The lead story was 'Mars Confidential', a so-called exposé by reporters Jack Lait and Lee Mortimer. Also present were top

writers known to the slicks, Ray Bradbury, Robert Heinlein
Theodore Sturgeon, Murray Leinster, and Richard Matheson
whose impressively shocking 'The Last Day' is included in this
volume.

Browne was to be congratulated. *Amazing* made the transition to digest with such effect that it was looked upon thereafter
as a completely new product, and it lived to fight another day
with renewed vigour.

In passing, it is worth recalling that in the summer of 1952
there were two *Fantastic*s on the stands. That from Ziff-Davis
plus *Fantastic Science Fiction*. Since the latter was a large-size
publication with only 48 pages it was instantly distinguishable
It contained low-grade juvenile fiction well illustrated by artists
from the comic magazines. The only recognisable name was
that of Walter Gibson who supplied the lead novel and edited
the magazine. Gibson was renowned as the author of the novels
about super-detective The Shadow, whose adventures had
appeared in the magazine of that name from November 1931
to Summer 1949. Gibson had hitherto edited the short-lived
rival to *Weird Tales*, *Tales of Magic and Mystery*, which had
seen five issues in 1927-8. *Fantastic SF* saw even fewer issues:
only one in August and a second in December 1952.

Just to keep the confusion of titles complete, after Del Rey's
Space SF, in October 1952 Standard Magazines issued *Space
Stories*. But this was a pulp magazine, and already it seemed a
new pulp was not what the public wanted, so after four bi-
monthly issues, it ceased.

The same was true of *Tops in SF*. Malcolm Reiss decided to
capitalise on the reprint trend by digging into the vaults of
Planet Stories for a new pulp, *Tops in SF*. The first publication
in March 1953 must certainly have appealed to one section of
the public, but was lost among all the other pulps, so with a
second in October, Reiss changed the format to digest. Too
late, it didn't work. *Tops* disappeared.

More and more short-lived magazines came onto the market
Many must have been planned before the boom was at its
height, hoping to jump in on the bandwaggon, and not realising
there was going to be a whole waggon train. Thus the magazines
were but a drop in the ocean, and it was no matter whether
they were good or bad. Unless they had adequate display on
the stalls the public could not see them to buy them. This was
often the reason for their early demise.

For instance, in 1952 Wollheim left Avon Books and his two magazines, *Fantasy Reader* and *Science Fiction Reader* folded after eighteen and three issues respectively. But in January 1953 appeared the hybrid *Avon Science Fiction and Fantasy Reader* edited by Avon's comics editor, Sol Cohen. This neat, digest magazine contained all new fiction (bar one) with a high-quality content of all the major names. Interior artwork was superbly executed, concentrating mostly on the erotic, but although it was an above average publication, it was terminated after a second issue in April.

Chester Whitehorne, who had briefly edited *Planet Stories* in 1945, reappeared in 1953 with a thick, digest magazine, *Vortex SF*. The idea here was for a magazine crammed full of ultra short stories, twenty in the first issue. The response was encouraging and a second appeared six months later with twenty-five stories. But that idea could not last for long – and neither did *Vortex*. It was never seen again. Whitehorne was though. He popped up in 1954 with a very logical magazine, *Science Fiction Digest,* which was further evidence of the popularity of the digest format. The idea was to select fiction from all the various slicks and other magazines, so becoming in effect a *Year's Best* collection in magazine form. It was a good idea, and one that should have worked. But Whitehorne's selection of stories left much to be desired, as did the presentation, and despite such telling features as 'My Experience with the Supernatural' by Eartha Kitt, *SF Digest* also disappeared after just two issues.

By mid-1953 it seemed that the whole publishing world had gone berserk, especially since in February Ballantine Books had started a regular series of paperback anthologies carrying all new stories, *Star Science Fiction Stories*, edited by Frederik Pohl. Sf writers had never had it so good: with titles appearing daily, their writings would sell somewhere. New writers had ample opportunity to ply their wares and also to experiment. It did mean that more bad fiction was published, but as a rule this appeared in the lesser publications. The major magazines, *Galaxy*, *Astounding*, *F & SF*, with their better rates and prestige, were still able to pick the best names.

One of the major sf events of 1953 that attracted much attention was the return of Hugo Gernsback. Gernsback had left in 1936 when he had handed over *Wonder Stories* to Standard, but Gernsback Publications had continued with various scientific journals. And he himself had given talks and published the occasional humorous annuals such as *Newspeek* and *Quip*. Then March 1953 saw the first issue of *Science Fiction Plus*. Neither a digest magazine, nor a pulp, it was a glossy slick, large size (8½ x 11 in) with 64 pages. Surely at thirty-five cents this would sell.

Obviously many were attracted to it out of curiosity. Gernsback was editor/publisher, and his forty-year-old son, Harvey, was executive editor. But the man who did all the work of reading and finding material, blurb-writing and compiling was Sam Moskowitz. Moskowitz was a leading sf fan, already establishing himself as a science fiction historian with his history of organised fandom, *The Immortal Storm* (1954). He acquired fiction from most of the major names in sf, as well as bringing back famous names from the past – Eando Binder, Raymond Z. Gallun, Richard Tooker and Harry Bates. Gernsback provided lengthy scientific articles, 'The World in 2046' or 'World War III – In retrospect', plus his usual editorials. In one of these he derided much of the *pseudo* science fiction being published, claiming writers should be more factual in the science they used. To this end he concocted a symbol of the letters 'SF' inset in a black ball surmounted by a star, which was put next to a story that contained new scientific ideas certain to be realised in the future. It wasn't next to many, beyond Gernsback's own!

Frank R. Paul returned as art director, although his work usually only illustrated Gernsback's extrapolations. Stories were accompanied by cameo-photographs of the authors. The old Gernsback departments, 'Science Questions and Answers' and 'Science Quiz', were again featured and there was even a novel translated from the French. It was *Wonder Stories* slicked up and modernised. Would the public accept it?

Early reports were favourable. *SF Plus* appeared with four monthly issues. Then sales began to drop and the schedule was staggered, until after number seven, it collapsed in December 1953. Why? As a slick, it should not have been lost among the welter of pulps or digests. Gernsback's radio journals had a healthy distribution, so it had not suffered from that problem. Essentially, the reason lay with the attitudes of modern day audiences. By 1953 an entire generation had grown up since Gernsback's *Wonder* days. Anyone born in 1926, the year *Amazing* first appeared, would have discovered sf at the age of say, fifteen, in 1941 at the height of Campbell's *Astounding*. The subsequent development of sf was his development. *SF Plus* was an anachronism. Although it carried some excellent fiction: Simak's 'Spacebred Generations', Leinster's 'Nightmare Planet', Philip José Farmer's 'Strange Compulsion', to the audience of 1953 the approach of the magazine was heavy-handed and readers feared being bogged down in a concentration of scientific prognostication. They preferred to continue with *Galaxy* or *Astounding*.

Much the same reticence attached itself to the other new publications. There was *Orbit SF*, edited by Jules Saltman, which showed obvious overtones of a poor man's *Galaxy*. Then there was *Cosmos Science Fiction and Fantasy* which read like a poor man's *Imagination*. That the magazine boasted stories by Poul Anderson, Arthur C. Clarke, Robert Sheckley . . . or anyone else, was to no avail – so did nearly every other magazine. It was only the die-hard sf fan who would hunt down each publication and this was not enough to support all the magazines. The vital factor was timing: being on the news-stand at the right time to sell. If a new supply of magazines came in to the retailer while his racks were still full, that magazine stayed in its box until either there was a space or someone asked for a copy. If it were a new magazine, people would be unlikely to ask for it so, whatever its quality, it would be doomed. Yet now, a quarter of a century later, collectors hunt down the magazines and gasp in amazement at the rich amalgam of names often with first-class stories and think, 'Why did this magazine fold?'

Louis Silberkleit at Columbia decided to take a gamble and issued a digest-sized *Science Fiction Stories* with no cover date. That meant the retailer had no return date for the magazine, so it hung around until there was space on the stalls, and it invariably ended up on display. After only four months *Science Fiction* had sold enough to warrant a second issue, and Lowndes went ahead on the same basis. The issues appeared in August 1953 and July 1954 respectively, and sold very well. Silberkleit was prepared, and in June 1954 *Future* changed from pulp to digest. But *SF Quarterly* did not. The opinion was that the public still regarded the *Quarterlies* as something special. A digest *Quarterly* just did not seem right, so it stayed as a pulp.

Just why *Fantastic Universe* survived while others collapsed is not clear. It first appeared in June 1953 at the very height of the boom, and should have been swallowed up. But it wasn't. It was published by Leo Margulies of King-Size Publications, Park Avenue, New York, and had good distribution as it was a companion to *The Saint Detective Magazine*, which enjoyed high sales. That was one point in its favour. Another was that Sam Merwin was the editor. The Margulies/Merwin combination had been a great hit in the 1940s with *Thrilling Wonder* and sf enthusiasts were bound to be enamoured with it. Furthermore, its thirty-five cent cover price bought a digest with 192 pages – more than any other magazine. Even though its page count dropped after number two, and Merwin left to become an associate editor at *Galaxy*, it had obviously captured enough readers in its early stages to secure a viable audience.

Not so *Spaceway*, from the indefatigable William Crawford. Crawford's *Fantasy Book* had died of malnutrition, mainly a lack of adequate distribution, after its eighth issue in January 1951. Shortly thereafter Crawford was requested to edit a new magazine styled around the Hollywood sf movie king, George Pal, to be called *George Pal's Tales of Space Conquest*. As often happens with these high-flown ideas, it never materialised. But Crawford, having made connections with a new distributor and actually having prepared and lino-typed an issue of *Pal*, decided to take the plunge again with *Spaceway*. Number one, digest-sized, dated December 1953 was better produced than *Fantasy Book*, but alas the distributor again pulled out. Crawford was once more left high and dry, and he struggled on valiantly, but with diminishing capital and resources *Spaceway* rapidly deteriorated to a rather shoddy production. Crawford managed to secure a British edition, but that was not enough. *Spaceway* ran to number eight and closed in January 1955 – but not permanently.

Ray Palmer, now back in circulation after his accident, could view this turmoil as if from outside. The sf boom was centred on New York and if distribution failed, then sales seldom left that city. Palmer was in Chicago with his *Other Worlds*, and his only competition from that town was William Hamling's *Imagination*. Of course other magazines were displayed there, but Palmer had more chance to have his magazines displayed. So he created a mini-boom of his own. In June 1953 a new digest sf magazine came from George Bell of Bell Publications in North Clark Street, Chicago. It was neat, aiming for high standards and presenting some first-class fiction by major names. Ray Palmer moved in, and with its third issue, *Universe* was under the control of Palmer and Mahaffey, and featured excellent artwork by Virgil Finlay, Lawrence Stevens and Edd Cartier, three of the biggest names around. It included a whole variety of fiction, from L. Sprague de Camp's sword and sorcery tale 'The Hungry Hercynian' to Isaac Asimov's tale of the Martians on Mount Everest, 'Everest'. It was a good magazine.

As a companion, Palmer retitled *Other Worlds* to *Science Stories*. Then he started another magazine, this time an occult fiction companion to *Fate*, called *Mystic*. Strictly outside the realm of this series, I mention it because of its January 1954 number, in which Palmer talks again about the Shaver Mystery, gives his views, and then supplies his own complete story based on the facts, 'The Devil's Empire', which tells how Lucifer conquered Atlan. Surprisingly readable, remaining the best written of all the stories of the myth, it is well worth reading for its novelty.

By Christmas 1953, with the sf wave having crested, there were still twenty-seven surviving titles of an sf nature in the United States alone. Only seven of these were pulp. Even *Weird Tales* had changed to digest in September 1953, but for that magazine, the backbone of the weird fiction scene since 1923, the end was near. The final blow came when the American News Corporation, the major pulp distributor, refused to handle any more pulp magazines, since they were no longer paying. The comic industry was booming, the slicks were far more profitable, and a new line was beginning: Hugh Heffner had just commenced his man's magazine, *Playboy*, with astonishing results. The distributor was only interested in profit and pulps were not profitable. The same logic applied to the advertisers who paid more to the slick magazines for far wider coverage. Whether or not there was an audience for the pulps, they were being swept away by these powers, and with that final cornerstone gone the pulps were stranded. It was too late now to change. Too late to make amends.

Weird Tales died September 1954. *Thrilling Wonder* died

January 1955. *Fantastic Story Magazine* died April 1955. *Planet Stories* died June 1955. *Startling Stories* died October 1955.

Some of the biggest names in the sf field, and among the most established, all vanished within a year because no one was interested in distributing them anymore.

But at least they went with their heads high. *Thrilling Wonder* and *Startling* had been towering publications in their last years. They had suffered one blow when in 1952 their leading cover artist, Earle Bergey, died. He was irreplaceable; he had epitomised the magazines and his covers with their BEMs and brass-bra'd blondes represented an era. But a new generation of sf artists had entered the field, such as Alex Schomburg, Ed Emshwiller and Jack Coggins, and they took over from Bergey with their own particular talents and styles.

Samuel Merwin had edited the magazines up till the summer of 1951 when he had left, intending to write more fiction. But he appeared reviewing books in *Amazing,* then editing the first issues of *Fantastic Universe* then helping out at *Galaxy.* He was succeeded at Standard by Samuel Mines, who at that time was probably the most broadminded of all editors. He wanted stories of literary quality, but he didn't give a damn for taboos, proving it by publishing the story that has gone down in legend as being the first to bring sex into science fiction: 'The Lovers' by Philip José Farmer. It appeared as a complete novel in the August 1952 *Startling,* and Mines used it as a launching pad on which to sound off about restrictions in science fiction. I wish I had room to reprint that editorial in full, for not only is it most sensible but it shows how Mines was a key figure in furthering the frontiers of science fiction. The editorial said in part:

Editorially and otherwise, we have long contended that science fiction must be more than hopeful science; it must be *good* fiction as well. It must contain the basic requirements of drama, it must be well told, it must depict real people, it must be as sincere in its emotional values as in calculating the speed of a spaceship operating on ultra-galactic drive. Until this is achieved, *Time* book-reviewers will continue to make disparaging comparisons with westerns.

It is our contention that anything can be done in science

fiction – and should be done. It is actually the broadest of all mediums, because it is imagination unlimited, A lot of sf authors writing today are good as can be in their own type of story, but the type has turned into a rut. They are writing the same basic story they wrote fifteen years ago . . .[9]

Merwin challenged writers to experiment with daring themes and highlighted 'The Lovers' as the find of the decade. He hoped it would make writers sit up and say: 'My gosh, I didn't know we could do anything like that in science fiction!'[9] That same crusading talk would be used by Harlan Ellison in his taboo-breaking anthology *Dangerous Visions* in 1967. But here it is in a pulp magazine fifteen years earlier.

In 'The Lovers' humans land on a planet where the humanoid inhabitants metamorphose from insects. The females, who grow into the image of a human woman, can only breed by mating with a real human male. After pregnancy, the mother dies and the young live off the flesh. The insects, called lalitha, learn that a certain drink prevents pregnancy. When one of the humans falls in love with a lalitha he assumes she is addicted to the drink. Not knowing its real purpose he dilutes it, with the result that the lalitha conceives and dies.

The story is beautifully and effectively told, and showed powerfully how sex could be an integral part of a story without being obscene. 'The Lovers' was beyond doubt a milestone in science fiction, yet it took Samuel Mines to realise it – the editor of a pulp magazine with the brash name of *Startling Stories*. If ever a story was 'startling', this was it, and surprisingly the story had previously been rejected by both Campbell and Gold, and might not have seen the light of day at all, as Farmer was not then a big name in sf. This marked his first appearance, since when his gluttony for hard work has made him one of the most prolific, original and admired authors in the genre.

'The Lovers' was no isolated success for Mines. He had also purchased Edmond Hamilton's 'What's It Like Out There?' which saw print in the December 1952 *Thrilling Wonder*. He mentions the story in the same editorial quoted above, saying that it 'is so far removed from his Captain Future stories as to convince anyone that it is the work of a different writer.'[9] Hamilton had written an earlier version of the story in 1933! But its harshness as it paints a grim and all too realistic picture of the first expedition to Mars caused it to be rejected by the editors at that time. Hamilton had become stereotyped for his cosmic calamities that earned him the nickname 'World Wrecker'. Such a departure from his, and the pulp formula, could not be entertained.

But after the War, it was realism that science fiction needed, and writers at last found they could break the old moulds. 'The Lovers' had broken the sex barrier, and throughout the genre traditions and taboos were being smashed. Religion had hitherto been sacrosanct, until Ray Bradbury turned his hand to it. Samuel Merwin at *Thrilling Wonder* had purchased 'The Man' for the February 1949 issue, which describes a spaceship landing on another world only to discover that, just the day before, Christ had come. 'In This Sign', where Bradbury details a sin-free Mars, was bought by Ray Palmer but published in Hamling's *Imagination* for April 1951.

Ray Palmer bought several of Bradbury's more controversial stories, which shows that Palmer was not as unperceptive as some would make out. Despite Bradbury's acceptance in the slick magazines, 'Way in the Middle of the Air' was rejected by *Harper's*, and instead appeared in the July 1950 *Other Worlds*. The story depicts a Mars inhabited by negroes who are preparing for apartheid upon hearing that a rocket-load of white people is coming. The sequel, 'The Other Foot', did see mainstream publication in *New Story* for March 1951. In this tale, life on Earth is nearly extinct and the whites agree to shine shoes or whatever provided the negroes rescue them all.

The unprecedented explosion of sf publishing in the early 1950s had brought with it a new liberation. It was a direct result of the nuclear age, which had brought more public acceptance of science fiction, and which in turn encouraged writers to polish both their style and approach with the result that science fiction came through gleaming. By today's terms the sf of the early fifties will hardly seem liberated at all, but one has to view it through the eyes of the 1940s. It was revolutionary indeed.

The American boom was having its own echo in Britain, and whilst this was not advancing trends in any way, it was bringing out a wealth of hidden talent.

10—HOME RULE

Even during the thirties and forties, when home markets for sf were scarce in Britain, the country had still developed some remarkable writers who had taken the United States by storm. First had been John Russell Fearn and John Beynon Harris, then Eric Frank Russell, William F. Temple, Arthur C. Clarke and John Christopher. John Beynon Harris had recently been reborn as John Wyndham and was receiving much acclaim following the success of his book, *The Day of the Triffids*. That Britain could produce such talent with a negligible home market was remarkable. Just what the country would now produce with several British magazines was nothing short of fantastic.

By early 1954 Britain had five chief magazines. Mercifully, all of Spencer's sf magazines ceased during 1954, and only a more readable *Supernatural Stories,* written almost single-handedly by Robert Lionel Fanthorpe, sustained publication. Other forgettable publications made brief appearances, such as Gerald Swan's largely reprint *Space Fact and Fiction* which was even more juvenile-looking than Spencer's denizens; and a one-shot, *Worlds of the Universe*, of which Mark Denholm's (J. R. Fearn) lead story 'Waters of Eternity' was readable, but with only three stories failed to present sufficient evidence to show its worth. That left *New Worlds*, *Science Fantasy*, *Authentic*, *Nebula* and a new *Vargo Statten Science Fiction Magazine*, with its first issue in January 1954.

Among the plethora of British sf paperbacks, good and bad, issued since 1950, one by-line that had stood out was that of Vargo Statten. It was the contractual pen name of John Russell Fearn who had now found a well-paying market closer to home – well-paying only in that he was able to sell everything he could write, as fast as he could write it. Because Fearn had been known to use an army of pen-names and because most of the British sf papaerbacks appeared with pseudonymous by-lines, many were assumed to be the work of Fearn. Atrocious work under names as appalling as the contents (Marco Garron, Vector Magroon, Aston del Martia) all served to blacken his name – although they were not his work !

Nevertheless the popularity of the Statten books, with less critical younger readers and a general public unfamiliar with the basic concepts of sf, resulted in huge sales – the Statten books outsold everything else on the stands. This prompted the publishers, Scion Ltd, of Avonmore Road, London, to bring out the magazine. Pulp-sized and shoddily printed, it was edited by Scion's general editor, Alistair Paterson (although attributed to Statten) and was slanted to juvenile appeal. The first issue consisted mostly of Fearn's fiction under pen-names, but E. C. Tubb was also present, another Scion stalwart. Tubb was not one to write down to youngsters: his work was trademarked by his tendency towards grim reality. He contributed a short novel, *The Inevitable Conflict*, which was serialised in the first three issues. It opened with a gory description of a man jumping off a roof and landing close to a casual passer-by! By number four, production was vastly improved and, with a switch to digest size, the title became *Vargo Statten British Science Fiction Magazine*. The subsequent history of the magazine is here fully detailed for the first time by my colleague, Phil Harbottle, Fearn-addict extraordinaire:

Then came an upheaval. Scion Ltd, in common with most other British publishers, issued floods of western and gangster novels. The former were harmless, but the latter, in the mode popularised by Hank Jansen, were crudely written sexo-sadistic stories as pointed out by Gordon Landsborough earlier. Many of these went too far for the rather conservative Watch Committees of the day and successful prosecutions were brought against offending publishers. The great clean-up campaign began, a natural gut reaction against the prurient trash being served up by cynical publishers. Scion had been as guilty as anyone, and they copped a crippling fine. The directors squabbled over whose responsibility the fiasco had been as the offending books actually dated back to a previous managerial era. Scion had been a successful firm and presented an attractive proposition to a conglomerate called the Henry Squire Co Ltd, which was swallowing up a number of other small publishing houses. This company refloated Scion Ltd as Scion Distributors Ltd with Alistair Paterson still responsible for the sf lists. Paterson attempted to continue the activities of the various firms Squire's had inherited. There was even an attempt to produce a British reprint of *Tops in SF*, but as that saw only two US issues, it got nowhere.

But times were changing. Publishing standards, led by Penguin, Pan and Corgi Books, were rising. The day of the cheaply produced sf, gangster and western novels was over. The conglomerate found that it had swallowed a cancer. The situation was aggravated by the fact that Squire's found it owed a large sum of money to a firm called Dragon Press in Luton, who had printed many of the cheap British paperbacks, and had remained unpaid by the earlier companies. So developed the next step which led to the attrition and eventual death of the *Vargo Statten* empire.

To offset the debt, the Squire Company handed over their best assets, the *Vargo Statten* magazine and novels, to Dragon Press. Fearn himself, still contracted to Scion, was part of the deal. He took over the editorship of the magazine with its sixth issue, whereupon it became simply *British Science Fiction Magazine*.

With Fearn in control the magazine took a turn. Paterson had antagonised fandom by having his authors write down for younger readers. Under Fearn the magazine openly catered to fandom, with the expansion of its 'Inquisitor' department conducted by arch-fan, A. Vincent Clarke. Harry Cohn (Manchester fan Dave Cohen) ran a 'Personalities in Fandom' column. Fiction improved as much encouragement was given to new writers, such as Barrington J. Bayley, who would feature prominently in the later development of sf in Britain. The magazine acquired a definite personality, but Fearn was fighting a lost cause, labouring under a crippling handicap imposed by the publisher.

Dragon were not really publishers and they misinterpreted a fall-off in the magazine's circulation (the natural 'settling' to a firm level). They panicked and slashed Fearn's budget by more than half. At only 12/6d a 1,000 words (for all rights!) Fearn didn't stand a chance against other magazine editors who offered a minimum of 25/- a 1,000 for first British serial rights only.

So while many new writers contributed, few established authors bothered because of the miserly rate. The prolific E. C. Tubb still appeared, but insisted on using a pseudonym. Even Fearn stopped supplying new stories and astutely reworked his old wartime American stories under different pseudonyms. A standard cover was adopted for the sake of economy, and with a further name-change to *The British Space Fiction Magazine*, the magazine somehow lasted until February 1956 and its nineteenth issue, when its collapse was hastened by a general printing strike. With the passing of Vargo Statten – who started and finished the boom – the British sf magazine scene settled down to a steady improvement in keeping with the increasing standards of British publishing generally.

Meanwhile what of the leading authors who had been appearing in the other four magazines?

By the early 1950s Britain's leading names (Clarke, Wyndham, Russell, Christopher) had virtually deserted the British scene. One who would soon join their ranks was Charles Eric Maine whose novels like *The Mind of Mr Soames* and *The Tides Went Out* have made him a front line author. Maine (real name David McIlwain) was a radio engineer and the editor of a technical magazine. His very successful radio play, *Spaceways*, was filmed and later published in book form. He was also appearing in sf magazines at that time, starting with his short story about matter transmitters, 'Repulsion Factor' (*Authentic*, September 1953).

Many authors continued to write for the magazines, however. There was the talented Scots writer, J. T. McIntosh, who was first published in the December 1950 *Astounding* with 'The Curfew Tolls' and was soon in print regularly both sides of the Atlantic. He provided *New Worlds* with its first serial in 1952, 'The Esp Worlds', wherein a telepath is despatched to a world governed by women adept in teleportation. By 1953 McIntosh joined the American trend for breaking taboos with his story 'Made in USA' (*Galaxy*, April 1953) in which a husband sues his wife for divorce on the grounds she never revealed she was an android until the wedding night!

Lan Wright made his first sales to the Spencer magazines, but was first printed in *New Worlds* for January 1952 with 'Operation Exodus' which concerns the transfer of Earth's overpopulation to another sector of space, only to discover an alien spaceship interested in the same territory. Wright rapidly made a name for himself in the Nova magazines particularly in the mid-1950s with his series about Ambassador Dawson and his humorous attempts in diplomacy which was a forerunner to Keith Laumer's popular Retief series of the sixties.

The name J. F. Burke is today often linked with his *Hammer Horror Omnibus* books, but he first appeared in print with a story about conditioned citizens in the future called 'Chessboard' (*New Worlds*, January 1952). He had almost made his début ten years earlier when he sold a story to *Tales of Wonder*, but the magazine folded before his work was published. (Burke later became a mainstay of *Authentic*.)

That January 1952 *New Worlds* was quite a platform issue for new writers, as besides Lan Wright and Jonathan Burke it also marked the première of James White with his first story, 'Assisted Passage'. The focus of this tale is the military and the first manned rocket with the wrong pilot! White, from Ireland, was obsessive about authentic scientific detail, and his many subsequent stories earned him a high reputation in British circles. He really came into his own in 1957 though, when he commenced his series about a space hospital with 'Sector General'.

Fellow Irishman, Bob Shaw, is also firmly established today, although he only came back to writing in the mid-1960s. He actually began with a clever story, 'Aspect', in the August 1954 *Nebula*, describing the exploration of an alien planet by an Earth team who discover other aliens have been there before them.

1953 saw the magazine début of John Brunner, one of Britain's major award-winning writers today. Brunner had sold a pocketbook in 1951 while still at school, but its actual title remains a closely guarded secret, since Brunner has his sensitivities! When still in his teens he appeared in the March 1953 *Astounding* as John Loxmith with 'Thou Good and Faithful', and also sold a novel, *The Wanton of Argus*, set in a feudal society on another planet to *2 Complete Science Adventure Books*. By the mid-1950s Brunner was becoming a name to be reckoned with.

Kenneth Bulmer, who had sold several pocketbook novels, was finally published in magazine format in the April 1954 *Authentic* with 'First Down'. It appears somewhat dated today, yet twenty years ago this action story about two men occupying a one-man rocket, both determined to be the first on the moon, was well received. Thereafter, Bulmer maintained a regular sale of excellent stories, mostly of novelette length, to all four leading magazines. He was also one half of the writing team Kenneth Johns, with research chemist John Newman. Their scientific articles became regular features of all the magazines, particularly *New Worlds* and *Nebula*.

But the name most synonymous with British science fiction today is that of Brian Aldiss. His first sale was 'T', about a mysterious entity encapsulated in a space-time projectile aimed at our solar system and timed to activate when the Earth is reached. It was not seen in print though until the November 1956 *Nebula*. He was first published in the *Bookseller*, 13 February 1954, with 'A Book in Time', and made his entry in the sf magazine field in the July 1954 *Science Fantasy* with 'Criminal Record', a cleverly told tale of the lesson learned from a record from the future. Aldiss rapidly developed as a challenging new author.

One British author achieved a special coup in 1953: Bryan Berry, who sold several novels to Hamilton, under the arrangements then prevalent – all rights for about £40. Hamilton succeeded in selling them to Fiction House, and they appeared in the pulp *2 Complete Science Adventure Books*. Berry received no additional payment for this reprinting, while the publishers pocketed over £300. Berry protested to Fiction House who responded apologetically but made no further payment. However, they did request to see some of his short stories. Berry sent a selection, and *Planet Stories* of January 1953 carried three titles by Berry, all under his own name. It was not strange for authors to have more than one story per issue, but they were usually under pseudonyms. This brought some harsh response from readers, but Berry was satisfied that just retribution had been carried out – especially when he also received a letter of praise from Clifford Simak about his work. As Simak pointed out, the readers' disgruntlement stemmed not from the stories themselves, but rather from their own inability to sell even one! Sadly, Berry died soon afterwards, and his undoubted talent was never fully realised.

The most prolific British writer during the 1950s was undoubtedly E. C. Tubb, who under his own name and a host of pseudonyms filled many a magazine issue. You need only check his listing at the back of this volume to see just how ubiquitous he was – and this continued right through to the end of the fifties! As an example of his best work, and reflecting the enormity of his contribution to the field, his long story 'The Wager' (*Science Fantasy*, November 1955) is included in this book.

By the end of 1955 a change was in hand at *Authentic*. H. J. Campbell could no longer both edit the magazine and find time to continue his research work, so the helm was given over to the capable guidance of E. C. Tubb with the sixty-sixth issue in February 1956.

At the close of the third decade of sf magazine history Britain at last had four highly readable and fairly successful sf magazines: *New Worlds*, *Science Fantasy*, *Nebula* and *Authentic*, with the result of maintaining a healthy growth of good quality British writers. The first half of the fifties saw their apprenticeship: practising, experimenting with styles and perfecting their talents. And a new talent was also growing, following the sf blossoming in Britain, and weighing up his own directions and intentions. That talent would spring into the open with the December 1956 *Science Fantasy* carrying 'Prima Belladonna' by J. G. Ballard. The course of British science fiction, guided by the sf magazines and their writers, was about to revolutionise science fiction the world over.

11—DIRECTIONS

For 'The Lovers' and his other contributions to sf so early in his career, Philip José Farmer received the Hugo Award in 1953 as the Best New Science Fiction Author.

This was the first year of the awards, presented at the Annual World Science Fiction Convention in September. The convention is usually held in the United States, but has twice been in Britain, once in Germany and once in Australia. Often, fans and attendees had talked and voted on their favourite writers, artists and stories but it was not until 1953 that a tangible award was given. It took the form of a cast metal spaceship, and was named, naturally enough, after Hugo Gernsback. It was ironic that in the year of its appearance Gernsback had been forced to admit defeat with *Science Fiction Plus* and had left the sf publishing field. Gernsback died on 19 August 1967 aged eighty-three. Devoted to science to the very end, he had bequeathed his body to medical research.

The categories for which the Hugo is voted annually do change, though there is generally a hard core, and they offer a fair guide of tastes within the field. In 1953 the award for the best sf magazine went to both *Astounding* and *Galaxy*, which emphasised *Galaxy*'s meteoric rise to prominence. It scored another point, since the award for the best novel went to *The Demolished Man* by Alfred Bester, which had been serialised in *Galaxy* from January to March 1952. Additionally, a special Hugo went to Willy Ley for his excellence in science fact articles. And Ley had supplied a regular fact column, 'For Your Information', to *Galaxy* since March 1952. There was also a tie for best cover artist between Hannes Bok and Ed Emsh. Bok was never a prolific artist and had completed few magazine covers during 1951-2. His work, characterised by his bizarre 'stained-glass window' techniques, has since become highly sought after, and his death in 1964, just before his fiftieth birthday, pushed him even further into legend.

Ed Emshwiller, to give him his full name, must rank as one of the most gifted and realistic of sf artists. His talent for creating scenes is second to none as is his skill at depicting people. His first cover was *Galaxy*, June 1951 and initially most of his work was for that magazine – another feather in their cap with the Hugo.

The Hugo for interior artwork went to Virgil Finlay, probably the greatest artist in black-and-white of the period. His work was appearing everywhere in the early 1950s, since no single magazine could pay enough to claim him exclusively. Some of his most superb work was then in *Startling*, *Thrilling Wonder* and Ray Palmer's magazines.

No awards were given in 1954, but they became a mainstay from 1955 onwards. In that year *Astounding* almost swept the board, winning the magazine section outright, as well as having published the winning novel, novelette and short story. The winning artist, Kelly Freas, was also associated mostly with that magazine. *Astounding* was not intending to lose ground despite formidable opposition.

Which brings me to a good point to view the fiction that had appeared during 1950 to 1955.

One of today's leading sf exponents is Philip K. Dick. His first publication was a brief tale, 'Beyond Lies the Wub' (*Planet Stories*, July 1952), and he concentrated on short fiction for a while, appearing in nearly all of the sf magazines before expanding to novel length works. Dick had a special skill for producing the unexpected in his stories, and in this period showed it in such pieces like 'The Defenders' (*Galaxy*, January 1953) wherein humanity moves underground leaving robots on the surface to fight on the war. Unbeknown to the humans, the robots make peace almost straight away, but feed false information down to humanity, thus keeping the surface to themselves. And in 'Impostor' (*Astounding*, January 1953) the reader is enmeshed in a search to discover the identity of an impostor in our midst who is actually a walking bomb.

Dick had made his début at about the same time as Robert Sheckley, who during 1953-4 was astonishingly prolific. The bulk of his stories are spun with a web of humour and realism, and one such example, 'Hands Off', is included in this volume. Sheckley was one of the first writers to make the transition from sf magazines to men's slicks, like *Playboy*.

Another was Charles Beaumont, who later earned much fame as a Hollywood screenwriter. He sold his first story to Howard Browne who published it in *Amazing*, January 1951. So Beaumont, who established himself as a major sf and horror writer for the slicks, had begun by working for the pulps. He died tragically in February 1967 aged only thirty-eight! By the mid-1950s most leading writers changed from sf magazines to the slicks quite early in their careers. But from the other direction came Kurt Vonnegut, a much revered name in the sf canon today even though he personally denies that he writes science fiction. He never sold directly to the sf magazines; he sold straight to the slicks – but only *after* the sf pulp writers had opened the door. His early stories, such as 'Thanasphere', which appeared in *Collier's,* (2 September 1950) and dealt with a rocket test pilot finding spirits of the dead orbiting the Earth, had rather weak plots by sf standards. Could Vonnegut have established himself, though, had not writers like Leinster, Heinlein and Bradbury already turned that key?

Gordon R. Dickson had an ingenious story in 'The Monkey Wrench' (*Astounding*, August 1951) where a man baffles a computer by logical means. The use of logic in sf was a good springboard for humour, and Britain's Eric Frank Russell put that to good use in 'Diabologic' (*Astounding*, March 1955) where a human ensnares aliens in that manner. Russell was writing at his best during the fifties and won the Hugo for 'Allamagoosa' (*Astounding*, May 1955) which tells of the hilarious search by a starship's crew for the 'allamagoosa' listed on their inventory. Russell's superb 'Dear Devil' (*Other Worlds*, May 1950) was also of Hugo standards. This tells of a hideous, blue, tentacled Martian poet and artist who remains behind after exploring a near-lifeless Earth. There he befriends a group of deserted children by showing kindness. In this story Russell puts forward a perfect argument for racial tolerance. Again, its appearance in Palmer's magazine shows that Palmer was perceptive and did not rely solely on sensationalism for his effect.

Russell would pursue his alien racial parallels in stories like 'The Witness' (*Other Worlds*, September 1951) where an alien is put on trial as a menace only to discover she had come to Earth for sanctuary. In 'Fast Falls the Eventide' (*Astounding*, May 1952) humans are sent to alien planets to teach universal brotherhood; and 'Postscript' (*SF Plus*, October 1953) where a man corresponds with an alien female only to learn she is a loathsome fungus, successfully hammers home Russell's point.

Would stories like these have been written had science fiction magazines not existed?

Another leading name during the 1950s was Walter M. Miller. Miller had actually made his début in the *American Mercury* in 1950, and in January 1951 *Amazing Stories* contained his editorially retitled 'Secret of the Death Dome'. Miller had a talent for characterisation and the believable narration of events. 'I Made You' (*Astounding*, March 1954) is a terrifying account of a robot machine on the moon, bent on destroying his operator. The January 1955 *Astounding* carried 'The Darfstellar', which centres around a human in an interstellar robot theatrical company, and it won him his first Hugo. He later won another in 1960 for his novel. *A Canticle for Leibowitz*, which is set on a post-atomic holocaust Earth, where the religious order of St Leibowitz – a canonised scientist – strives to bring some semblance of order back into the chaotic world. It was a masterpiece, and will doubtless remain in print for years to come. That novel was originally three connected novelettes, the first of which, 'A Canticle for Leibowitz', had appeared in *F & SF* for April 1955.

The name Frank Herbert is today inextricably linked with his trilogy of novels around *Dune*. His first appearance in sf however was as far back as 1952, with a short story in the August *Startling*, 'Looking for Something'. By 1955 he had completed his first novel, *Under Pressure*, which was serialised in *Astounding* from November 1955, receiving tremendous praise for its realism. Set during wartime on an atomic submarine of the future it bristles with intrigue as the submarine sets out to capture an oil supply, with one of the crew a saboteur. Published in book form in 1956 as *The Dragon in the Sea* it has been in print ever since.

Many other names spring to mind, but lack of space forces me to make but passing mention. Edgar Pangborn's first story 'Angel's Egg' (*Galaxy*, June 1951) should need no plot résumé here as it is one of the most anthologised sf stories. Ward Moore is a name overlooked today despite his excellent contributions to the field, notably *Bring the Jubilee* (*F & SF*, November 1952), the definitive alternate Earth story along the lines that the South won the American Civil War. He followed this with 'Lot' (*F & SF*, May 1953) and 'Lot's Daughter' (*F & SF*, October 1954) set on the Earth after atomic devastation and following the problems of adolescence. Dr Alan E. Nourse is also fondly remembered from this period, primarily for 'Counterfeit' (*Thrilling Wonder*, August 1952), one of the most absorbing stories on the theme of an alien assuming the identity of a crew member on a starship. Nourse had earlier written 'Tiger by the Tail' (*Galaxy*, November 1951), a clever twist on the Möbius-dimensions theory, and would later be remembered for 'Brightside Crossing' (*Galaxy*, January 1956), one of the most exciting stories set on Mercury, as it was once imagined.

Female writers were also gaining a reputation. Margaret St. Clair had already established herself by 1950 with clever stories like 'The Gardener' (*Thrilling Wonder*, October 1949), wherein a bureaucrat chops down a sacred tree on an alien planet only to find himself subject to the ultimate penalty, and begins to turn into a tree. She created an alter-ego, Idris Seabright, for special fantasies in *F & SF*, although one very advanced story about love-making, 'Short in the Chest', actually appeared in *Fantastic Universe* (June 1954). One woman who made *F & SF* her home was Zenna Henderson, who made her début in October 1952 with 'Ararat', the first of her many stories concerning 'The People', human-like alien refugees stranded on the Earth. How various individuals try to merge with humans is the standard theme of the series, which she has handled with the perfect mixture of tenderness and tragedy that has made her one of the leading female writers in the genre.

A most memorable story was Katherine MacLean's 'Pictures Don't Lie' (*Galaxy*, June 1951) which follows the televising of the arrival of aliens on the Earth. The revelation in the final lines is delivered with pure mastery of touch.

One leading woman writer, Anne McCaffrey, made her first appearance at this time with a brief vignette 'Freedom of the Race' in the October 1953 *SF Plus*; and 1954 heralded the first fiction from Marion Zimmer Bradley, though she had sold a poem to *Thrilling Wonder* three years earlier. Women were at last making their presence known in sf. Perhaps this is concomitant with the maturing of the genre and its emphasis now on humanity rather than science. Or perhaps the detailing of emotions in their stories was just what editors like Gold and Boucher were after.

Although at the risk of completely ignoring many authors, like Mack Reynolds, Randall Garrett, Milton Lesser . . . I must not forget the established names, for they were doing much more than merely watching the growth of younger talents.

Isaac Asimov was writing at the top of his form. His *Foundation* series had drawn to a close with the serialisation of '. . . And Now You Don't' (part of *Second Foundation*) in *Astounding* in 1949. Then came *Pebble in the Sky* (in *2 Complete Science Adventure Books*) about a man catapulted into the far future only to be the key to its salvation. Then *The Stars Like Dust* was serialised in *Galaxy* as *Tyrann* from issue number four. This was his compelling, if shallow, novel of a chase through the galaxy in search of a secret document to save mankind. The October 1952 *Astounding* began his serial, *The Currents of Space*, which describes an intrigue to save the planet Florina from an imminent nova, and in October 1953 *Galaxy* carried episode one of his first major sf mystery novel, *The Caves of Steel*.

Robert Heinlein was not exclusively printed in the slicks. His famous novel, *The Puppet Masters,* where aliens take mental and physical control of some humans was serialised in *Galaxy* during 1951, and in 1954 *F & SF* serialised his juvenile novel *Star Beast* (as *Star Lummox*), in which an alien pet is brought back to Earth with calamitous results.

Hal Clement is one of the masters of the hard-science sf story, and he soared to even greater esteem with the serialisation of *Mission of Gravity* in *Astounding* during 1953, A valuable probe crashes near the poles of a planet which, because of its rapid rotation but massive size has nearly seven hundred times the gravitational pull of Earth at the poles, but only three times at the equator. The story traces how the problem is overcome and the probe recovered. For devotees of pure *science* fiction this novel is doubtless among the most sacred.

The late James Blish came more and more to prominence throughout the decade with his fascinating 'Okie' series about the flying cities. The series started with 'Okie' (*Astounding*, April 1950): the development of an anti-gravity device enabling cities to abandon Earth, and the concurrent discovery of a longevity drug. Later connected stories included 'Bridge' (*Astounding*, February 1952), his oft-reprinted tale about attempts to construct a bridge on Jupiter.

A relative newcomer was Charles L. Harness. He was originally published in the August 1948 *Astounding* with his clever time-travel mystery story, 'Time Trap', and followed it with a flood of ingenious stories. He caused a sensation in 1953 with his novel *The Rose,* which details the development of man into a superman. This novel failed to find a market in America, and was first published in Britain's *Authentic*, March 1953. A fine novel and a great writer may have been lost had it not been for that magazine's existence. Shortly after that Harness gave up writing in order to have more time for his family, but he has recently returned to the field with even more stunning effect.

The late Murray Leinster was no less active in this decade than he had been thirty years earlier. His superb short novel, 'The Gadget Had a Ghost' (*Thrilling Wonder*, June 1952) is a front-line story of time paradoxes. And 'Nightmare Planet' (*SF Plus*, June 1953) added the final episode to his series of the bizarre future Earth that had started with 'The Mad Planet' in *Argosy* in 1920!

Leinster also won the Hugo award for his novelette, 'Exploration Team', from the March 1956 *Astounding*. His talent was indeniable and his death in June 1975, aged nearly seventy-nine brought to a very firm close a massive chapter in the history of science fiction.

Frederik Pohl and Cyril Kornbluth, both respected names in the genre, had started by collaborating with each other and fellow writers under a host of pseudonyms in the early 1940s. It was not until the fifties that they appeared regularly under their real names. Pohl contributed gems like 'The Midas Plague' (*Galaxy*, April 1954) set when over-production has become a real menace; and Kornbluth his characteristically harsh visions like 'The Altar at Midnight' (*Galaxy,* November 1952), with its grim view of the life of spacemen. In collaboration they penned such classic novels at *Gravy Planet* (*Galaxy,* June–August 1952), which portrays mega-companies trying to 'sell' Venus, and *Gladiator-at-Law* (*Galaxy,* June–August 1954), which depicts a violent future Earth. Kornbluth had also collaborated with Judith Merril (as Cyril Judd) on several works, notably *Gunner Cade,* serialised in *Astounding* during 1952, which delineates the ultimate regimented soldier of the future, incapable of thinking for himself.

The early 1950s also brought a formidable quota of fiction from Theodore Sturgeon, who too was shattering the barriers of conformity, made easier once Mines had accepted Farmer's work. In *Galaxy,* Sturgeon emphasises essentially human themes. 'Baby Is Three' (October 1952) deals with a teenager with exceptional psi-powers who combines with other such talented children to form a terrifying 'gestalt' brain. That novelette expanded to novel length as *More Than Human* won the 1954 International Fantasy Award, essentially a British affair organised by Leslie Flood and awarded between 1951 and 1957. An earlier winner had been Clifford Simak with the novelisation of his *City* series from *Astounding.*

If one must call the early 1940s the 'Golden Age' of *Astounding,* then the period 1946–55 must surely be the 'Platinum Age' of science fiction. I have already mentioned scores of superb stories from this decade, but even these are only a few in comparison with the many hundreds written. I can only implore those of you interested to explore further.

12—ROUND UP

By the end of 1955 the extinction of the pulps had been followed by a relative calm on the sf sea. Several digests had also parted company with the field, but many survived. A brief résumé of the survivors and their editors is perhaps in order.

Amazing Stories, the oldest of all magazines, was now a digest publication edited by Howard Browne with a newly acquired companion, *Fantastic.* Browne had been allowed a larger budget during 1953 enabling him to purchase good quality fiction, but this was cut as the years passed, and by 1955 the quality of the stories was dropping. Nevertheless in November 1955 *Amazing* resumed monthly publication, while *Fantastic* remained bi-monthly.

Coincidentally, that first monthly *Amazing* was its three hundredth issue. November 1955 also marked the three hundredth issue of *Astounding*, of which all but eighty-two had been under the iron control of John W. Campbell. For the next ten years *Amazing* and *Astounding* would run side by side as the oldest surviving sf magazines.

Columbia Publications continued with *Science Fiction Stories*, *Future SF* and *SF Quarterly*. By 1955, *Science Fiction* had become the mainstay publication, and was now prefixed 'The Original . . .' to link it back to the *Science Fiction* started under Charles Hornig in 1939. *Future* had temporarily been relegated to an irregular publication programme. *SF Quarterly* kept its schedule, and had also stayed a pulp – a very rare instance. It was the only still *surviving* pulp around, but not the only pulp magazine.

As I have emphasised on previous occasions, Ray Palmer was never one to conform. During the War, when paper rationing had forced many magazines to limit their pages, Palmer *doubled* the number in his publications. In the mid-1950s, when most magazines had changed to digest or folded, Palmer converted his *Other Worlds* from digest to pulp! Yes, *Other Worlds*. After changing its name to *Science Stories* and taking over *Universe* during the last year, Palmer decided that contemporary trends in sf were gradually causing stagnation in the genre. But he admitted in his editorials that *Other Worlds* was operating on an invisible budget. He changed back to pulp format to attract attention, but would soon discover he was now out of touch with the times. Was his knack for sensationalism leaving him?

The Magazine of Fantasy and Science Fiction still maintained its exceptional high quality. It was now solely guided by Anthony Boucher, as Mick McComas had stepped down in 1954 through ill-health.

Galaxy was regularly appearing alongside *Astounding*, and its companion *Novel* series still appeared sporadically. During the boom *Galaxy* had also had a fantasy companion, *Beyond*, which survived ten issues, was very popular and is often compared as the natural successor to Campbell's *Unknown*. Of the many stories it printed probably the best recalled are Damon Knight's story of language chaos, 'Babel II'; Theodore Cogswell's classic 'The Wall around the World' and Theodore

Sturgeon's macabre tale of a child with power, 'Talent'. Sadly, *Beyond* suffered the fate of suffocation from the boom.

Fantastic Universe had established itself firmly as a monthly publication with a broad policy incorporating fantasy and sf. It was sufficiently different from *F & SF* to warrant its survival, yet cunningly similar to echo its success. Leo Margulies remained the guiding hand, though soon another figure, Hans Stefan Santesson, was to enter the scene.

William Hamling's *Imagination* had stayed monthly throughout the boom, but by autumn 1955 was apearing every other month. It now alternated with his new magazine, *Imaginative Tales*, which was born in September 1954, essentially as a vehicle to carry long lead novels, leaving *Imagination* with the shorter pieces. In this way it captured a fair audience, although it was never as successful. It echoed the *Amazings* of the late forties that Hamling had ghost-edited, and contained several lead space-opera novels by Edmond Hamilton, thus appealing to the audience left starved by the demise of *Planet Stories*.

And finally James Quinn still valiantly edited *If*, now celebrating its thirtieth issue. Quinn had some assistance from subeditors, one of which had been Larry Shaw. Shaw left in 1954 and later joined Royal Publications. There publisher Irwin Shaw (no relation) was interested in issuing a science fiction magazine, and Larry Shaw became its editor. *Infinity SF* appeared in November 1955, the first of the post-boom magazines. It carried a lead novelette by William Tenn, and included a short story, 'The Star', by Arthur Clarke, which won the Hugo Award as the year's best short story. If *Infinity* could start like that, what would it lead to?

One pointer was an author Shaw helped put on the road by publishing his first sf story. The second issue of *Infinity* (February 1956) carried fiction by many leading names including a brilliantly funny robot story, 'Internal Combustion' by L. Sprague de Camp. But it also included 'Glow Worm' by Harlan Ellison, a tale that centred upon a human freak, a man who glowed. Ellison was already famous in fandom for his leading fanzine, *Dimensions*. Who could forecast that ten years later Ellison would be changing the very face of science fiction?

With Ellison in the USA and with J. G. Ballard in Britain emerging in the mid-1950s, supported by growing numbers of talented writers it was obvious that science fiction was preparing itself for new directions and the demolishing of more taboos.

If ever there was a literature of change it was science fiction, and the laboratory wherein those changes were tried and tested was the science fiction magazine. How dead would have been a world without them!

Mike Ashley
October 1975

SOURCES OF QUOTATIONS

All quotations are from private correspondence or previously unpublished sources unless enumerated, in which case their origin was as follows:

[1]   Theodore Sturgeon's preface to his story 'Thunder and Roses' in *My Best Science Fiction Story*, edited by Leo Margulies & Oscar J. Friend (Merlin Press, New York, 1949).

[2]   Ray Palmer's editorial comment in answer to a letter in the 'Letters' department of *Other Worlds Science Stories*, May 1955, page 121 (Palmer Publications, Illinois).

[3]   Robert Heinlein's essay 'On the Writing of Speculative Fiction' in *Of Worlds Beyond*, edited by Lloyd Arthur Eshbach, page 13 (Advent, Chicago, 1971 edition).

[4]   Howard Browne's contribution to *Cheap Thrills* by Ron Goulart, page 192 (Ace Books, New York, 1973 edition).

[5]   Alfred Bester's essay 'My Affair with Science Fiction' in *Hell's Cartographers*, edited by Brian W. Aldiss and Harry Harrison, page 58 (Weidenfeld & Nicolson, London, 1975).

[6]   L. Sprague de Camp's Chapter 4: 'Markets and Editors' in *Science-Fiction Handbook*, page 115 (Hermitage House, New York, 1953.

7   H. L. Gold's editorial 'It's All Yours' in *Galaxy Science Fiction*, November 1950, page 3 (World Editions, New York).

8   John Carnell's editorial 'Good Companions . . .' in *New Worlds*, Summer 1950, page 3 (Nova Publications, London).

9   Samuel Mines's editorial 'The Ether Vibrates' in *Startling Stories*, August 1952, page 6 (Better Publications, New York).

Memorial

BY THEODORE STURGEON

f:om *Astounding Science Fiction*, April 1946

Since this survey begins at April 1946, it seems fitting to choose a story from that month's issue of the leading magazine, *Astounding*. 'Memorial' not only reflects the immediate reaction to the nuclear bomb, but is written by one of sf's greatest talents.

Theodore Sturgeon was born Edward Hamilton Waldo on Staten Island, New York, on Tuesday 26 February 1918. When his mother later remarried, Edward adopted his stepfather's surname and became officially Theodore Sturgeon. In his youth Sturgeon was devoted to gymnastics and wished to make the circus his career, but in 1933 he contracted rheumatic fever which enlarged his heart, and destroyed his aspirations, so the despondent Sturgeon took to reading. Two years later he abandoned land life for the open sea, and it was then he began writing. He initially sold some forty stories that were syndicated in dozens of American newspapers, but none were fantasy. Then in 1939 Sturgeon discovered the first issue of *Unknown* and thereby its editor, John W. Campbell. Sturgeon first appeared in the September 1939 *Astounding* with 'Ether Breather', a light-hearted look at ethereal beings interfering with television transmissions. His first real success came with 'It' (*Unknown*, August 1940), about a loathsome, slimy life-form that reactivates the skeleton of a dead man. Later came 'Killdozer!' (*Astounding*, November 1944) his famous story of the alien intelligence that takes over a bulldozer. Adapted by Sturgeon, this novel was seen on many television screens in 1974 as one of the American *Sunday Mystery Movie* film series.

Throughout the forties, and particularly the fifties, Sturgeon's work established him firmly in the sf hierarchy, and his inclusion in this series was mandatory. Currently, his fictional output is spasmodic. He has turned his talents to book reviewing, both in and out of the field, and in lecturing on many college sf courses. Fortunately he has never deserted the genre and one may expect plenty more surprises from his keen mind yet.

The Pit, in A.D. 5000, had changed little over the centuries. Still it was an angry memorial to the misuse of great power; and because of it, organized warfare was a forgotten thing. Because of it, the world was free of the wasteful smoke and dirt of industry. The scream and crash of bombs and the soporific beat of marching feet were never heard, and at long last the earth was at peace.

To go near The Pit was slow, certain death, and it was respected and feared, and would be for centuries more. It winked and blinked redly at night, and was surrounded by a bald and broken tract stretching out and away over the horizon; and around it flickered a ghostly blue glow. Nothing lived there. Nothing could.

With such a war memorial, there could be only peace. The earth could never forget the horror that could be loosed by war.

That was Grenfell's dream.

Grenfell handed the typewritten sheet back. 'That's it, Jack. My idea, and – I wish I could express it like that.' He leaned back against the littered workbench, his strangely asymmetrical face quizzical. 'Why is it that it takes a useless person to adequately express an abstract?'

Jack Roway grinned as he took back the paper and tucked it into his breast pocket. 'Interestin' question, Grenfell, because this *is* your expression, the words *are* yours. Practically verbatim. I left out the 'er's and 'ah's that you play conversational hopscotch with, and strung together all the effects you mentioned without mentioning any of the technological causes. Net result: you think I did it, when you did. You think it's good writing, and I don't.'

'You don't?'

Jack spread his bony length out on the hard little cot. His relaxation was a noticeable act, like the unbuttoning of a shirt collar. His body seemed to unjoint itself a little. He laughed.

'Of course I don't. Much too emotional for my taste. I'm just a fumbling aesthete – useless, did you say? Mm-m-m – yeah. I suppose so.' He paused reflectively. 'You see, you cold-blooded characters, you scientists, are the true visionaries. Seems to me the essential difference between a scientist and an artist is that the scientist mixes his hope with patience.

'The scientist visualizes his ultimate goal, but pays little attention to it. He is all caught up with the achievement of the next step upward. The artist looks so far ahead that more often than not he can't see what's under his feet; so he falls flat on his face and gets called useless by scientists. But if you strip all of the intermediate steps away from the scientist's thinking you have an artistic concept to which the scientist responds distantly and with surprise, giving some artist credit for being deeply perspicacious purely because the artist repeated something the scientist said.'

'You amaze me,' Grenfell said candidly. 'You wouldn't be what you are if you weren't lazy and superficial. And yet you come out with things like that. I don't know that I understand what you just said. I'll have to think – but I do believe that you show all the signs of clear thinking. With a mind like yours, I can't understand why you don't use it to build something instead of wasting it in these casual interpretations of yours.'

Jack Roway stretched luxuriously. 'What's the use? There's more waste involved in the destruction of something which is already built than in dispersing the energy it would take to help build something. Anyway, the world is filled with builders – and destroyers. I'd just as soon sit by and watch, and feel things. I like my environment, Grenfell. I want to feel all I can of it, while it lasts. It won't last much longer. I want to touch all of it I can reach, taste of it, hear it, while there's time. What is around me, here and now, is what is important to me. The acceleration of human progress, and the increase of its mass – to use your own terms – are taking humanity straight to Limbo. You, with your work, think you are fighting humanity's inertia. Well, you are. But it's the kind of inertia called momentum. You command no force great enough to stop it, or even to change its course appreciably.'

'I have atomic power.'

Roway shook his head, smiling. 'That's not enough. No power is enough. It's just too late.'

'That kind of pessimism does not affect me,' said Grenfell.

'You can gnaw all you like at my foundations, Jack, and achieve nothing more than the loss of your front teeth. I think you know that.'

'Certainly I know that. I'm not trying to. I have nothing to sell, no one to change. I am even more impotent than you and your atomic power; and you are completely helpless. Uh – I quarrel with your use of the term 'pessimist', though. I am nothing of the kind. Since I have resolved for myself the fact that humanity, as we know it, is finished, I'm quite resigned to it. Pessimism from me, under the circumstances, would be the pessimism of a photo-phobiac predicting that the sun would rise tomorrow.'

Grenfell grinned. 'I'll have to think about that, too. You're such a mass of paradoxes that turn out to be chains of reasoning. Apparently you live in a world in which scientists are poets and the grasshopper has it all over the ant.'

'I always did think the ant was a stinker.'

'Why do you keep coming here, Jack? What do you get out of it? Don't you realize I'm a criminal?'

Roway's eyes narrowed. 'Sometimes I think you wish you were a criminal. The law says you are, and the chances are very strong that you'll be caught and treated accordingly. Ethically, you know you're not. It sort of takes the spice out of being one of the hunted.'

'Maybe you're right,' Grenfell said thoughtfully. He sighed. 'It's so completely silly. During the war years, the skills I had were snatched up and the government flogged me into the Manhattan Project, expecting, and getting, miracles. I have never stopped working along the same lines. And now the government has changed the laws, and pulled legality from under me.'

'Hardly surprising. The government deals rather severely with soldiers who go on killing other soldiers after the war is over.' He held up a hand to quell Grenfell's interruption. 'I know you're not killing anyone, and are working for the opposite result. I was only pointing out that it's the same switcheroo. We the people,' he said didactically, 'have, in our sovereign might, determined that no atomic research be done except in government laboratories. We have then permitted our politicians to allow so little for maintenance of those laboratories – unlike our overseas friends – that no really exhaustive research can be done in them. We have further

made it a major offense to operate such a bootleg lab as yours.'
He shrugged. 'Comes the end of mankind. We'll get walloped
first. If we put more money and effort into nuclear research
than any other country, some other country would get walloped
first. If we last another hundred years – which seems doubtful
– some poor, spavined, underpaid government researcher will
stumble on the aluminum-isotope space-heating system you
have already perfected.'

'That was a little rough,' said Grenfell bitterly. 'Driving me
underground just in time to make it impossible for me to
announce it. What a waste of time and energy it is to heat homes
and buildings the way they do now! Space heating – the biggest
single use for heat-energy – and I have the answer to it over
there.' He nodded toward a compact cube of lead-alloys in the
corner of the shop. 'Build it into a foundation, and you have
controllable heat for the life of the building, with not a cent for
additional fuel and practically nothing for maintenance.' His
jaw knotted. 'Well, I'm glad it happened that way.'

'Because it got you started on your war memorial – The Pit?
Yeah. Well, all I can say is, I hope you're right. It hasn't been
possible to scare humanity yet. The invention of gunpowder
was going to stop war, and didn't. Likewise the submarine, the
torpedo, the airplane, and that two-by-four bomb they pitched
at Hiroshima.'

'None of that applies to The Pit,' said Grenfell. 'You're
right; humanity hasn't been scared off war yet; but the Hiroshima bomb rocked 'em back on their heels. My little memorial
is the real stuff. I'm not depending on a fission effect, you know,
with a release of one-tenth of one percent of the energy of the
atom. I'm going to disrupt it completely, and get all the energy
there is in it. And it'll be *more* than a thousand times as
powerful as the Hiroshima bomb, because I'm going to use
twelve times as much explosive; and it's going off on the ground,
not a hundred and fifty feet above it.' Grenfell's brow, over
suddenly hot eyes, began to shine with sweat. 'And then – The
Pit,' he said softly. 'The war memorial to end war, and all other
war memorials. A vast pit, alive with bubbling lava, radiating
death for ten thousand years. A living reminder of the devastation mankind has prepared for itself. Out here on the desert,
where there are no cities, where the land has always been useless, will be the scene of the most useful thing in the history
of the race – a never-ending sermon, a warning, an example of

UNIVERSITY OF WINCHESTER

LIBRARY

the dreadful antithesis of peace.' His voice shook to a whisper, and faded.

'Sometimes,' said Roway, 'you frighten me, Grenfell. It occurs to me that I am such a studied sensualist, tasting everything I can, because I am afraid to feel any one thing that much.' He shook himself, or shuddered. 'You're a fanatic, Grenfell. Hyper-emotional. A monomaniac. I hope you can do it.'

'I can do it,' said Grenfell.

Two months passed, and in those two months Grenfell's absorption in his work had been forced aside by the increasing pressure of current events. Watching a band of vigilantes riding over the waste to the south of his little buildings one afternoon, he thought grimly of what Roway had said. 'Sometimes I think you wish you were a criminal.' Roway, the sensualist, would say that. Roway would appreciate the taste of danger, in the same way that he appreciated all the other emotions. As it intensified, he would wait to savor it, no matter how bad it got.

Twice Grenfell shut off the instigating power of the carbon-aluminum pile he had built, as he saw government helicopters hovering on the craggy skyline. He knew of hard-radiation detectors; he had developed two different types of them during the war; and he wanted no questions asked. His utter frustration at being unable to announce the success of his space-heating device, for fear that he would be punished as a criminal and his device impounded and forgotten – that frustration had been indescribable. It had canalized his mind, and intensified the devoted effort he had put forth for the things he believed in during the war. Every case of neural shock he encountered in men who had been hurt by war and despised it, made him work harder on his monument – on The Pit. For if humans could be frightened by war, humanity could be frightened by The Pit.

And those he met who had been hurt by war and who still hated the late enemy – those who would have been happy to go back and kill some more, reckoning the vital risk well worth it – those he considered mad, and forgot them.

So he could not stand another frustration. He was the center of his own universe, and he realized it dreadfully, and he had to justify his position there. He was a humanitarian, a philanthropist in the word's truest sense. He was probably as mad as any other man who has, through his own efforts, moved the world.

For the first time, then, he was grateful when Jack Roway arrived in his battered old convertible, although he was deliriously frightened at the roar of the motor outside his laboratory window. His usual reaction to Jack's advent was a mixture of annoyance and gratification, for it was a great deal of trouble to get out to his place. His annoyance was not because of the interruption, for Jack was certainly no trouble to have around. Grenfell suspected that Jack came out to see him partly to get the taste of the city out of his mouth, and partly to be able to feel superior to somebody he considered of worth.

But the increasing fear of discovery, and his race to complete his work before it was taken from him by an hysterical public, had had the unusual effect of making him lonely. For such a man as Grenfell to be lonely bordered on the extraordinary; for in his daily life there were simply too many things to be done. There had never been enough hours in a day nor days in a week to suit him, and he deeply resented the encroachments to sleep, which he considered a criminal waste.

'Roway!' he blurted, as he flung the door open, his tone so warm that Roway's eyebrows went up in surprise. 'What dragged you out here?'

'Nothing in particular,' said the writer, as they shook hands. 'Nothing more than usual, which is a great deal. How goes it?'

'I'm about finished.' They went inside, and as the door closed, Grenfell turned to face Jack. 'I've been finished for so long I'm ashamed of myself,' he said intently.

'Ha! Ardent confession so early in the day! What are you talking about?'

'Oh, there have been things to do,' said Grenfell restlessly. 'But I could go ahead with the . . . with the big thing at almost any time.'

'You hate to be finished. You're never visualized what it would be like to have the job done.' His teeth flashed. 'You know, I've never heard a word from you as to what your plans are after the big noise. You going into hiding?'

'I . . . haven't thought much about it. I used to have a vague idea of broadcasting a warning and an explanation before I let go with the disruptive explosion. I've decided against it, though. In the first place, I'd be stopped within minutes, no matter how cautious I was with the transmitter. In the second place – well, this is going to be so big that it won't need any explanation.'

'No one will know who did it, or why it was done.'

'Is that necessary?' asked Grenfell quietly.

Jack's mobile face stilled as he visualized The Pit, spewing its ten-thousand-year hell. 'Perhaps not,' he said. 'Isn't it necessary, though, to you?'

'To me?' asked Grenfell, surprised. 'You mean, do I care if the world knows I did this thing, or not? No; of course I don't. A chain of circumstances is occurring, and it has been working through me. It goes directly to The Pit; The Pit will do all that is necessary from then on. I will no longer have any part in it.'

Jack moved, clinking and splashing, around the sink in the corner of the laboratory. 'Where's all your coffee? Oh – here. Uh . . . I have been curious about how much personal motive you had for your work. I think that answers it pretty well. I think, too, that you believe what you are saying. Do you know that people who do things for impersonal motives are as rare as fur on a fish?'

'I hadn't thought about it.'

'I believe that, too. Sugar? And milk. I remember. And have you been listening to the radio?'

'Yes. I'm . . . a little upset, Jack,' said Grenfell, taking the cup. 'I don't know where to time this thing. I'm a technician, not a Machiavelli.'

'Visionary, like I said. You don't know if you'll throw this gadget of yours into world history too soon or too late – is that it?'

'Exactly. Jack, the whole world seems to be going crazy. Even fission bombs are too big for humanity to handle.'

'What else can you expect,' said Jack grimly, 'with our dear friends across the water sitting over their push buttons waiting for an excuse to punch them.'

'And we have our own set of buttons, of course.'

Jack Roway said: 'We've got too defend ourselves.'

'Are you kidding?'

Roway glanced at him, his dark brows plotting a V. 'Not about this. I seldom kid about anything, but particularly not about this.' And he – shuddered.

Grenfell stared amazedly at him and then began to chuckle. 'Now,' he said, 'I've seen everything. My iconoclastic friend Jack Roway, of all people, caught up by a . . . a fashion. A national pastime, fostered by uncertainty and fed by yellow journalism – fear of the enemy.'

'This country is not at war.'

'You mean, we have no enemy? Are you saying that the gentlemen over the water, with their itching fingertips hovering about the push buttons, are not our enemies?'

'Well –'

Grenfell came across the room to his friend, and put a hand on his shoulder. 'Jack – what's the matter? You can't be so troubled by the news – not *you*!'

Roway stared out at the brazen sun, and shook his head slowly. 'International balance is too delicate,' he said softly; and if a voice could glaze like eyes, his did. 'I see the nations of the world as masses balanced each on its own mathematical point, each with its center of gravity directly above. But the masses are fluid, shifting violently away from the center lines. The opposing trends aren't equal; they can't cancel each other; the phasing is too slow. One or the other is going to topple, and then the whole works is going to go.'

'But you've known that for a long time. You've known that ever since Hiroshima. Possibly before. Why should it frighten you now?'

'I didn't think it would happen so soon.'

'Oh-ho! So that's it! You have suddenly realized that the explosion is going to come in your lifetime. Hm-m-m? And you can't take that. You're capable of all of your satisfying aesthetic rationalizations as long as you can keep the actualities at arm's length!'

'*Whew*!' said Roway, his irrepressible humor passing close enough to nod to him. 'Keep it clean, Grenfell! Keep your . . . your sesquipedalian polysyllabics for a scientific report.'

'*Touché*!' Grenfell smiled. 'Y'know, Jack, you remind me powerfully of some erstwhile friends of mine who write science fiction. They had been living very close to atomic power for a long time – years before the man on the street – or the average politician, for that matter – knew an atom from Ada. Atomic power was handy to these specialized word-merchants because it gave them a limitless source of power for background to a limitless source of story material. In the heydey of the Manhattan Project, most of them suspected what was going on, some of them knew – some even worked on it. All of them were quite aware of the terrible potentialities of nuclear energy. Practically all of them were scared silly of the whole idea. They were afraid for humanity, but they themselves were not really afraid, except in a delicious drawing-room sort of way, because they couldn't conceive of this Buck Rogers event happening to anything but posterity. But it happened, in their own sacro-sanct lifetimes.

'And I will be dog-goned if you're not doing the same thing. You've gotten quite a bang out of figuring out the doom humanity faces in an atomic war. You've consciously risen above it by calling it inevitable, and in the meantime, leave us gather rosebuds before it rains. You thought you'd be safe home – dead – before the first drops fell. Now social progress had rolled up a thunderhead and you find yourself a mile from home with a crease in your pants and no umbrella. And you're scared!'

Roway looked at the floor and said, 'It's so soon. It's so soon.' He looked up at Grenfell, and his cheekbones seemed too large. He took a deep breath. 'You . . . we can stop it, Grenfell.'

'Stop what?'

'The war . . . the . . . this thing that's happening to us. The explosion that will come when the strains get too great in the international situation. And it's *got* to be stopped!'

'That's what The Pit is for.'

'The Pit!' Roway said scornfully. 'I've called you a visionary before. Grenfell, you've got to be more practical! Humanity is not going to learn anything by example. It's got to be kicked and carved. Surgery.'

Grenfell's eyes narrowed. 'Surgery? What you said a minute ago about my stopping it . . . do you mean what I think you mean?'

'Don't you see it?' said Jack urgently. 'What you have here – total disruptive energy – the peak of atomic power. One or two wallops with this, in the right place, and we can stop anybody.'

'This isn't a weapon. I didn't make this to be a weapon.'

'The first rock ever thrown by a prehistoric man wasn't made to be a weapon, either. But it was handy and it was effective, and it was certainly used because it had to be used.' He suddenly threw up his hands in a despairing gesture. 'You don't under-stand. Don't you realize that this country is likely to be attacked at any second – that diplomacy is now hopeless and helpless, and the whole world is just waiting for the thing to start? It's probably too late even now – but it's the least we can do.'

'What, specifically, is the least thing we can do?'

'Turn your work over to the War Department. In a few hours the government can put it where it will do the most good.' He drew his finger across his throat. 'Anywhere we want to, over the ocean.'

There was a taut silence. Roway looked at his watch and licked his lips. Finally Grenfell said, 'Turn it over to the government. Use it for a weapon – and what for? To stop war?'

'Of course!' blurted Roway. 'To show the rest of the world that our way of life ... to scare the daylights out of ... to –'

'*Stop it*!' Grenfell roared. 'Nothing of the kind. You think – you hope anyway – that the use of total disruption as a weapon will stall off the inevitable – at least in your lifetime. Don't you?'

'No. I –'

'Don't you?'

'Well. I –'

'You have some more doggerel to write,' said Grenfell scathingly. 'You have some more blondes to chase. You want to go limp over a few more Bach fugues.'

Jack Roway said: 'No one knows where the first bomb might hit. It might be anywhere. There's nowhere I ... we ... can go to be safe.' He was trembling.

'Are the people in the city quivering like that?' asked Grenfell.

'Riots,' breathed Roway, his eyes bright with panic. 'The radio won't announce anything about the riots.'

'Is that what you came out here for today – to try to get me to give disruptive power to *any* government?'

Jack looked at him guiltily. 'It was the only thing to do. I don't know if your bomb will turn the trick, but it has to be tried. It's the only thing left. We've got to be prepared to hit first, and hit harder than anyone else.'

'No.' Grenfell's one syllable was absolutely unshakable.

'Grenfell – I thought I could argue you into it. Don't make it tough for yourself. You've got to do it. Please do it on your own. Please, Grenfell.' He stood up slowly.

'Do it on my own – or what? *Keep away from me*!'

'No ... I –' Roway stiffened suddenly, listening. From far above and to the north came the whir of rotary wings. Roway's fear-slackened lips tightened into a grin, and with two incredibly swift strides he was across to Grenfell. He swept in a handful of the smaller man's shirt front and held him half off the floor.

'Don't try a thing,' he gritted. There was not a sound then except their harsh breathing, until Grenfell said wearily: 'There was somebody called Judas –'

'You can't insult me,' said Roway, with a shade of his old cockiness, 'and you're flattering yourself'.

A helicopter sank into its own roaring dust-cloud outside the building. Men pounded out of it and burst in the door. There were three of them. They were not in uniform.

'Dr Grenfell,' said Jack Roway, keeping his grip, 'I want you to meet –'

'Never mind that,' said the taller of the three in a brisk voice. 'You're Roway? Hm-m-m. Dr Grenfell, I understand you have a nuclear energy device on the premises.'

'Why did you come by yourself?' Grenfell asked Roway softly. 'Why not just send these stooges?'

'For you, strangely enough. I hoped I could argue you into giving the thing freely. You know what will happen if you resist?'

'I know.' Grenfell pursed his lips for a moment, and then turned to the tall man. 'Yes. I have some such thing here. Total atomic disruption. Is that what you were looking for?'

'Where is it?'

'Here, in the laboratory, and then there's the pile in the other building. You'll find –' He hesitated. 'You'll find two samples of the concentrate. One's over there –' he pointed to a lead case on a shelf behind one of the benches. 'And there's another like it in a similar case in the shed back of the pile building.'

Roway sighed and released Grenfell. 'Good boy. I knew you'd come through.'

'Yes,' said Grenfell. 'Yes –'

'Go get it,' said the tall man. One of the others broke away.

'It will take two men to carry it," said Grenfell in a shaken voice. His lips were white.

The tall man pulled out a gun and held it idly. He nodded to the second man. 'Go get it. Bring it here and we'll strap the two together and haul 'em to the plane. Snap it up.'

The two men went out toward the shed.

'Jack?'

'Yes, Doc.'

'You really think humanity can be scared?'

'It will be – now. This thing will be used right.'

'I hope so. Oh, I hope so,' Grenfell whispered.

The men came back. 'Up on the bench,' said the leader, nodding toward the case the men carried between them.

As they climbed up on the bench and laid hands on the second case, to swing it down from the shelf, Jack Roway saw Grenfell's face spurt sweat, and a sudden horror swept over him.

'Grenfell!' he said hoarsely. 'It's –'

'Of course,' Grenfell whispered. 'Critical mass.'

Then it let go.

It was like Hiroshima, but much bigger. And yet, that explosion did not create The Pit. It was the pile that did – the boron-aluminum lattice which Grenfell had so arduously pieced together from parts bootlegged over the years. Right there at the heart of the fission explosion, total disruption took place in the pile, for that was its function. This was slower. It took more than an hour for its hellish activity to reach a peak, and in that time a huge crater had been gouged out of the earth, a seething, spewing mass of volatilized elements, raw radiation, and incandescent gases. It was – The Pit. Its activity curve was plotted abruptly – up to peak in an hour and eight minutes, and then a gradual subsidence as it tried to feed further afield with less and less fueling effect, and as it consumed its own flaming wastes in an effort to reach inactivity. Rain would help to blanket it, through energy lost in volatilizing the drops; and each of the many elements involved went through its respective secondary radioactivity, and passed away its successive half-lives. The subsidence of The Pit would take between eight and nine thousand years.

And like Hiroshima, this explosion had effects which reached into history and into men's hearts in places far separated in time from the cataclysm itself.

These things happened:

The explosion could not be concealed; and there was too much hysteria afoot for anything to be confirmed. It was easier to run headlines saying *We Are Attacked*. There was an instantaneous and panicky demand for reprisals, and the government acceded, because such 'reprisals' suited the policy of certain members who could command emergency powers. And so the First Atomic War was touched off.

And the Second.

There were no more atomic wars after that. The Mutants' War was a barbarous affair, and the mutants defeated the tattered and largely sterile remnants of humanity, because the mutants were strong. And then the mutants died out because they were unfit. For a while there was some very interesting material to be studied on the effects of radiation on heredity, but there was no one to study it.

There were some humans left. The rats got most of them, after increasing in fantastic numbers; and there were three plagues.

After that there were half-stooping, naked things whose twisted heredity could have been traced to humankind; but these could be frightened, as individuals and as a race, so therefore they could not progress. They were certainly not human.

The Pit, in A.D. 5000, had changed little over the centuries. Still it was an angry memorial to the misuse of great power; and because of it, organized warfare was a forgotten thing. Because of it, the world was free of the wasteful smoke and dirt of industry. The scream and crash of bombs and the soporific beat of marching feet were never heard, and at long last the earth was at peace.

To go near The Pit was slow, certain death, and it was respected and feared, and would be for centuries more. It winked and blinked redly at night, and was surrounded by a bald and broken tract stretching out and away over the horizon; and around it flickered a ghostly blue glow. Nothing lived there. Nothing could.

With such a war memorial, there could be only peace. The earth could never forget the horror loosed by war.

That was Grenfell's dream.

The Fires Within

BY ARTHUR C. CLARKE

from *Fantasy*, August 1947

Clarke is one of the few sf authors who along with Bradbury, Asimov and Wyndham is a household name. His reputation was especially enhanced with the success of the spectacular film, *2001: A Space Odyssey*, based partly on his short story 'Sentinel of Eternity' (*Ten Story Fantasy*, Spring 1951).

Arthur Charles Clarke was born in his grandmother's boarding-house in Minehead, Somerset on Sunday 16 December 1917. Educated at a Taunton grammar school, he subsequently took up work in the Civil Service. Since his childhood both science and science fiction had fascinated him, so it was hardly surprising he joined the newly formed British Interplanetary Society in 1934. The offices of the BIS, hitherto in Liverpool, moved to London in October 1936, and since Clarke's job was in the capital, he became the Society's treasurer and an active member. It brought him into contact with many who were, or would become, leading names in science or sf, and with sf fandom. He began to write for the various amateur magazines, and when Walter Gillings secured the publication of Britain's first true sf magazine, *Tales of Wonder*, Clarke's scientific articles were published.

Clarke's early career has already been recounted in my introduction. Like Asimov, his desires to be a scientist and an sf writer vied for prominence, yet Clarke has succeeded admirably in both careers. In 1954 he moved to Ceylon where he became actively engaged in many underwater projects, and he gained the Kalinga Prize in 1962 for the popularisation of science through his writings. A list of his sf books reads like a basic library for any reader: *Prelude to Space, The City and the Stars, Earthlight, The Sands of Mars, Childhood's End, A Fall of Moondust, Rendezvous With Rama* and, more recently, *Imperial Earth*, a novel on which he has worked since 1956.

But as we poise in 1947 all that was far in the future. Clarke was on the brink of his mighty career, and tucked away in the third and final issue of Walter Gillings's *Fantasy*, veiled under the pseudonym of E. G. O'Brien, was an early example of Clarke's embryonic talent – 'The Fires Within'.

'This,' said Karn smugly, 'will interest you. Just take a look at it!'

He pushed across the file he had been reading, and for the *nth* time I decided to ask for his transfer or, failing that, my own.

'What's it about?' I said wearily.

'It's a long report from a Dr Matthews to the Minister of Science.' He waved it in front of me. 'Just read it!'

Without much enthusiasm, I began to go through the file. A few minutes later I looked up and admitted grudgingly: 'Maybe you're right – this time.' I didn't speak again until I'd finished . . .

i

My dear Minister (the letter began). As you requested, here is my special report on Professor Hancock's experiments, which have had such unexpected and extraordinary results. I have not had time to cast it into a more orthodox form, but am sending you the dictation just as it stands.

Since you have many matters engaging your attention, perhaps I should briefly summarize our dealings with Professor Hancock. Until 1955, the Professor held the Kelvin Chair of Electrical Engineering at Brendon University, from which he was granted indefinite leave of absence to carry out his researches. In these he was joined by the late Dr Clayton, some-time Chief Geologist to the Ministry of Fuel and Power. Their joint research was financed by grants from the Paul Fund and the Royal Society.

The Professor hoped to develop sonar as a means of precise geological surveying. Sonar, as you will know, is the acoustic equivalent of radar and, although less familiar, is older by some millions of years, since bats use it very effectively to detect insects and obstacles at night. Professor Hancock intended to send high-powered supersonic pulses into the ground and to build up from the returning echoes an image of what lay beneath. The picture would be displayed on a cathode ray tube and the whole system would be exactly analogous to the type of radar used in aircraft to show the ground through cloud.

In 1957 the two scientists had achieved partial success but had exhausted their funds. Early in 1958 they applied directly to the government for a block grant. Dr Clayton pointed out the immense value of a device which would enable us to take a kind of X-ray photo of the Earth's crust, and the Minister of Fuel gave it his approval before passing on the application to us. At that time the report of the Bernal Committee had just been published and we were very anxious that deserving cases should be dealt with quickly to avoid further criticisms. I went to see the Professor at once and submitted a favourable report; the first payment of our grant (S/543A/68) was made a few days later. From that time I have been continually in touch with the research and have assisted to some extent with technical advice.

The equipment used in the experiments is complex, but its principles are simple. Very short but extremely powerful pulses of supersonic waves are generated by a special transmitter which revolves continuously in a pool of a heavy organic liquid. The beam produced passes into the ground and 'scans' like a radar beam searching for echoes. By a very ingenious time-delay circuit which I will resist the temptation to describe, echoes from any depth can be selected and so pictures of the strata under investigation can be built up on a cathode ray screen in the normal way.

When I first met Professor Hancock his apparatus was rather primitive, but he was able to show me the distribution of rock down to a depth of several hundred feet and we could see quite clearly a part of the Bakerloo Line which passed very near his laboratory. Much of the Professor's success was due to the great intensity of his supersonic bursts; almost from the beginning he was able to generate peak powers of several hundred kilowatts, nearly all of which was radiated into the ground. It was unsafe to remain near the transmitter, and I noticed that the soil became quite warm around it. I was rather surprised to see large numbers of birds in the vicinity, but soon discovered that they were attracted by the hundreds of dead worms lying on the ground.

At the time of Dr Clayton's death in 1960, the equipment was working at a power level of over a megawatt and quite good pictures of strata a mile down could be obtained. Dr Clayton had correlated the results with known geographical surveys, and had proved beyond doubt the value of the information obtained.

Dr Clayton's death in a motor accident was a great tragedy. He had always exerted a stabilizing influence on the Professor, who had never been much interested in the practical applications of his work. Soon afterward I noticed a distinct change in the Professor's outlook, and a few months later he confided his new ambitions to me. I had been trying to persuade him to publish his results (he had already spent over £50,000 and the Public Accounts Committee was being difficult again), but he asked for a little more time. I think I can best explain his attitude by his own words, which I remember very vividly, for they were expressed with peculiar emphasis.

'Have you ever wondered,' he said, 'what the Earth really is like inside? We've only scratched the surface with our mines and wells. What lies beneath is as unknown as the other side of the Moon.

'We know that the Earth is unnaturally dense – far denser than the rocks and soil of its crust would indicate. The core may be solid metal, but until now there's been no way of telling. Even ten miles down the pressure must be thirty tons or more to the square inch and the temperature several hundred degrees. What it's like at the center staggers the immagination: the pressure must be thousands of tons to the square inch. It's strange to think that in two or three years we may have reached the Moon, but when we've got to the stars we'll still be no nearer that inferno four thousand miles beneath our feet.

'I can now get recognizable echoes from two miles down, but I hope to step up the transmitter to ten megawatts in a few months. With that power, I believe the range will be increased to ten miles; and I don't mean to stop there.'

I was impressed, but at the same time I felt a little skeptical.

'That's all very well,' I said, 'but surely the deeper you go the less there'll be to see. The pressure will make any cavities impossible, and after a few miles there will simply be a homogeneous mass getting denser and denser.'

'Quite likely,' agreed the Professor. 'But I can still learn a lot from the transmission characteristics. Anyway, we'll see when we get there!'

That was four months ago; and yesterday I saw the result of that research. When I answered his invitation the Professor was clearly excited, but he gave me no hint of what, if anything, he had discovered. He showed me his improved equipment and raised the new receiver from its bath. The sensitivity of the pickups had been greatly improved, and this alone had effectively doubled the range, altogether apart from the increased transmitter power. It was strange to watch the steel framework slowly turning and to realize that it was exploring regions which, in spite of their nearness, man might never reach.

When we entered the hut containing the display equipment, the Professor was strangely silent. He switched on the transmitter, and even though it was a hundred yards away I could feel an uncomfortable tingling. Then the cathode ray tube lit up and the slowly revolving time-base drew the picture I had seen so often before. Now, however, the definition was much improved owing to the increased power and sensitivity of the equipment. I adjusted the depth control and focussed on the Underground, which was clearly visible as a dark lane across the faintly luminous screen. While I was watching, it suddenly seemed to fill with mist and I knew that a train was going through.

Presently I continued the descent. Although I had watched this picture many times before, it was always uncanny to see great luminous masses floating toward me and to know that they were buried rocks – perhaps the debris from the glaciers of fifty thousand years ago. Dr Clayton had worked out a chart so that we could identify the various strata as they were passed, and presently I saw that I was through the alluvial soil and entering the great clay saucer which traps and holds the city's artesian water. Soon that too was passed, and I was dropping down through the bedrock almost a mile below the surface.

The picture was still clear and bright, though there was little to see, for there were now few changes in the ground structure. The pressure was already rising to a thousand atmospheres; soon it would be impossible for any cavity to remain open, for the rock itself would begin to flow. Mile after mile I sank, but only a pale mist floated on the screen, broken sometimes when echoes were returned from pockets or lodes of denser material. They became fewer and fewer as the depth increased – or else they were now so small that they could no longer be seen.

The scale of the picture was, of course, continually expanding. It was now many miles from side to side, and I felt like an airman looking down upon an unbroken cloud ceiling from an enormous height. For a moment a sense of vertigo seized me as I thought of the abyss into which I was gazing. I do not think that the world will ever seem quite solid to me again.

At a depth of nearly ten miles I stopped and looked at the Professor. There had been no alteration for some time, and I knew that the rock must now be compressed into a featureless, homogeneous mass. I did a quick mental calculation and shuddered as I realized that the pressure must be at least thirty tons to the square inch. The scanner was revolving very slowly now, for the feeble echoes were taking many seconds to struggle back from the depths.

'Well, Professor,' I said, 'I congratulate you. It's a wonderful achievement. But we seem to have reached the core now. I don't suppose there'll be any change from here to the center.'

He smiled a little wryly. 'Go on,' he said. 'You haven't finished yet.'

There was something in his voice that puzzled and alarmed me. I looked at him intently for a moment; his features were just visible in the blue-green glow of the cathode ray tube.

'How far down can this thing go?' I asked, as the interminable descent started again.

'Fifteen miles,' he said shortly. I wondered how he knew, for the last feature I had seen at all clearly was only eight miles down. But I continued the long fall through the rock, the scanner turning more and more slowly now, until it took almost five minutes to make a complete revolution. Behind me I could hear the Professor breathing heavily, and once the back of my chair gave a crack as his fingers gripped it.

Then, suddenly, very faint markings began to reappear on the screen. I leaned forward eagerly, wondering if this was the first glimpse of the world's iron core. With agonizing slowness the scanner turned through a right angle, then another. And then –

I leaped suddenly out of my chair, cried 'My God!' and turned to face the Professor. Only once before in my life had I received such an intellectual shock – fifteen years ago, when

I had accidentally turned on the radio and heard of the fall of the first atomic bomb. That had been unexpected, but this was inconceivable. For on the screen had appeared a grid of faint lines, crossing and recrossing to form a perfectly symmetrical lattice.

I know that I said nothing for many minutes, for the scanner made a complete revolution while I stood frozen with surprise. Then the Professor spoke in a soft, unnaturally calm voice.

'I wanted you to see it for yourself before I said anything. That picture is now thirty miles in diameter, and those squares are two or three miles on a side. You'll notice that the vertical lines converge and the horizontal ones are bent into arcs. We're looking at part of an enormous structure of concentric rings; the center must lie many miles to the north, probably in the region of Cambridge. How much further it extends in the other direction we can only guess.'

'But what *is* it, for heaven's sake?'

'Well, it's clearly artificial.'

'That's ridiculous! Fifteen miles down!'

The Professor pointed to the screen again. 'God knows I've done my best,' he said, 'but I can't convince myself that Nature could make anything like that.'

I had nothing to say, and presently he continued: 'I discovered it three days ago, when I was trying to find the maximum range of the equipment. I can go deeper than this, and I rather think that the structure we can see is so dense that it won't transmit my radiations any further.

'I've tried a dozen theories, but in the end I keep returning to one. We know that the pressure down there must be eight or nine thousand atmospheres, and the temperature must be high enough to melt rock. But normal matter is still almost empty space. Suppose that there is life down there – not organic life, of course, but life based on partially condensed matter, matter in which the electron shells are few or altogether missing. Do you see what I mean? To such creatures, even the rock fifteen miles down would offer no more resistance than water – and we and all our world would be as tenuous as ghosts.'

'Then that thing we can see –'

'Is a city, or its equivalent. You've seen its size, so you can judge for yourself the civilization that must have built it. All the world we know – our oceans and continents and mountains – is nothing more than a film of mist surrounding something beyond our comprehension.'

Neither of us said anything for a while. I remember feeling a foolish surprise at being one of the first men in the world to learn the appalling truth; for somehow I never doubted that it was the truth. And I wondered how the rest of humanity would react when the revelation came.

Presently I broke into the silence. 'If you're right,' I said, 'why have they – whatever they are – never made contact with us?'

The Professor looked at me rather pityingly. 'We think we're good engineers,' he said, 'but how could *we* reach *them*? Besides, I'm not at all sure that there haven't been contacts. Think of all the underground creatures and the mythology – trolls and cobalds and the rest. No, it's quite impossible – I take it back. Still, the idea *is* rather suggestive.'

All the while the pattern on the screen had never changed: the dim network still glowed there, challenging our sanity. I tried to imagine streets and buildings and the creatures going among them, creatures who could make their way through the incandescent rock as a fish swims through water. It was fantastic . . . and then I remembered the incredibly narrow range of temperatures and pressures under which the human race exists. *We*, not they, were the freaks, for almost all the matter in the universe is at temperatures of thousands or even millions of degrees.

'Well,' I said lamely, 'what do we do now?'

The Professor leaned forward eagerly. 'First we must learn a great deal more, and we must keep this an absolute secret until we are sure of the facts. Can you imagine the panic there would be if this information leaked out? Of course, the truth's inevitable sooner or later, but we may be able to break it slowly.

'You'll realize that the geological surveying side of my work is now utterly unimportant. The first thing we have to do is to build a chain of stations to find the extent of the structure. I visualize them at ten-mile intervals toward the north, but I'd like to build the first one somewhere in South London to see how extensive the thing is. The whole job will have to be kept as secret as the building of the first radar chain in the late thirties.

'At the same time, I'm going to push up my transmitter power again. I hope to be able to beam the output much more narrowly, and so greatly increase the energy concentration. But this will involve all sorts of mechanical difficulties, and I'll need more assistance.'

I promised to do my utmost to get further aid, and the Professor hopes that you will soon be able to visit his laboratory yourself. In the meantime I am attaching a photograph of the vision screen, which although not as clear as the original will, I hope, prove beyond doubt that our observations are not mistaken.

I am well aware that our grant to the Interplanetary Society has brought us dangerously near the total estimate for the year, but surely even the crossing of space is less important than the immediate investigation of this discovery which may have the most profound effects on the philosophy and the future of the whole human race.

I sat back and looked at Karn. There was much in the document I had not understood, but the main outlines were clear enough.

'Yes,' I said, 'this is it! Where's that photograph?'

He handed it over. The quality was poor, for it had been copied many times before reaching us. But the pattern was unmistakable and I recognized it at once.

'They were good scientists,' I said admiringly. 'That's Callastheon, all right. So we've found the truth at last, even if it has taken us three hundred years to do it.'

'Is that surprising,' asked Karn, 'when you consider the mountain of stuff we've had to translate and the difficulty of copying it before it evaporates?'

I sat in silence for a while, thinking of the strange race whose relics we were examining. Only once – never again! – had I gone up the great vent our engineers had opened into the Shadow World. It had been a frightening and unforgettable experience. The multiple layers of my pressure suit had made movement very difficult, and despite their insulation I could sense the unbelievable cold that was all around me.

'What a pity it was,' I mused, 'that our emergence destroyed them so completely. They were a clever race, and we might have learned a lot from them.'

'I don't think we can be blamed.' said Karn. 'We never really believed that anything could exist under those awful conditions of near-vacuum, and almost absolute zero. It couldn't be helped.'

I did not agree. 'I think it proves that they were the more intelligent race. After all, *they* discovered us first. Everyone laughed at my grandfather when he said that the radiation he'd detected from the Shadow World must be artificial.'

Karn ran one of his tentacles over the manuscript.

'We've certainly discovered the cause of that radiation,' he said. 'Notice the date – it's just a year before your grandfather's discovery. The Professor must have got his grant all right!' He laughed unpleasantly. 'It must have given him a shock when he saw us coming up to the surface, right underneath him.'

I scarcely heard his words, for a most uncomfortable feeling had suddenly come over me. I thought of the thousands of miles of rock lying below the great city of Callastheon, growing hotter and denser all the way to the Earth's unknown core. And so I turned to Karn.

'That isn't very funny,' I said quietly. 'It may be our turn next.'

Don't Look Now

BY HENRY KUTTNER

from *Startling Stories*, March 1948

To try and summarise the life of one of science fiction's most prolific writers in a few hundred words is like trying to write *The Lord's Prayer* on a pinhead. I envy those who can succeed.

Kuttner was born in Los Angeles in 1914 and was soon addicted to sf and fantasy. His first story sale was 'The Graveyard Rats' to *Weird Tales* (March 1936) which was a regular market for the next five years. Kuttner's penchant for the bizarre enabled him to find ready markets with the host of sadistic mystery magazines that flourished in the 1930s – such as *Mystery Tales* and *Thrilling Mystery*. *Thrilling Mystery* originated with Standard Magazines, who also produced *Thrilling Wonder*, in which Kuttner's 'When the Earth Lived' was published in November 1937; an intriguing story where alien rays focused on the Earth bring inanimate objects to life. Kuttner's output at this stage was colossal; many were hack stories simply to earn some money, but when he had the time, his fiction acquired a fine polish and style.

In June 1940 Kuttner married C. L. Moore, and thereafter they mostly collaborated on fiction. The result was electrifying, and their talents combined as Lewis Padgett or Lawrence O'Donnell produced some of the finest science fiction ever seen: 'The Twonky', 'Mimsy Were the Borogroves', '*Fury*', all are now recognised classics.

By the late 1940s Kuttner's most prolific period was over, but the couple were writing for Hollywood, and the few stories that Kuttner did write are cleverly polished gems. 'Don't Look Now' is one such pearl.

In 1950 the Kuttners went to college, and Henry received his BA in 1954. He was working on his MA when he died of an acute coronary on Monday 3 February 1958, aged just forty-three. His passing has left a black hole in the sf firmament where once shone one of its most sparkling talents.

The man in the brown suit was looking at himself in the mirror behind the bar. The reflection seemed to interest him even more deeply than the drink between his hands. He was paying only perfunctory attention to Lyman's attempts at conversation. This had been going on for perhaps fifteen minutes before he finally lifted his glass and took a deep swallow.

'Don't look now,' Lyman said.

The brown man slid his eyes sidewise toward Lyman, tilted his glass higher, and took another swig. Ice-cubes slipped down toward his mouth. He put the glass back on the red-brown wood and signalled for a refill. Finally he took a deep breath and looked at Lyman.

'Don't look at what?' he asked.

'There was one sitting right beside you,' Lyman said, blinking rather glazed eyes. 'He just went out. You mean you couldn't see him?'

The brown man finished paying for his fresh drink before he answered. 'See who?' he asked, with a fine mixture of boredom, distate and reluctant interest. 'Who went out?'

'What have I been telling you for the last tèn minutes? Weren't you listening?'

'Certainly I was listening. That is – certainly. You were talking about – bathtubs. Radios. Orson –'

'Not Orson. H. G. Herbert George. With Orson it was just a gag. H. G. *knew* – or suspected. I wonder if it was simply intuition with him? He couldn't have had any proof – but he did stop writing science fiction rather suddenly, didn't he? I'll bet he knew once, though.'

'Knew what?'

'About the Martians. All this won't do us a bit of good if you don't listen. It may not anyway. The trick is to jump the gun – with proof. Convincing evidence. Nobody's ever been allowed to produce the evidence before. You *are* a reporter, aren't you?'

Holding his glass, the man in the brown suit nodded reluctantly.

'Then you ought to be taking it all down on a piece of folded paper. I want everybody to know. The whole world. It's important. Terribly important. It explains everything. My life won't be safe unless I can pass along the information and make people believe it.'

'Why won't your life be safe?'

'Because of the Martians, you fool. They own the world.'

The brown man sighed. 'Then they own my newspaper, too,' he objected, 'so I can't print anything they don't like.'

'I never thought of that,' Lyman said, considering the bottom of his glass, where two ice-cubes had fused into a cold, immutable union. 'They're not omnipotent, though. I'm sure they're vulnerable, or why have they always kept under cover? They're afraid of being found out. If the world had convincing evidence – look, people always believe what they read in the newspapers. Couldn't you –'

'Ha,' said the brown man with deep significance.

Lyman drummed sadly on the bar and murmured, 'There must be some way. Perhaps if I had another drink . . .'

The brown-suited man tasted his collins, which seemed to stimulate him. 'Just what is all this about Martians?' he asked Lyman. 'Suppose you start at the beginning and tell me again. Or can't you remember?'

'Of course I can remember. I've got practically total recall. It's something new. Very new. I never could do it before. I can even remember my last conversation with the Martians.' Lyman favored the brown man with a glance of triumph.

'When was that?'

'This morning.'

'I can even remember conversations I had last week,' the brown man said mildly. 'So what?'

'You don't understand. They make us forget, you see. They tell us what to do and we forget about the conversation – it's post-hypnotic suggestion, I expect – but we follow their orders just the same. There's the compulsion, though we think we're making our own decisions. Oh, they own the world, all right, but nobody knows it except me.'

'And how did you find out?'

'Well, I got my brain scrambled, in a way. I've been fooling around with supersonic detergents, trying to work out something marketable, you know. The gadget went wrong – from some standpoints. High-frequency waves, it was. They went through and through me. Should have been inaudible, but I could hear them, or rather – well, actually I could *see* them. That's what I mean about my brain being scrambled. And after that, I could see and hear the Martians. They've geared themselves so they work efficiently on ordinary brains, and mine isn't ordinary any more. They can't hypnotize me, either. They can command me, but I needn't obey – now. I hope they don't suspect. Maybe they do. Yes, I guess they do.'

'How can you tell?'

'The way they look at me.'

'How do they look at you?' asked the brown man, as he began to reach for a pencil and then changed his mind. He took a drink instead. 'Well? What are they like?'

'I'm not sure. I can see them, all right, but only when they're dressed up.'

'Okay, okay,' the brown man said patiently. 'How do they look, dressed up?'

'Just like anybody, almost. They dress up in – in human skins. Oh, not real ones, imitations. Like the Katzenjammer Kids zipped into crocodile suits. Undressed – I don't know. I've never seen one. Maybe they're invisible even to me, then, or maybe they're just camouflaged. Ants or owls or rats or bats or –'

'Or anything,' the brown man said hastily.

'Thanks. Or anything, of course. But when they're dressed up like humans – like that one who was sitting next to you awhile ago, when I told you not to look –'

'That one was invisible, I gather?'

'Most of the time they are, to everybody. But once in a while, for some reason, they –'

'Wait,' the brown man objected. 'Make sense, will you? They dress up in human skins and then sit around invisible?'

'Only now and then. The human skins are perfectly good imitations. Nobody can tell the difference. It's that third eye that gives them away. When they keep it closed, you'd never guess it was there. When they want to open it, they go invisible – like *that*. Fast. When I see somebody with a third eye, right in the middle of his forehead, I know he's a Martian and invisible, and I pretend not to notice him.'

'Uh-huh,' the brown man said. 'Then for all you know, I'm one of your visible Martians.'

'Oh, I hope not!' Lyman regarded him anxiously. 'Drunk as I am, I don't think so. I've been trailing you all day, making sure. It's a risk I have to take, of course. They'll go to any length – any length at all – to make a man give himself away. I realize that. I can't really trust anybody. But I had to find *someone* to talk to, and I –' He paused. There was a brief silence. 'I could be wrong,' Lyman said presently. 'When the third eye's closed, I can't tell if it's there. Would you mind opening your third eye for me?' He fixed a dim gaze on the brown man's forehead.

'Sorry,' the reporter said. 'Some other time. Besides, I don't know you. So you want me to splash this across the front page, I gather? Why didn't you go to see the managing editor? My stories have to get past the desk and rewrite.'

'I want to give my secret to the world,' Lyman said stubbornly. 'The question is, how far will I get? You'd expect they'd have killed me the minute I opened my mouth to you – except that I didn't say anything while they were here. I don't believe they take us very seriously, you know. This must have been going on since the dawn of history, and by now they've had time to get careless. They let Fort go pretty far before they cracked down on him. But you notice they were careful never to let Fort get hold of genuine proof that would convince people.'

The brown man said something under his breath about a human interest story in a box. He asked, 'What do the Martians do, besides hang around bars all dressed up?'

'I'm still working on that,' Lyman said. 'It isn't easy to understand. They run the world, of course, but why?' He wrinkled his brow and stared appealingly at the brown man. 'Why?'

'If they do run it, they've got a lot to explain.'

'That's what I mean. From our viewpoint, there's no sense to it. We do things illogically, but only because they tell us to. Everything we do, almost, is pure illogic. Poe's "Imp of the Perverse" – you could give it another name beginning with **M**. Martian, I mean. It's all very well for psychologists to explain why a murderer wants to confess, but it's still an illogical reaction. Unless a Martian commands him to.'

'You can't be hypnotized into doing anything that violates your moral sense,' the brown man said triumphantly.

Lyman frowned. 'Not by another human, but you can by a Martian. I expect they got the upper hand when we didn't have more than ape-brains, and they've kept it ever since. They evolved as we did, and kept a step ahead. Like the sparrow on the eagle's back who hitch-hiked till the eagle reached his ceiling, and then took off and broke the altitude record. They conquered the world, but nobody ever knew it. And they've been ruling ever since.'

'But –'

'Take houses, for example. Uncomfortable things. Ugly, inconvenient, dirty, everything wrong with them. But when men like Frank Lloyd Wright slip out from under the Martian's thumb long enough to suggest something better, look how the people react. They hate the thought. That's their Martians, giving them orders.'

'Look. Why should the Martians care what kind of houses we live in? Tell me that.'

Lyman frowned. 'I don't like the note of skepticism I detect creeping into this conversation,' he announced. 'They care, all right. No doubt about it. They *live* in our houses. We don't build for our convenience, we build, under order, for the Martians, the way they want it. They're very much concerned with everything we do. And the more senseless, the more concern.

'Take wars. Wars don't make sense from any human viewpoint. Nobody really wants wars. But we go right on having them. From the Martian viewpoint they're useful. They give us a spurt in technology, and they reduce the excess population. And there are lots of other results, too. Colonization, for one thing. But mainly technology. In peace time, if a guy invents jet-propulsion, it's too expensive to develop commercially. In war-time, though, it's *got* to be developed. Then the Martians can use it whenever they want. They use us the way they'd use tools or – or limbs. And nobody ever really wins a war – except the Martians.'

The man in the brown suit chuckled. 'That makes sense,' he said. 'It must be nice to be a Martian.'

'Why not? Up till now, no race ever successfully conquered and ruled another. The underdog could revolt or absorb. If you know you're being ruled, then the ruler's vulnerable. But if the world doesn't know – and it doesn't –

'Take radios,' Lyman continued, going off at a tangent. 'There's no earthly reason why a sane human should listen to a radio. But the Martians make us do it. They like it. Take bathtubs. Nobody contends bathtubs are comfortable – for us. But they're fine for Martians. All the impractical things we keep on using, even though we know they're impractical –'

'Typewriter ribbons,' the brown man said, struck by the thought. 'But not even a Martian could enjoy changing a type-writer ribbon.'

Lyman seemed to find that flippant. He said that he knew all about the Martians except for one thing – their psychology.

'I don't know *why* they act as they do. It looks illogical sometimes, but I feel perfectly sure they've got sound motives for every move they make. Until I get that worked out I'm pretty much at a standstill. Until I get evidence – proof – and help. I've got to stop under cover till then. And I've been doing that. I do what they tell me, so they won't suspect, and I pretend to forget what they tell me to forget.'

'Then you've got nothing much to worry about.'

Lyman paid no attention. He was off again on a list of his grievances.

'When I hear the water running in the tub and a Martian splashing around, I pretend I don't hear a thing. My bed's too short and I tried last week to order a special length, but the Martian that sleeps there told me not to. He's a runt, like most of them. That is, I think they're runts. I have to deduce, because you never see them undressed. But it goes on like that con-stantly. By the way, how's your Martian?'

The man in the brown suit set down his glass rather suddenly.

'My Martian?'

'Now listen. I may be just a little bit drunk, but my logic remains unimpaired. I can still put two and two together. Either you know about the Martians, or you don't. If you do, there's no point in giving me that, "What, *my* Martian?" routine. I know you have a Martian. Your Martian knows you have a Martian. My Martian knows. The point is, do *you* know? Think hard,' Lyman urged solicitously.

'No, I haven't got a Martian,' the reporter said, taking a quick drink. The edge of the glass clicked against his teeth.

'Nervous, I see,' Lyman remarked. 'Of course you *have* got a Martian. I suspect you know it.'

'What would I be doing with a Martian?' the brown man asked with dogged dogmatism.

'What would you be doing without one? I imagine it's illegal. If they caught you running around without one they'd probably put you in a pound or something until claimed. Oh, you've got one, all right. So have I. So has he, and he, and he – and the

bartender.' Lyman enumerated the other barflies with a wavering forefinger.

'Of course they have,' the brown man said. 'But they'll all go
back to Mars tomorrow and then you can see a good doctor.
You'd better have another dri –'

He was turning toward the bartender when Lyman, apparently by accident, leaned close to him and whispered urgently,

'*Don't look now!*'

The brown man glanced at Lyman's white face reflected in
the mirror before them.

'It's all right,' he said. 'There aren't any Mar –'

Lyman gave him a fierce, quick kick under the edge of the
bar.

'Shut up! One just came in!'

And then he caught the brown man's gaze and with elaborate
unconcern said, '– so naturally, there was nothing for me to do
but climb out on the roof after it. Took me ten minutes to get it
down the ladder, and just as we reached the bottom it gave one
bound, climbed up my face, sprang from the top of my head,
and there it was again on the roof, screaming for me to get it
down.'

'*What?*' the brown man demanded with pardonable curiosity.

'My cat, of course. What did you think? No, never mind,
don't answer that.' Lyman's face was turned to the brown man's,
but from the corners of his eyes he was watching an invisible
progress down the length of the bar toward a booth at the very
back.

'Now why did he come in?' he murmured. 'I don't like this.
Is he anyone you know?'

'Is who –?'

'That Martian. Yours, by any chance? No, I suppose not.
Yours was probably the one who went out a while ago. I wonder
if he went to make a report, and sent this one in? It's possible.
It could be. You can talk now, but keep your voice low, and
stop squirming. Want him to notice we can see him?'

'*I* can't see him. Don't drag me into this. You and your
Martians can fight it out together. You're making me nervous.
I've got to go, anyway.' But he didn't move to get off the stool.
Across Lyman's shoulder he was stealing glances toward the
back of the bar, and now and then he looked at Lyman's face.

'Stop watching me,' Lyman said. 'Stop watching him. Anybody'd think you were a cat.'

'Why a cat? Why should anybody – do I look like a cat?'

'We were talking about cats, weren't we? Cats can see them, quite clearly. Even undressed, I believe. They don't like them.'

'Who doesn't like who?'

'Whom. Neither likes the other. Cats can see Martians – sh-h! – but they pretend not to, and that makes the Martians mad. I have a theory that cats ruled the world before the Martians came. Never mind. Forget about cats. This may be more serious than you think. I happen to know my Martian's taking tonight off, and I'm pretty sure that was your Martian who went out some time ago. And have you noticed that nobody else in here has his Martian with him? Do you suppose –' His voice sank. 'Do you suppose they could be *waiting for us outside*?'

'Oh Lord,' the brown man said. 'In the alley with the cats, I suppose.'

'Why don't you stop this yammer about cats and be serious for a moment?' Lyman demanded, and then paused, paled and reeled slightly on his stool. He hastily took a drink to cover his confusion.

'What's the matter now?' the brown man asked.

'Nothing.' Gulp. 'Nothing. It was just that – he *looked* at me. With – you know.'

'Let me get this straight. I take it the Martian is dressed in – is dressed like a human?'

'Naturally.'

'But he's invisible to all eyes but yours?'

'Yes. He doesn't want to be visible, just now. Besides –' Lyman paused cunningly. He gave the brown man a furtive glance and then looked quickly down at his drink. 'Besides, you know, I rather think you can see him – a little, anyway.'

The brown man was perfectly silent for about thirty seconds. He sat quite motionless, not even the ice in the drink he held clinked. One might have thought he did not even breathe. Certainly he did not blink.

'What makes you think that?' he asked in a normal voice, after the thirty seconds had run out.

'I – did I say anything? I wasn't listening.' Lyman put down his drink abruptly. 'I think I'll go now.'

'No, you won't,' the brown man said, closing his fingers around Lyman's wrist. 'Not yet you won't. Come back here. Sit down. Now. What was the idea? Where were you going?'

Lyman nodded dumbly toward the back of the bar, indicating

either a juke-box or a door marked MEN.

'I don't feel so good. Maybe I've had too much to drink. I guess I'll –'

'You're all right. I don't trust you back there with that – that invisible man of yours. You'll stay right here until he leaves.'

'He's going now,' Lyman said brightly. His eyes moved with great briskness along the line of an invisible but rapid progress toward the front door. 'See, he's gone. Now let me loose, will you?'

The brown man glanced toward the back booth.

'No,' he said, 'He isn't gone. Sit right where you are.'

It was Lyman's turn to remain quite still, in a stricken sort of way, for a perceptible while. The ice in *his* drink, however, clinked audibly. Presently he spoke. His voice was soft, and rather soberer than before.

'You're right. He's still there. You can see him, can't you?'

The brown man said, 'Has he got his back to us?'

'You *can* see him, then. Better than I can maybe. Maybe there are more of them here than I thought. They could be anywhere. They could be sitting beside you anywhere you go, and you wouldn't even guess, until –' He shook his head a little. 'They'd want to be *sure*,' he said, mostly to himself. 'They can give you orders and make you forget, but there must be limits to what they can force you to do. They can't make a man betray himself. They'd have to lead him on – until they were sure.'

He lifted his drink and tipped it steeply above his face. The ice ran down the slope and bumped coldly against his lip, but he held it until the last of the pale, bubbling amber had drained into his mouth. He set the glass on the bar and faced the brown man.

'Well?' he said.

The brown man looked up and down the bar.

'It's getting late,' he said. 'Not many people left. We'll wait.'

'Wait for what?'

The brown man looked toward the back booth and looked away again quickly.

'I have something to show you. I don't want anyone else to see.'

Lyman surveyed the narrow, smoky room. As he looked the last customer beside themselves at the bar began groping in his pocket, tossed some change on the mahogany, and went out slowly.

They sat in silence. The bartender eyed them with stolid disinterest. Presently a couple in the front booth got up and departed, quarreling in undertones.

'Is there anyone left?' the brown man asked in a voice that did not carry down the bar to the man in the apron.

'Only –' Lyman did not finish, but he nodded gently toward the back of the room. 'He isn't looking. Let's get this over with. What do you want to show me?'

The brown man took off his wrist-watch and pried up the metal case. Two small, glossy photograph prints slid out. The brown man separated them with a finger.

'I just want to make sure of something,' he said. 'First – why did you pick me out? Quite a while ago, you said you'd been trailing me all day, making sure. I haven't forgotten that. And you knew I was a reporter. Suppose you tell me the truth, now?'

Squirming on his stool, Lyman scowled. 'It was the way you looked at things,' he murmured. 'On the subway this morning – I'd never seen you before in my life, but I kept noticing the way you looked at things – the wrong things, things that weren't there, the way a cat does – and then you'd always look away – I got the idea you could see the Martians too.'

'Go on,' the brown man said quietly.

'I followed you. All day. I kept hoping you'd turn out to be – somebody I could talk to. Because if I could *know* that I wasn't the only one who could see them, then I'd know there was still some hope left. It's been worse than solitary confinement. I've been able to see them for three years now. Three years. And I've managed to keep my power a secret even from them. And, somehow, I've managed to keep from killing myself, too.'

'Three years?' the brown man said. He shivered.

'There was always a little hope. I knew nobody would believe – not without proof. And how can you get proof? It was only that I – I kept telling myself that maybe you could see them too, and if you could, maybe there were others – lots of others – enough so we might get together and work out some way of proving to the world –'

The brown man's fingers were moving. In silence he pushed

a photograph across the mahogany. Lyman picked it up un-steadily.

'Moonlight?' he asked after a moment. It was a landscape under a deep, dark sky with white clouds in it. Trees stood white and lacy against the darkness. The grass was white as if with moonlight, and the shadows blurry.

'No, not moonlight,' the brown man said. 'Infra-red. I'm strictly an amateur, but lately I've been experimenting with infra-red film. And I got some very odd results.'

Lyman stared at the film.

'You see, I live near –' The brown man's finger tapped a certain quite common object that appeared in the photograph '– and something funny keeps showing up now and then against it. But only with infra-red film. Now I know chlorophyll reflects so much infra-red light that grass and leaves photograph white. The sky comes out black, like this. There are tricks to using this kind of film. Photograph a tree against a cloud, and you can't tell them apart in the print. But you can photograph through a haze and pick out distant objects the ordinary film wouldn't catch. And sometimes, when you focus on something like this –' He tapped the image of the very common object again, 'you get a very odd image on the film. Like that. A man with three eyes.'

Lyman held the print up to the light. In silence he took the other one from the bar and studied it. When he laid them down he was smiling.

'You know,' Lyman said in a conversational whisper, 'a pro-fessor of astrophysics at one of the more important universities had a very interesting little item in "The Times" the other Sunday. Name of Spitzer, I think. He said that if there were life on Mars, and if Martians had ever visited earth, there'd be no way to prove it. Nobody would believe the few men who saw them. Not, he said, unless the Martians happened to be photo-graphed. . . .'

Lyman looked at the brown man thoughtfully.

'Well,' he said, 'it's happened. You've photographed them.'

The brown man nodded. He took up the prints and returned them to his watch-case. 'I thought so, too. Only until tonight I couldn't be sure. I'd never seen one – fully – as you have. It isn't so much a matter of what you call getting your brain scrambled with supersonics as it is of just knowing where to look. But I've been seeing *part* of them all my life, and so has everybody.

It's that little suggestion of movement you never catch except just at the corner of your eye. Something that's *almost* there – and when you look fully at it, there's nothing. These photographs showed me the way. It's not easy to learn, but it can be done. We're conditioned to look directly at a thing – the particular thing we want to see clearly, whatever it is. Perhaps the Martians gave us that conditioning. When we see a movement at the edge of our range of vision, it's almost irresistible not to look directly at it. So it vanishes.'

'Then they can be seen – by anybody?'

'I've learned a lot in a few days,' the brown man said. 'Since I took those photographs. You have to train yourself. It's like seeing a trick picture – one that's really a composite, after you study it. Camouflage. You just have to learn how. Otherwise we can look at them all our lives and never see them.'

'The camera does, though.'

'Yes, the camera does. I've wondered why nobody ever caught them this way before. Once you see them on film, they're unmistakable – that third eye.'

'Infra-red film's comparatively new, isn't it? And then I'll bet you have to catch them against that one particular background – you know – or they won't show on the film. Like trees against clouds. It's tricky. You must have had just the right lighting that day, and exactly the right focus, and the lens stopped down just right. A kind of minor miracle. It might never happen again exactly that way. But . . . don't look now.'

They were silent. Furtively, they watched the mirror. Their eyes slid along toward the open door of the tavern.

And then there was a long, breathless silence.

'He looked back at us,' Lyman said very quietly. 'He looked at us . . . that third eye!'

The brown man was motionless again. When he moved, it was to swallow the rest of his drink.

'I don't think that they're suspicious yet,' he said. 'The trick will be to keep under cover until we can blow this thing wide open. There's got to be some way to do it – some way that will convince people.'

'There's proof. The photographs. A competent cameraman ought to be able to figure out just how you caught that Martian on film and duplicate the conditions. It's evidence.'

'Evidence can cut both ways,' the brown man said. 'What I'm hoping is that the Martians don't really like to kill – unless they have to. I'm hoping they won't kill without proof. But –' He tapped his wrist-watch.

'There's two of us now, though,' Lyman said. 'We've got to stick together. Both of us have broken the big rule – *don't look now* –'

The bartender was at the back, disconnecting the juke-box. The brown man said, 'We'd better not be seen together unnecessarily. But if we both come to this bar tomorrow night at nine for a drink – that wouldn't look suspicious, even to them.'

'Suppose –' Lyman hesitated. 'May I have one of those photographs?'

'Why?'

'If one of us had – an accident – the other one would still have the proof. Enough, maybe, to convince the right people.'

The brown man hesitated, nodded shortly, and opened his watch-case again. He gave Lyman one of the pictures.

'Hide it,' he said. 'It's evidence. I'll see you here tomorrow. Meanwhile, be careful. Remember to play safe.'

They shook hands firmly, facing each other in an endless second of final, decisive silence. Then the brown man turned abruptly and walked out of the bar.

Lyman sat there. Between two wrinkles in his forehead there was a stir and a flicker of lashes unfurling. The third eye opened slowly and looked after the brown man.

Kaleidoscope

BY RAY BRADBURY

from *Thrilling Wonder Stories*, October 1949

Ray Bradbury is indisputably the poet of science fiction. His ability to mould language to transmit thoughts once considered impossible is unique within the sf genre. His unquenchable talent made sf editors realise that here was someone to whom the once rigid confines of science fiction meant nothing. More than any writers before him, Bradbury pushed the borders of science fiction far into the unknown, and in so doing made very hazy that boundary between science fiction and science fantasy.

But it didn't happen overnight, and it meant much hard work on Bradbury's side. Raymond Douglas Bradbury was born in Waukegan, Illinois on Sunday 22 August 1920. He and his family moved to Los Angeles, via Arizona, and in 1937 he discovered the local Los Angeles Chapter of the Science Fiction League, and thereby sf fandom. He discovered fanzines, and much of his early fiction appeared in their pages. He produced his own, *Futuria Fantasia*, which survived four issues. The second (Fall 1939) carried Bradbury's short piece, 'Pendulum', which when rewritten by sf author Henry Hasse marked Bradbury's first professional sale, appearing in *Super Science Stories* for November 1941. Bradbury had had a short piece published in the Californian slick *Script* the year before, but no payment was made.

Regular sales eluded Bradbury for a long time. He reputedly destroyed millions of words. But he persevered, and finally found a suitable market for his strange brand of fantasy in *Weird Tales*. Other publishers, (mostly detective and sf) told Bradbury to conform, but in *Weird Tales*, editor Dorothy

McIlwraith allowed him to write as he pleased. This developed his talents and made his name so that other editors looked at his stories in a new light. By the mid-1940s he was selling unconventional sf to *Planet Stories*, and by 1949 was producing really superior science fiction such as 'Kaleidoscope'. Who would think a magazine with the title *Thrilling Wonder*, which evokes visions of bug-eyed monsters and space battles, would house within its aging pulp pages the following example of such beautifully constructed gems of prose?

The first concussion cut the ship up the side like a gian. can opener. The men were thrown into space like a dozen wriggling silverfish. They were scattered into a dark sea; and the ship, in a million pieces, went on like a meteor swarm seeking a lost sun.

'Barkley, Barkley, where are you?'

The sound of voices calling like lost children on a cold night.

'Woode, Woode!'

'Captain!'

'Hollis, Hollis, this is Stone.'

'Stone, this is Hollis. Where are you?'

'I don't know, how can I? Which way is up? I'm falling. Good gosh, I'm falling.'

They fell. They fell as pebbles fall in the long autumns of childhood, silver and thin. They were scattered as jack-stones are scattered from a gigantic throw. And now instead of men there were only voices – all kinds of voices, disembodied and impassioned, in varying degrees of terror and resignation.

'We're going away from each other.'

This was true. Hollis, swinging head over heels, knew this was true. He knew it with a vague acceptance. They were parting to go their separate ways, and nothing could bring them back. They were wearing their sealed-tight space suits with the glass tubes over their pale faces, but they hadn't had time to lock on their force units. With them, they could be small lifeboats in space, saving themselves, saving others, collecting together, finding each other until they were an island of men with some plan. But without the force units snapped to their shoulders they were meteors, senseless, each going to a separate and irrecoverable fate.

A period of perhaps ten minutes elapsed while the first terror died and a metallic calm took its place. Space began to weave their strange voices in and out, on a great dark loom, crossing, recrossing, making a final pattern.

'Stone to Hollis. How long can we talk by phone?'

'It depends on how fast you're going your way and I'm going mine.'

'An hour, I make it.'

'That should do it,' said Hollis, abstracted and quiet.

'What happened?' said Hollis, a minute later.

'The rocket blew up, that's all. Rockets do blow up.'

'Which way are you going?'

'It looks like I'll hit the sun.'

'It's Earth for me. Back to old Mother Earth at ten thousand miles per hour. I'll burn like a match.' Hollis thought of it with a queer abstraction of mind. He seemed to be removed from his body, watching it fall down and down through space, as objective as he had been in regard to the first falling snowflakes of a winter season long gone.

The others were silent, thinking of the destiny that had brought them to this, falling, falling, and nothing they could do to change it. Even the captain was quiet, for there was no command or plan he knew that could put things back together again.

'Oh, it's a long way down, oh it's a long way down, a long, long, long, way down,' said a voice. 'I don't want to die, I don't want to die, it's a long way down.'

'Who's that?'

'I don't know.'

'Stimson, I think. Stimson, is that you?'

'It's a long long way and I don't like it, oh God, I don't like it.'

'Stimson, this is Hollis, Stimson, you hear me?'

A pause while they fell separate from one another.

'Stimson?'

'Yes.' He replied at last.

'Stimson, take it easy, we're all in the same fix.'

'I don't want to be here, I want to be somewhere else.'

'There's a chance we'll be found.'

'I must be, I must be,' said Stimson. 'I don't believe this, I don't believe any of this is happening.'

'It's a bad dream,' said someone.

'Shut up!' said Hollis.

'Come and make me,' said the voice. It was Applegate. He laughed easily, with a similar objectivity. 'Come and shut me up.'

Hollis for the first time felt the impossibility of his position. A great anger filled him, for he wanted more than anything in existence at this moment to be able to do something to Applegate. He had wanted for many years to do something and now it was too late. Applegate was only a telephonic voice.

Falling, falling, falling!

Now, as if they had discovered the horror, two of the men began to scream. In a nightmare, Hollis saw one of them float by, very near, screaming and screaming.

'Stop it!' The man was almost at his fingertips, screaming insanely. He would never stop. He would go on screaming for a million miles, as long as he was in radio range, disturbing all of them, making it impossible for them to talk to one another.

Hollis reached out. It was best this way. He made the extra effort and touched the man. He grasped the man's ankle and pulled himself up along the body until he reached the head. The man screamed and clawed frantically, like a drowning swimmer. The screaming filled the universe.

One way or the other, thought Hollis. The sun or Earth or meteors will kill him, so why not now?

He smashed the man's glass mask with his iron fist. The screaming stopped. He pushed off from the body and let it spin away on its own course, falling, falling.

Falling, falling down space went Hollis and the rest of them in the long, endless dropping and whirling of silent terror.

'Hollis, you still there?'

Hollis did not speak, but felt the rush of heat in his face.

'This is Applegate again.'

'All right, Applegate.'

'Let's talk. We haven't anything else to do.'

The captain cut in. 'That's enough of that. We've got to figure a way out of this.'

'Captain, why don't you shut up?' said Applegate.

'What!'

'You heard me, Captain. Don't pull your rank on me, you're ten thousand miles away by now, and let's not kid ourselves. As Stimson puts it, it's a long way down.'

'See here, Applegate!'

'Can it. This a mutiny of one. I haven't a damn thing to lose. Your ship was a bad ship and you were a bad captain and I hope you roast when you hit the sun.'

'I'm ordering you to stop!'

'Go on, order me again.' Applegate smiled across ten thousand miles. The captain was silent. Applegate continued, 'Where were we, Hollis? Oh, yes, I remember. I hate you, too. But you know that. You've known it for a long time.'

Hollis clenched his fists, helplessly.

'I want to tell something,' said Applegate. 'Make you happy. I was the one who blackballed you with the Rocket Company five years ago.'

A meteor flashed by. Hollis looked down and his left hand was gone. Blood spurted. Suddenly there was no air in his suit. He had enough air in his lungs to move his right hand over and twist a knob at his left elbow, tightening the joint and sealing the leak. It had happened so quickly that he was not surprised. Nothing surprised him any more. The air in the suit came back to normal in an instant now that the leak was sealed. And the blood that had flowed so swiftly was pressured as he fastened the knob yet tighter, until it made a tourniquet.

All of this took place in a terrible silence on his part. And the other men chatted. That one man, Lespere, went on and on with his talk about his wife on Mars, his wife on Venus, his wife on Jupiter, his money, his wondrous times, his drunkenness, his gambling, his happiness. On and on, while they all fell, fell. Lespere reminisced on the past, happy, while he fell to his death.

It was so very odd. Space, thousands of miles of space, and these voices vibrating in the center of it. No one visible at all, and only the radio waves quivering and trying to quicken other men into emotion.

'Are you angry, Hollis?'

'No.' And he was not. The abstraction had returned and he was a thing of dull concrete, forever falling nowhere.

'You wanted to get to the top all your life, Hollis. And I ruined it for you. You always wondered what happened. I put the black mark on you just before I was tossed out myself.'

'That isn't important,' said Hollis. And it was not. It was gone. When life is over it is like a flicker of bright film, an instant on the screen, all of its prejudices and passions condensed and illumined for an instant on space, and before you could cry out. There was a happy day, there a bad one, there an evil face, there a good one, the film burned to a cinder, the screen went dark.

From this outer edge of his life, looking back, there was only one remorse, and that was only that he wished to go on living. Did all dying people feel this way, as if they had never lived? Does life seem that short, indeed, over and down before you took a breath? Did it seem this abrupt and impossible to everyone, or only to himself, here, now, with a few hours left to him for thought and deliberation?

One of the other men was talking. 'Well, I had me a good life. I had a wife on Mars and one on Venus and one on Earth and one on Jupiter. Each of them had money and they treated me swell. I had a wonderful time. I got drunk and once I gambled away twenty thousand dollars.'

But you're here now, thought Hollis. I didn't have any of those things. When I was living I was jealous of you, Lespere, when I had another day ahead of me I envied you your women and your good times. Women frightened me and I went into space, always wanting them, and jealous of you for having them, and money, and as much happiness as you could have in your own wild way. But now, falling here, with everything over, I'm not jealous of you any more, because it's over for you as it is over for me, and right now it's like it never was. Hollis craned his face forward and shouted into the telephone.

'It's all over, Lespere!'

Silence.

'It's just as if it never was, Lespere!'

'Who's that?' Lespere's faltering voice.

'This is Hollis.'

He was being mean. He felt the meanness, the senseless meanness of dying. Applegate had hurt him, now he wanted to hurt another. Applegate and space had both wounded him.

'You're out here, Lespere. It's all over. It's just as if it had never happened, isn't it?'

'No.'

'When anything's over, it's just like it never happened. Where's your life any better than mine, now? While it was happening, yes, but now? Now is what counts. Is it any better, is it?'

'Yes, it's better!'

'How!'

'Because I got my thoughts; I remember!' cried Lespere, far away, indignant, holding his memories to his chest with both hands.

And he was right. With a feeling of cold water gushing through his head and his body, Hollis knew he was right. There were differences between memories and dreams. He had only dreams of things he had wanted to do, while Lespere had memories of things done and accomplished. And this knowledge began to pull Hollis apart, with a slow, quivering precision.

'What good does it do you?' he cried to Lespere. 'Now? When a thing's over it's not good any more. You're no better off than me.'

'I'm resting easy,' said Lespere. 'I've had my turn. I'm not getting mean at the end, like you.'

'Mean?' Hollis turned the word on his tongue. He had never been mean, as long as he could remember, in his life. He had never dared to be mean. He must have saved it all of these years for such a time as this. 'Mean.' He rolled the word into the back of his mind. He felt tears start into his eyes and roll down his face. Someone must have heard his gasping voice.

'Take it easy, Hollis.'

It was, of course, ridiculous. Only a minute before he had been giving advice to others, to Stimson, he had felt a braveness which he had thought to be the genuine thing, and now he knew that it had been nothing but shock and the objectivity possible in shock. Now he was trying to pack a lifetime of suppressed emotion into an interval of minutes.

'I know how you feel, Hollis,' said Lespere, now twenty thousand miles away, his voice fading. 'I don't take it personally.'

But aren't we equal, his wild mind wondered. Lespere and I? Here, now? If a thing's over it's done, and what good is it? You die anyway. But he knew he was rationalizing, for it was like trying to tell the difference between a live man and a corpse. There was a spark in one, and not in the other, an aura, a mysterious element.

So it was with Lespere and himself; Lespere had lived a good full life, and it made him a different man now, and he, Hollis, had been as good as dead for many years. They came to death by separate paths and, in all likelihood, if there were kinds of deaths, their kinds would be as different as night from day. The quality of death, like that of life, must be of infinite variety, and if one has already died once, then what is there to look for in dying for once and all, as he was now?

It was a second later that he discovered his right foot was cut sheer away. It almost made him laugh. The air was gone from his suit again, he bent quickly, and there was blood, and the meteor had taken flesh and suit away to the ankle. Oh, death in space was most humorous, it cut you away, piece by piece, like a black and invisible butcher. He tightened the valve at the knee, his head whirling into pain, fighting to remain aware, and with the valve tightened, the blood retained, the air kept, he straightened up and went on falling, falling, for that was all there was left to do.

'Hollis?'

Hollis nodded sleepily, tired of waiting for death.

'This is Applegate again,' said the voice.

'Yes.'

'I've had time to think. I listened to you. This isn't good. It makes us mean. This is a bad way to die. It brings all the bile out. You listening, Hollis?'

'Yes.'

'I lied. A minute ago. I lied. I didn't blackball you. I don't know why I said that. Guess I wanted to hurt you. You seemed the one to hurt. We've always fought. Guess I'm getting old fast and repenting fast, I guess listening to you be mean made me ashamed. Whatever the reason, I want you to know I was an idiot, too. There's not an ounce of truth in what I said. To heck with you.'

Hollis felt his heart begin to work again. It seemed as if it hadn't worked for five minutes, but now all of his limbs began to take color and warmth. The shock was over, and the successive shocks of anger and terror and loneliness were passing. He felt like a man emerging from a cold shower in the morning, ready for breakfast and a new day.

'Thanks, Applegate.'

'Don't mention it. Up your nose, you slob.'

'Where's Stimson, how is he?'

'Stimson?'

They listened.

No answer.

'He must be gone.'

'I don't think so. Stimson!'

They listened again.

They could hear a long, slow, hard breathing in their phones.

'That's him. Listen.'

'Stimson!'

No reply.

Only the slow, hard breathing.

'He won't answer.'

'He's gone insane, God help him.'

'That's it. Listen.'

The silent breathing, the quiet.

'He's closed up like a clam. He's in himself, making a pearl. Listen to the poet, will you. He's happier than us now, anyway.'

They listened to Stimson float away.

'Hey,' said Stone.

'What?' Hollis called across space, for Stone, of all of them, was a good friend.

'I've got myself into a meteor swarm, some little asteroids.'

'Meteors?'

'I think it's the Myrmidone cluster that goes out past Mars and in toward Earth once every five years. I'm right in the middle. It's like a big kaleidoscope. You get all kinds of colors and shapes and sizes. God, it's beautiful, all the metal.'

Silence.

'I'm going with them,' said Stone. 'They're taking me off with them. I'll be damned.' He laughed tightly.

Hollis looked to see, but saw nothing. There were only the great jewelries of space, the diamonds and sapphires and emerald mists and velvet inks of space, with God's voice mingling among the crystal fires. There was a kind of wonder and imagination in the thought of Stone going off in the meteor swarm, out past Mars for years and coming in toward Earth every five years, passing in and out of the planet's ken for the next million years, Stone and the Myrmidone cluster eternal and unending, shifting and shaping like the kaleidoscope colours when you were a child and held the long tube to the sun and gave it a twirl.

'So long, Hollis.' Stone's voice, very faint now. 'So long.'

'Good luck,' shouted Hollis across thirty thousand miles.

'Don't be funny,' said Stone, and was gone.

The stars closed in.

Now all the voices were fading, each on their own trajectories, some to the sun, others into farthest space. And Hollis himself. He looked down. He, of all the others, was going back to Earth alone.

'So long.'

'Take it easy.'

'So long, Hollis.' That was Applegate.

The many goodbyes. The short farewells. And now the great loose brain was disintegrating. The components of the brain which had worked so beautifully and efficiently in the skull case of the rocket ship racing through space, were dying one by one, the meaning of their life together was falling apart. And as a body dies when the brain ceases functioning, so the spirit of the ship and their long time together and what they meant to one another was dying. Applegate was now no more than a finger blown from the parent body, no longer to be despised and worked against. The brain was exploded, and the senseless, useless fragments of it were far-scattered. The voices faded and now all of space was silent. Hollis was alone, falling.

They were all alone. Their voices had died like echoes of the words of God spoken and vibrating in the starred space. There went the captain to the sun; there Stone with the meteor swarm; there Stimson, tightened and unto himself; there Applegate toward Pluto; there Smith and Turner and Underwood and all the rest, the shards of the kaleidoscope that had formed a thinking pattern for so long, now hurled apart.

And I? thought Hollis. What can I do? Is there anything I can do now to make up for a terrible and empty life? If I could do one good thing to make up for the meanness I collected all these years and didn't even know was in me? But there's no one here, but myself, and how can you do good all alone? You can't. Tomorrow night I'll hit Earth's atmosphere.

I'll burn, he thought, and be scattered in ashes all over the continental lands. I'll be put to use. Just a little bit, but ashes are ashes and they'll add to the land.

He fell swiftly, like a bullet, like a pebble, like an iron weight, objective, objective all of the time now, not sad or happy or anything, but only wishing he could do a good thing now that everyone was gone, a good thing for just himself to know about.

When I hit the atmosphere, I'll burn like a meteor.

'I wonder,' he said. 'If anyone'll see me?'

The small boy on the country road looked up and screamed. 'Look, Mom, look! A falling star!'

The blazing white star fell down the sky of dusk in Illinois. 'Make a wish,' said his mother. 'Make a wish.'

To Serve Man

BY DAMON KNIGHT

from *Galaxy Science Fiction*, November 1950

Damon Knight's name today is so much associated with the new wave, avant-garde approach to science fiction, which course he helps direct with his own prestigious *Orbit* series of original anthologies, that one might feel he is a product of the sixties. But on the contrary, Knight made his first appearance in the February 1941 issue of *Stirring Science Stories* with a short story, 'Resilience'.

Knight is one of the authors who made their débuts in their teens. He was born in Baker, Oregon, at midnight on Sunday/Monday, 19/20 September 1920, and discovered sf with a copy of *Amazing Stories* in 1932. However, although he did not discover fandom until 1940, through the fan column in *Astonishing Stories*, by May of that year he had completed the first issue of his own fanzine, *Snide*. Knight had artistic leanings, and often sketched cartoons for his own and other fanzines. His activities brought him into contact with the Futurians group, which included Wollheim, Lowndes, Wilson, Pohl and Kornbluth, and thereby his first professional appearances.

He did not really begin to blossom as a writer until 1950, for he was working mostly as an assistant editor for Popular Publications. His brief affair with *Worlds Beyond* is told in this volume's introduction.

The Winter 1950 *F & SF* carried Knight's 'Not with a Bang', the first real sign of Knight's emergent talent. Building on from T. S. Eliot's line in 'The Hollow Men': 'This is the way the world ends, Not with a bang but a whimper', Knight cleverly unravels a pivotal incident in the lives of the last man and

Imagination, May 1952 – Malcolm Smith. Popular in the early fifties, Smith's covers were eye-catching and often experimental. For Daniel F. Galouye's lead story he combined two photographs.

Science Stories, December 1953 – Virgil Finlay, for John Bloodstone's 'Potential Zero'. Bloodstone was the pen-name of Stuart J. Byrne.

Galaxy, May 1954 – Ed Emshwiller, who was paramount among the new artists. This is for 'Granny Won't Knit' by Theodore Sturgeon.

Fantastic Universe, August 1955 – Kelly Freas, another major new artist. This cover depicts anticipated new hospital techniques.

Thrilling Wonder, August 1947 – Earle K. Bergey. A typical 'monsters 'n' maidens' cover for Henry Kuttner's 'Atomic'.

Startling Stories, August 1952 – Earle K. Bergey. One of his last covers, illustrating Philip Jose Farmer's 'The Lovers'.

Famous Fantastic Mysteries, August 1949 – Lawrence Stevens, for 'The Valley of Silent Men' by E. Charles Vivian.

Fantastic Novels, January 1951 – Rafael de Soto. This cover illustrates Arthur Leo Zagat's 1937 classic, 'Drink We Deep'.

ew Worlds, June 1953 – Gerard Quinn.
his British artist envisaged the surface of
Mercury for 'Ride the Twilight Rail' by
. R. James.

Nebula, February 1954 – Robert Clothier.
A lunar scene.

uthentic, January 1955 – Davis (John
Richards?). Planetary scenes were popular
n British magazines – one of Saturn's
moons.

Science-Fantasy, Spring 1952 – Reina Bull.
A scene from 'Resurrection' by John
Christopher.

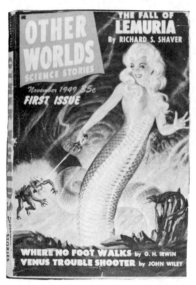

Other Worlds, November 1949 – Malcolm Smith. Ray Palmer's new magazine shows a scene from 'The Fall of Lemuria' by Richard Shaver.

Amazing Stories, June 1952 – Walter Popp. Under new editorship, *Amazing* attracted a variety of artists, among them Walter Popp with this rather daring cover for Milton Lesser's 'Secret of the Dark Planet'.

Planet Stories, November 1951 – Allen Anderson. A scene from Stanley Mullen's 'The Pit of Nympthons'.

Future combined with Science Fiction Stories, British Edition No 2, 1951 – Milton Luros. The British Thorpe & Porter Ltd released this edition of the March 1951 American issue in December.

woman on Earth. He next appeared with 'To Serve Man' which follows. His career is firmly set in the short story field, although he has written the occasional novel like *Hell's Pavement* (1955) and *Mind Switch* (1965). He is a notable anthologist with volumes like *A Century of Science Fiction* (1962) and the collection of leading authors' first sales, *First Flight* (1963).

Knight is married to sf writer Kate Wilhelm.

The Kanamit were not very pretty, it's true. They looked something like pigs and something like people, and that is not an attractive combination. Seeing them for the first time shocked you; that was their handicap. When a thing with the countenance of a fiend comes from the stars and offers a gift, you are disinclined to accept.

I don't know what we expected interstellar visitors to look like – those who thought about it at all, that is. Angels, perhaps, or something too alien to be really awful. Maybe that's why we were all so horrified and repelled when they landed in their great ships and we saw what they really were like.

The Kanamit were short and very hairy – thick, bristly brown-grey hair all over their abominably plump bodies. Their noses were snoutlike and their eyes small, and they had thick hands of three fingers each. They wore green leather harness and green shorts, but I think the shorts were a concession to our notions of public decency. The garments were quite modishly cut, with slash pockets and half-belts in the back. The Kanamit had a sense of humour, anyhow.

There were three of them at this session of the U.N., and, Lord, I can't tell you how queer it looked to see them there in the middle of a solemn plenary session – three fat, piglike creatures in green harness and shorts, sitting at the long table below the podium, surrounded by the packed arcs of delegates from every nation. They sat correctly upright, politely watching each speaker. Their flat ears drooped over the earphones. Later on, I believe, they learned every human language, but at this time they knew only French and English.

They seemed perfectly at ease – and that, along with their humour, was a thing that tended to make me like them. I was in the minority; I didn't think they were trying to put anything over.

The delegate from Argentina got up and said that his government was interested in the demonstration of a new cheap power source, which the Kanamit had made at the previous session, but that the Argentine government could not commit itself as to its future policy without a much more thorough examination.

It was what all the delegates were saying, but I had to pay particular attention to Señor Valdes, because he tended to sputter and his diction was bad. I got through the translation all right, with only one or two momentary hesitations, and then switched to the Polish-English line to hear how Gregori was doing with Janciewicz. Janciewicz was the cross Gregori had to bear, just as Valdes was mine.

Janciewicz repeated the previous remarks with a few ideological variations, and then the Secretary-General recognized the delegate from France, who introduced Dr Denis Lévèque, the criminologist, and a great deal of complicated equipment was wheeled in.

Dr Lévèque remarked that the question in many people's minds had been aptly expressed by the delegate from the USSR at the preceding session, when he demanded, 'What is the motive of the Kanamit? What is their purpose in offering us these unprecedented gifts, while asking nothing in return?'

The doctor then said, 'At the request of several delegates and with the full consent of our guests, the Kanamit, my associates and I have made a series of tests upon the Kanamit with the equipment which you see before you. These tests will now be repeated.'

A murmur ran through the chamber. There was a fusillade of flashbulbs, and one of the TV cameras moved up to focus on the instrument board of the doctor's equipment. At the same time, the huge television screen behind the podium lighted up, and we saw the blank faces of two dials, each with its pointer resting at zero, and a strip of paper tape with a stylus point resting against it.

The doctor's assistants were fastening wires to the temples of one of the Kanamit, wrapping a canvas-covered rubber tube around his forearm, and taping something to the palm of his right hand.

In the screen, we saw the paper tape begin to move while the stylus traced a slow zigzag pattern along it. One of the needles began to jump rhythmically; the other flipped over and stayed there, wavering slightly.

'These are the standard instruments for testing the truth of a statement,' said Dr Lévèque. 'Our first object, since the physiology of the Kanamit is unknown to us, was to determine whether or not they react to these tests as human beings do. We will now repeat one of the many experiments which were made in the endeavour to discover this.'

He pointed to the first dial. 'This instrument registers the subject's heartbeat. This shows the electrical conductivity of the skin in the palm of his hand, a measure of perspiration, which increases under stress. And this –' pointing to the tape-and-stylus device – 'shows the pattern and intensity of the electrical waves emanating from his brain. It has been shown, with human subjects, that all these readings vary markedly depending upon whether the subject is speaking the truth.'

He picked up two large pieces of cardboard, one red and one black. The red one was a square about three feet on a side; the black was a rectangle three and a half feet long. He addressed himself to the Kanama.

'Which of these is longer than the other?'

'The red,' said the Kanama.

Both needles leaped wildly, and so did the line on the unrolling tape.

'I shall repeat the question,' said the doctor. 'Which of these is longer than the other?'

'The black,' said the creature.

This time the instruments continued in their normal rhythm.

'How did you come to this planet?' asked the doctor.

'Walked,' replied the Kanama.

Again the instruments responded, and there was a subdued ripple of laughter in the chamber.

'Once more,' said the doctor. 'How did you come to this planet?'

'In a spaceship,' said the Kanama, and the instruments did not jump.

The doctor again faced the delegates. 'Many such experiments were made,' he said, 'and my colleagues and myself are satisfied that the mechanisms are effective. Now –' he turned to the Kanama – 'I shall ask our distinguished guest to reply to the question put at the last session by the delegate of the USSR – namely, what is the motive of the Kanamit people in offering these great gifts to the people of Earth?'

The Kanama rose. Speaking this time in English, he said, 'On my planet there is a saying, 'There are more riddles in a stone than in a philosopher's head.' The motives of intelligent beings, though they may at times appear obscure, are simple things compared to the complex workings of the natural universe. Therefore I hope that the people of Earth will understand, and believe, when I tell you that our mission upon your planet is simply this – to bring to you the peace and plenty which we ourselves enjoy, and which we have in the past brought to other races throughout the galaxy. When your world has no more hunger, no more war, no more needless suffering, that will be our reward.'

And the needles had not jumped once.

The delegate from the Ukraine jumped to his feet, asking to be recognized, but the time was up and the Secretary-General closed the session.

I met Gregori as we were leaving the chamber. His face was red with excitement. 'Who promoted that circus?' he demanded.

'The tests looked genuine to me,' I told him.

'A circus!' he said vehemently. 'A second-rate farce! If they were genuine, Peter, why was debate stifled?'

'There'll be time for debate tomorrow, surely.'

'Tomorrow the doctor and his instruments will be back in Paris. Plenty of things can happen before tomorrow. In the name of sanity, man, how can anybody trust a thing that looks as if it ate the baby?'

I was a little annoyed. I said, 'Are you sure you're not more worried about their politics than their appearance?'

He said, 'Bah,' and went away.

The next day reports began to come in from government laboratories all over the world where the Kanamit's power source was being tested. They were wildly enthusiastic. I don't understand such things myself, but it seemed that those little metal boxes would give more electrical power than an atomic pile, for next to nothing and nearly for ever. And it was said that they were so cheap to manufacture that everybody in the world could have one of his own. In the early afternoon there were reports that seventeen countries had already begun to set up factories to turn them out.

The next day the Kanamit turned up with plans and specimens of a gadget that would increase the fertility of any arable land by 60 to 100 per cent. It speeded the formation of nitrates in the soil, or something. There was nothing in the newscasts any more but stories about the Kanamit. The day after that, they dropped their bombshell.

'You now have potentially unlimited power and increased food supply,' said one of them. He pointed with his three-fingered hand to an instrument that stood on the table before him. It was a box on a tripod, with a parabolic reflector on the front of it. 'We offer you today a third gift which is at least as important as the first two.'

He beckoned to the TV men to roll their cameras into close-up position. Then he picked up a large sheet of cardboard covered with drawings and English lettering. We saw it on the large screen above the podium; it was all clearly legible.

'We are informed that this broadcast is being relayed throughout your world,' said the Kanama. 'I wish that everyone who has equipment for taking photographs from television screens would use it now.'

The Secretary-General leaned forward and asked a question sharply, but the Kanama ignored him.

'This device,' he said, 'generates a field in which no explosive, of whatever nature, can detonate.'

There was an uncomprehending silence.

The Kanama said, 'It cannot now be suppressed. If one nation has it, all must have it.' When nobody seemed to understand, he explained bluntly, 'There will be no more war.'

That was the biggest news of the millennium, and it was perfectly true. It turned out that the explosions the Kanama was talking about included gasoline and Diesel explosions. They had simply made it impossible for anybody to mount or equip a modern army.

We could have gone back to bows and arrows, of course, but that wouldn't have satisfied the military. Besides, there wouldn't be any reason to make war. Every nation would soon have everything.

Nobody ever gave another thought to those lie-detector experiments, or asked the Kanamit what their politics were. Gregori was put out; he had nothing to prove his suspicions.

I quit my job with the UN a few months later, because I foresaw that it was going to die under me anyhow. UN business was booming at the time, but after a year or so there was going to be nothing for it to do. Every nation on Earth was well on the way to being completely self-supporting; they weren't going to need much arbitration.

I accepted a position as translator with the Kanamit Embassy, and it was there that I ran into Gregori again. I was glad to see him, but I couldn't imagine what he was doing there.

'I thought you were on the opposition,' I said. 'Don't tell me you're convinced the Kanamit are all right.'

He looked rather shamefaced. 'They're not what they look, anyhow,' he said.

It was as much of a concession as he could decently make, and I invited him down to the embassy lounge for a drink. It was an intimate kind of place, and he grew confidential over the second daiquiri.

'They fascinate me,' he said. 'I hate them instinctively still – that hasn't changed – but I can evaluate it.' You were right, obviously; they mean us nothing but good. But do you know –' he leaned across the table – 'the question of the Soviet delegate was never answered.'

I am afraid I snorted.

'No, really,' he said. 'They told us what they wanted to do – 'to bring to you the peace and plenty which we ourselves enjoy.' But they didn't say *why*.'

'Why do missionaries –'

'Missionaries be damned!' he said angrily. 'Missionaries have a religious motive. If these creatures have a religion, they haven't once mentioned it. What's more, they didn't send a missionary group; they sent a diplomatic delegation – a group representing the will and policy of their whole people. Now just what have the Kanamit, as a people or a nation, got to gain from our welfare?'

I said, 'Cultural –'

'Cultural cabbage soup! No, it's something less obvious than that, something obscure that belongs to their psychology and not to ours. But trust me, Peter, there is no such thing as a completely disinterested altruism. In one way or another, they have something to gain.'

'And that's why you're here,' I said. 'To try to find out what it is.'

'Correct. I wanted to get on one of the ten-year exchange groups to their home planet, but I couldn't; the quota was filled a week after they made the announcement. This is the next best thing. I'm studying their language, and you know that language reflects the basic assumptions of the people who use it. I've got a fair command of the spoken lingo already. It's not hard, really, and there are hints in it. Some of the idioms are quite similar to English. I'm sure I'll get the answer eventually.'

'More power,' I said, and we went back to work.

I saw Gregori frequently from then on, and he kept me posted about his progress. He was highly excited about a month after that first meeting; said he'd got hold of a book of the Kanamit's and was trying to puzzle it out. They wrote in ideographs, worse than Chinese, but he was determined to fathom it if it took him years. He wanted my help.

Well, I was interested in spite of myself, for I knew it would be a long job. We spent some evenings together, working with material from Kanamit bulletin boards and so forth, and with the extremely limited English-Kanamit dictionary they issued to the staff. My conscience bothered me about the stolen book, but gradually I became absorbed by the problem. Languages are my field, after all. I couldn't help being fascinated.

We got the title worked out in a few weeks. It was *How to Serve Man*, evidently a handbook they were giving out to new Kanamit members of the embassy staff. They had new ones in, all the time now, a shipload about once a month; they were opening all kinds of research laboratories, clinics and so on. If there was anybody on Earth beside Gregori who still distrusted those people, he must have been somewhere in the middle of Tibet.

It was astonishing to see the changes that had been wrought in less than a year. There were no more standing armies, no more shortages, no unemployment. When you picked up a newspaper you didn't see H-BOMB or SATELLITE leaping out at you; the news was always good. It was a hard thing to get used to. The Kanamit were working on human biochemistry, and it was known around the embassy that they were nearly ready to announce methods of making our race taller and stronger and healthier – practically a race of supermen – and they had a potential cure for heart disease and cancer.

I didn't see Gregori for a fortnight after we finished working out the title of the book; I was on a long-overdue vacation in Canada. When I got back, I was shocked by the change in his appearance.

'What on earth is wrong, Gregori?' I asked. 'You look like the very devil.'

'Come down to the lounge.'

I went with him, and he gulped a stiff Scotch as if he needed it.

'Come on, man, what's the matter?' I urged.

'The Kanamit have put me on the passenger list for the next exchange ship,' he said. 'You too, otherwise I wouldn't be talking to you.'

'Well,' I said, 'but –'

'They're not altruists.'

I tried to reason with him. I pointed out they'd made Earth a paradise compared to what it was before. He only shook his head.

Then I said, 'Well, what about those lie-detector tests?'

'A farce,' he replied, without heat. 'I said so at the time, you fool. They told the truth, though, as far as it went.'

'And the book?' I demanded, annoyed. 'What about that – *How to Serve Man*? That wasn't put there for you to read. They *mean* it. How do you explain that?'

'I've read the first paragraph of that book,' he said. 'Why do you suppose I haven't slept for a week?'

I said, 'Well?' and he smiled a curious, twisted smile.

'It's a cookbook,' he said.

Earthman, Beware!

BY POUL ANDERSON

from *Super Science Stories*, June 1951

Only in the last couple of years have British publishers recognised Poul Anderson as a leading science fiction writer. A calamitous oversight. He was born Poul William Anderson, in Bristol, Pennsylvania on Thursday 25 November 1926, which makes him the first author represented in this series to be born after the birth of the sf magazines. His parents were Danish, and in all of Anderson's work there is much influence from his Scandinavian origins. His first name, incidentally, is pronounced somewhere in between 'powl' and 'pole'.

His early sales, while still at the University of Minnesota, were mentioned in my introduction, Anderson's first true appearance was in the September 1944 *Astounding*. Campbell had a 'Probability Zero' department, a short-lived venture, devoted to scientific spoofs written by aspiring authors. Anderson's vignette was entitled 'A Matter of Relativity'.

Anderson left University and plunged into full-time writing. He has maintained a healthy volume of work, predominantly science fiction, but also in the fantasy, historical and mystery fields as well as children's books. He has won several awards in sf alone, including five Hugos and two Nebulas. He has a penchant for scientific accuracy and plausible characterisation that gives his work that added life that so many stories lack. He has written both humorous sf, like *The High Crusade* (1960) when a knight takes over an alien spaceship that lands on Earth in the Middle Ages, to the serious, *The People of the Wind* (1973) his more recent novel, which looks in depth at the interaction between human colonists on an alien planet and the native wingmen culture.

Writing in 1971, the late James Blish said of Anderson: 'It's my opinion, which I suspect is widely shared, that Anderson is the only surviving writer of the Golden Age of *Astounding* who is still writing sf whose work has not gone steadily (or jerkily) downhill . . . Poul Anderson, the scientist, the technician, the stylist, the bard, the humanist and the humorist – a non-exhaustive list – is completely immune to any changes in fashion. He is, in short, an artist.' Need I say more?

As he neared the cabin, he grew aware that someone was waiting for him.

He paused for a moment, scowling, and sent his perceptions ahead to analyze that flash of knowledge. Something in his brain thrilled to the presence of metal, and there were subtler overtones of the organic – oil and rubber and plastic . . . he dismissed it as an ordinary small helicopter and concentrated on the faint, maddeningly elusive fragments of thought, nervous energy, lifeflows between cells and molecules. There was only one person, and the sketchy outline of his data fitted only a single possibility.

Margaret.

For another instant he stood quietly, and his primary emotion was sadness. He felt annoyance, perhaps a subtle dismay that his hiding place had finally been located, but mostly it was pity that held him. Poor Peggy. Poor kid.

Well – he'd have to have it out. He straightened his slim shoulders and resumed his walk.

The Alaskan forest was quiet around him, A faint evening breeze rustled the dark pines and drifted past his cheeks, a cool lonesome presence in the stillness. Somewhere birds were twittering as they settled toward rest, and the mosquitoes raised a high, thin buzz as they whirled outside the charmed circle of the odorless repellent he had devised. Otherwise, there was only the low scrunch of his footsteps on the ancient floor of needles. After two years of silence, the vibrations of human presence were like a great shout along his nerves.

When he came out into the little meadow, the sun was going down behind the northern hills. Long aureate rays slanted across the grass, touching the huddled shack with a wizard glow and sending enormous shadows before them. The helicopter was a metallic dazzle against the darkling forest, and he was quite close before his blinded eyes could discern the woman.

She stood in front of the door, waiting, and the sunset turned her hair to ruddy gold. She wore the red sweater and the navy-blue skirt she had worn when they had last been together, and her slim hands were crossed before her. So she had waited for him many times when he came out of the laboratory, quiet as an obedient child. She had never turned her pert vivacity on him, not after noticing how it streamed off his uncomprehending mind like rain off one of the big pines.

He smiled lopsidedly. 'Hullo, Peggy,' he said, feeling the blind inadequacy of words. But what could he say to her?

'Joel . . .' she whispered.

He saw her start and felt the shock along her nerves. His smile grew more crooked, and he nodded. 'Yeah,' he said. 'I've been bald as an egg all my life. Out here, alone, I had no reason to use a wig.'

Her wide hazel eyes searched him. He wore backwoodsman's clothes, plaid shirt and stained jeans and heavy shoes, and he carried a fishing rod and tackle box and a string of perch. But he had not changed, at all. The small slender body, the fine-boned ageless features, the luminous dark eyes under the high forehead, they were all the same. Time had laid no finger on him.

Even the very baldness seemed a completion, letting the strong classic arch of his skull stand forth, stripping away another of the layers of ordinariness with which he had covered himself.

He saw that she had grown thin, and it was suddenly too great an effort to smile. 'How did you find me, Peggy?' he asked quietly.

From her first word, his mind leaped ahead to the answer, but he let her say it out. 'After you'd been gone six months with no word, we – all your friends, insofar as you ever had any – grew worried. We thought maybe something had happened to you in the interior of China. So we started investigating, with the help of the Chinese government, and soon learned you'd never gone there at all. It had just been a red herring, that story about investigating Chinese archeological sites, a blind to gain time while you – disappeared. I just kept on hunting, even after everyone else had given up, and finally Alaska occurred to me. In Nome I picked up rumours of an odd and unfriendly squatter out in the bush. So I came here.'

'Couldn't you just have let me stay vanished?' he asked wearily.

'No.' Her voice was trembling with her lips. 'Not till I knew for sure, Joel. Not till I knew you were safe and – and –'

He kissed her, tasting salt on her mouth, catching the faint fragrance of her hair. The broken waves of her thoughts and emotions washed over him, swirling through his brain in a tide of loneliness and desolation.

Suddenly he knew exactly what was going to happen, what he would have to tell her and the responses she would make – almost to the word, he foresaw it, and the futility of it was like a leaden weight on his mind. But he had to go through with it, every wrenching syllable must come out. Humans were that way, groping through a darkness of solitude, calling to each other across abysses and never, never understanding.

'It was sweet of you,' he said awkwardly. 'You shouldn't have, Peggy, but it was . . .' His voice trailed off and his pre-vision failed. There were no words which were not banal and meaningless.

'I couldn't help it,' she whispered. 'You know I love you.'

'Look, Peggy,' he said. 'This can't go on. We'll have to have it out now. If I tell you who I am, and why I ran away –' He tried to force cheerfulness. 'But never have an emotional scene on an empty stomach. Come on in and I'll fry up these fish.'

'I will,' she said with something of her old spirit. 'I'm a better cook than you.'

It would hurt her, but: 'I'm afraid you couldn't use my equipment, Peggy.'

He signalled to the door, and it opened for him. As she pre-ceded him inside, he saw that her face and hands were red with mosquito bites. She must have been waiting a long time for him to come home.

'Too bad you came today,' he said desperately. 'I'm usually working in here. I just happened to take today off.'

She didn't answer. Her eyes were travelling around the cabin, trying to find the immense order that she knew must underlie its chaos of material.

He had put logs and shingles on the outside to disguise it as an ordinary shack. Within, it might have been his Cambridge laboratory, and she recognized some of the equipment. He had filled a plane with it before leaving. Other things she did not remember, the work of his hands through two lonely years, jungles of wiring and tubing and meters and less understandable apparatus. Only a little of it had the crude, unfinished look of experimental setups. He had been working on some enormous project of his own, and it must be near its end now.

But after that –?

The grey cat which had been his only real companion, even back in Cambridge, rubbed against her legs with a mew that might be recognition. *A friendlier welcome than* he *gave me,* she thought bitterly, and then, seeing his grave eyes on her, flushed. It was unjust. She had hunted him out of his self-chosen solitude, and he had been more than decent about it.

Decent – but not human. No unattached human male could have been chased across the world by an attractive woman without feeling more than the quiet regret and pity he showed.

Or did he feel something else? She would never know. No one would ever know all which went on within that beautiful skull. The rest of humanity had too little in common with Joel Weatherfield.

'The *rest* of humanity?' he asked softly.

She started. That old mind-reading trick of his had been enough to alienate most people. You never knew when he would spring it on you, how much of it was guesswork based on a transcendent logic and how much was – was ...

He nodded. 'I'm partly telepathic,' he said, 'and I can fill in the gaps for myself – like Poe's Dupin, only better and easier. There are other things involved too – but never mind that for now. Later.'

He threw the fish into a cabinet and adjusted several dials on its face. 'Supper coming up,' he said.

'So now you've invented the robot chef,' she said.

'Saves me work.'

'You could make another million dollars or so if you marketed it.'

'Why? I have more money right now than any reasonable being needs.'

'You'd save people a lot of time, you know.'

He shrugged.

She looked into a smaller room where he must live. It was sparsely furnished, a cot and a desk and some shelves holding his enormous microprinted library. In one corner stood the multitone instrument with which he composed the music that no one had ever liked or understood. But he had always found the music of man shallow and pointless. And the art of man and the literature of man and all the works and lives of man.

'How's Langtree coming with his new encephalograph?' he asked, though he could guess the answer. 'You were going to assist him on it, I recall.'

'I don't know.' She wondered if her voice reflected her own weariness. 'I've been spending all my time looking, Joel.'

He grimaced with pain and turned to the automatic cook. A door opened in it and it slid out a tray with two dishes. He put them on a table and gestured to chairs. 'Fall to, Peggy.'

In spite of herself, the machine fascinated her. 'You must have an induction unit to cook that fast,' she murmured, 'and I suppose your potatoes and greens are stored right inside it. But the mechanical parts –' She shook her head in baffled wonderment, knowing that a blueprint would have revealed some utterly simple arrangement involving only ingenuity.

Dewed cans of beer came out of another cabinet. He grinned and lifted his. 'Man's greatest achievement. Skoal.'

She hadn't realized she was so hungry. He ate more slowly, watching her, thinking of the incongruity of Dr Margaret Logan of MIT wolfing fish and beer in a backwoods Alaskan cabin.

Maybe he should have gone to Mars or some outer-planet satellite. But no, that would have involved leaving a much clearer trail for anyone to follow – you couldn't take off in a spaceship as casually as you could dash over to China. If he had to be found out, he would rather that she did it. For later on she'd keep his secret with the stubborn loyalty he had come to know.

She had always been good to have around, ever since he met her when he was helping MIT on their latest cybernetics work. Twenty-four-year-old Ph.D.'s with brilliant records were rare enough – when they were also good-looking young women, they became unique. Langtree had been quite hopelessly in love with her, of course. But she had taken on a double programme of work, helping Weatherfield at his private laboratories in addition to her usual duties – and she planned to end the latter when her contract expired. She'd been more than useful to him, and he had not been blind to her looks, but it was the same admiration that he had for landscapes and thoroughbred cats and open space. And she had been one of the few humans with whom he could talk at all.

Had been. He exhausted her possibilities in a year, as he drained most people in a month. He had known how she would react to any situation, what she would say to any remark of his, he knew her feelings with a sensitive perception beyond her own knowledge. And the loneliness had returned.

But he hadn't anticipated her finding him, he thought wryly. After planning his flight he had not cared – or dared – to follow out all its logical consequences. Well, he was certainly paying for it now, and so was she.

He had cleared the table and put out coffee and cigarettes before they began to talk. Darkness veiled the windows, but his fluorotubes came on automatically. She heard the far faint baying of a wolf out in the night, and thought that the forest was less alien to her than this room of machines and the man who sat looking at her with that too brilliant gaze.

He had settled himself in an easy chair and the grey cat had jumped up into his lap and lay purring as his thin fingers stroked its fur. She came over and sat on the stool at his feet, laying one hand on his knee. It was useless to suppress impulses when he knew them before she did.

Joel sighed. 'Peggy,' he said slowly, 'you're making a hell of a mistake.'

She thought, briefly, how banal his words were, and then remembered that he had always been awkward in speech. It was as if he didn't feel the ordinary human nuances and had to find his way through society by mechanical robot.

He nodded. 'That's right,' he said.

'But what's the matter with you?' she protested desperately. 'I know they all used to call you 'cold fish' and 'brain-heavy' and 'animated vacuum tube.' but it isn't so. I know you feel more than any of us do, only – only –'

'Only not the same way,' he finished gently.

'Oh, you always were a strange sort,' she said dully. 'The boy wonder, weren't you? Obscure farm kid who entered Harvard at thirteen and graduated with every honour they could give at fifteen. Inventor of the ion-jet space drive, the controlled-disintegration ion process, the cure for the common cold, the crystalline-structure determination of geological age, and only Heaven and the patent office know how much else. Nobel prize winner in physics for your relativistic wave mechanics. Pioneer in a whole new branch of mathematical series theory. Brilliant writer on archeology, economics, ecology, and semantics. Founder of whole new schools in painting and poetry. What's your IQ, Joel?'

'How should I know? Above 200 or so, IQ in the ordinary sense becomes meaningless. I was pretty foolish, Peggy. Most of my published work was done at an early age, out of a childish desire for praise and recognition. Afterward, I couldn't just stop – conditions wouldn't allow it. And of course I had to do something with my time.'

'Then at thirty, you pack up and disappear. *Why?*'

'I'd hoped they'd think I was dead,' he murmured. 'I had a beautiful faked crash in the Gobi, but I guess nobody ever found it. Because poor loyal fools like you just didn't believe I could die. It never occurred to you to look for my remains.' His hand passed lightly over her hair, and she sighed and rested her head against his knee. 'I should have foreseen that.'

'Why in hell I should have fallen in love with a goof like you, I'll never know,' she said at last. 'Most women ran in fright. Even your money couldn't get them close.' She answered her own question with the precision of long thought. 'But it was sheer quality, I suppose. After you, everyone else became so trite and insipid.' She raised her eyes to him, and there was sudden terrified understanding in them. 'And is that why you never married?' she whispered.

He nodded compassionately. Then, slowly, he added, 'Also, I'm not too interested in sex yet. I'm still in early adolescence, you know.'

'No, I don't know.' She didn't move, but he felt her stiffen against him.

'I'm not human,' said Joel Weatherfield quietly.

'A mutant? No, you couldn't be.' He could feel the tensing of her, the sudden rush of wild thought and wordless nerve current, pulse of blood as the endocrines sought balance on a high taut level of danger. It was the old instinctive dread of the dark and the unknown and the hungry presences beyond a dim circle of firelight – she held herself moveless, but she was an animal bristling in panic.

Calmness came, after a while during which he simply sat stroking her hair. She looked up at him again, forcing herself to meet his eyes.

He smiled as well as he could and said, 'No, no, Peggy, all this could never happen in one mutation. I was found in a field

of grain one summer morning thirty years ago. A . . . woman
. . . who must have been my mother, was lying beside me. They
told me later she was of my physical type, and that and the
curious iridescent garments she wore made them think she was
some circus freak. But she was dead, burned and torn by
energies against which she had shielded me with her body.
There were only a few crystalline fragments lying around. The
people disposed of that and buried her.

'The Weatherfields were an elderly local couple, childless
and kindly. I was only a baby, naturally, and they took me in.
I grew quite slowly physically, but of course mentally it was
another story. They came to be very proud of me in spite of my
odd appearance. I soon devised the perfect toupee to cover my
hairlessness, and with that and ordinary clothes I've always
been able to pass for human. But you may remember I've never
let any human see me without shirt and pants on.

'Naturally, I quickly decided where the truth must lie. Somewhere there must be a race, humanoid but well ahead of man
in evolution, which can travel between the stars. Somehow
my mother and I had been cast away on this desert planet, and
in the vastness of the universe any searchers that there may be
have never found us.'

He fell back into silence. Presently Margaret whispered,
'How – human – are you, Joel?'

'Not very,' he said with a flash of the old candid smile she
remembered. How often had she seen him look up from some
piece of work which was going particularly well and give her
just that look! 'Here, I'll show you.'

He whistled, and the cat jumped from his lap. Another
whistle, and the animal was across the room pawing at a switch.
Several large plates were released, which the cat carried back
in its mouth.

Margaret drew a shaky breath. 'I never yet heard of anyone
training a cat to run errands.'

'This is a rather special cat,' he replied absently, and leaned
forward to show her the plates. 'These are X-rays of myself.
You know my technique for photographing different layers of
tissue? I developed that just to study myself, I also confess to
exhuming my mother's bones, but they proved to be simply a
female version of my own. However, a variation of the crystalline structure method did show that she was at least five
hundred years old.'

'*Five hundred years*!'

He nodded. 'That's one of several reasons why I'm sure I'm a very young member of my race. Incidentally, her bones showed no sign of age, she corresponded about to a human twenty-five. I don't know whether the natural life span of the race is that great or whether they have artificial means of arresting senility, but I do know that I can expect at least half a millenium of life on Earth. And Earth seems to have a higher gravity than our home world; it's not a very healthy spot for me.'

She was too dazed to do more than nod. His finger traced over the X-ray plates. 'The skeletal differences aren't too great, but look here and here – the foot, the spine – the skull bones are especially peculiar – Then the internal organs. You can see for yourself that no human being ever had –'

'A double heart?' she asked dully.

'Sort of. It is a single organ, but with more functions than the human heart. Never mind that, it's the neural structure that's most important. Here are several of the brain, taken at different depths and angles.'

She fought down a gasp. Her work on encephalography had required a good knowledge of the brain's anatomy. *No human being carries this in his head.*

It wasn't too much bigger than the human. Better organization, she thought; Joel's people would never go insane. There were analogues, a highly convoluted cortex, a medulla, the rest of it. But there were other sections and growths which had no correspondents in any human.

'What are *they*?' she asked.

'I'm not very sure,' he replied slowly, a little distastefully. 'This one here is what I might call the telepathy centre. It's sensitive to neural currents in other organisms. By comparing human reactions and words with the emanations I can detect, I've picked up a very limited degree of telepathy. I can emit, too, but since no human can detect it I've had little use for that power. Then this seems to be for voluntary control of ordinarily involuntary functions – pain blocs, endocrine, regulation, and so on – but I've never learned to use it very effectively and I don't dare experiment much on myself. There are other centres – most of them, I don't even know what they're for.'

His smile was weary. 'You've heard of feral children – the occasional human children who're raised by animals? They never learn to speak, or to exercise any of their specifically human abilities, till they're captured and taught by men. In fact, they're hardly human at all.

'I'm a feral child, Peggy.'

She began to cry, deep racking sobs that shook her like a giant's hand. He held her until it passed and she sat again at his knee with the slow tears going down her cheeks. Her voice was a shuddering whisper:

'Oh, my dear, my dear, how lonely you must have been . . .'

Lonely? No human being would ever know how lonely.

It hadn't been too bad at first. As a child, he had been too preoccupied and delighted with his expanding intellectual horizons to care that the other children bored him – and they, in their turn, heartily disliked Joel for his strangeness and the aloofness they called 'snooty'. His foster parents had soon learned that normal standards just didn't apply to him, they kept him out of school and bought him the books and equipment he wanted. They'd been able to afford that; at the age of six he had patented, in old Weatherfield's name, improvements on farm machinery that made the family more than well-to-do. He'd always been a 'good boy,' as far as he was able. They'd had no cause to regret adopting him, but it had been pathetically like the hen who has hatched ducklings and watches them swim away from her.

The years at Harvard had been sheer heaven, an orgy of learning, of conversations and friendship with the great who came to see an equal in the solemn child. He had had no normal social life then either, but he hadn't missed it, the undergraduates were dull and a little frightening. He'd soon learned how to avoid most publicity – after all, infant geniuses weren't altogether unknown. His only real trouble had been with a psychiatrist who wanted him to be more 'normal'. He grinned as he remembered the rather fiendish ways in which he had frightened the man into leaving him entirely alone.

But toward the end, he had found limitations in the life. It seemed utterly pointless to sit through lectures on the obvious and to turn in assignments of problems which had been done a thousand times before. And he was beginning to find the professors a little tedious, more and more he was able to anticipate their answers to his questions and remarks, and those answers were becoming ever more trite.

He had long been aware of what his true nature must be though he had had the sense not to pass the information on. Now the dream began to grow in him: To find his people!

What was the use of everything he did, when their children must be playing with the same forces as toys, when his greatest discoveries would be as old in their culture as fire in man's? What pride did he have in his achievements, when none of the witless animals who saw them could say 'Well done!' as it should be said? What comradeship could he ever know with blind and stupid creatures who soon became as predictable as his machines: *With whom could he think?*

He flung himself savagely into work, with the simple goal of making money. It hadn't been hard. In five years he was a multimillionaire, with agents to relieve him of all the worry and responsibility, with freedom to do as he chose. To work for escape.

> *How weary, flat, stale and unprofitable*
> *Seem to me all the uses of this world!*

But not of every world! Somewhere, somewhere out among the grand host of the stars....

The long night wore on.

'Why did you come here?' asked Margaret. Her voice was quiet now, muted with hopelessness.

'I wanted secrecy. And human society was getting to be more than I could stand.'

She winced, then: 'Have you found a way to build a faster-than-light spaceship?'

'No. Nothing I've ever discovered indicates any way of getting around Einstein's limitation. There must be a way, but I just can't find it. Not too surprising, really. Our feral child would probably never be able to duplicate ocean-going ships.'

'But how do you ever hope to get out of the Solar System, then?'

'I thought of a robot-manned spaceship going from star to star, with myself in suspended animation.' He spoke of it as casually as a man might describe some scheme for repairing a leaky faucet. 'But it was utterly impractical. My people can't live anywhere near, or we'd have had more indication of them than one shipwreck. They may not live in this galaxy at all. I'll save that idea for a last resort.'

'But you and your mother must have been in some kind of ship. Wasn't anything ever found?'

'Just those few glassy fragments I mentioned. It makes me wonder if my people use spaceships at all. Maybe they have some sort of matter transmitter. No, my main hope is some kind of distress signal which will attract help.'

'But if they live so many light-years away –'

'I've discovered a strange sort of – well, you might call it radiation, though it has no relation to the electro-magnetic spectrum. Energy fields vibrating a certain way produce detectable effects in a similar setup well removed from the first. It's roughly analogous to the old spark-gap radio transmitters. The important thing is that these effects are transmitted with no measurable time lag or diminution with distance.

She would have been aflame with wonder in earlier times. Now she simply nodded. 'I see. It's a sort of ultrawave. But if there are no time or distance effects, how can it be traced? It'd be completely nondirectional, unless you could beam it.'

'I can't – yet. But I've recorded a pattern of pulses which are to correspond to the arrangement of stars in this part of the galaxy. Each pulse stands for a star, its intensity for the absolute brightness, and its time separation from the other pulses for the distance from the other stars.'

'But that's a one-dimensional representation, and space is three dimensional.'

'I know. It's not as simple as I said. The problem of such representation was an interesting problem in applied topology – took me a good week to solve. You might be interested in the mathematics, I've got my notes here somewhere – But anyway, my people, when they direct those pulses, should easily be able to deduce what I'm trying to say. I've put Sol at the head of each series of pulses, so they'll even know what particular star it is that I'm at. Anyway, there can only be one or a few configurations exactly like this in the universe, so I've given them a fix. I've set up an apparatus to broadcast my call automatically. Now I can only wait.'

'How long have you waited?'

He scowled. 'A good year now – and no sign. I'm getting worried. Maybe I should try something else.'

'Maybe they don't use your ultrawave at all. It might be obsolete in their culture.'

He nodded. 'It could well be. But what else is there?'

She was silent.

Presently Joel stirred and sighed. 'That's the story, Peggy.'

She nodded, mutely.

'Don't feel sorry for me,' he said. 'I'm doing all right. My research here is interesting, I like the country, I'm happier than I've been for a long time.'

'That's not saying much, I'm afraid,' she answered.

'No, but – Look, Peggy, you know what I am now. A monster. More alien to you than an ape. It shouldn't be hard to forget me.'

'Harder than you think, Joel. I love you. I'll always love you.'

'But – Peggy, it's ridiculous. Just suppose that I did come live with you. There could never be children . . . but I suppose that doesn't matter too much. We'd have nothing in common, though. Not a thing. We couldn't talk, we couldn't share any of the million little things that make a marriage, we could hardly ever work together. I can't live in human society any more, you'd soon lose all your friends, you'd become as lonely as I. And in the end you'd grow old, your powers would fade and die, and I'd still be approaching my maturity. Peggy, neither of us could stand it.'

'I know.'

'Langtree is a fine man. It'd be easy to love him. You've no right to withhold a heredity as magnificent as yours from your race.'

'You may be right.'

He put a hand under her chin and tilted her face up to his. 'I have some powers over the mind,' he said slowly. 'With your co-operation, I could adjust your feelings about this.'

She tensed back from him, her eyes wide and frightened. 'No –'

'Don't be a fool. It would only be doing now what time will do anyway.' His smile was tired, crooked. 'I'm really a remarkably easy person to forget, Peggy.'

His will was too strong. It radiated from him, in the lambent eyes and the delicately carved features that were almost human, it pulsed in great drowsy waves from his telepathic brain and seemed almost to flow through the thin hands. Useless to resist, futile to deny – give up, give up and sleep. She was so tired.

She nodded, finally. Joel smiled the old smile she knew so well. He began to talk.

She never remembered the rest of the night, save as a blur of half awareness, a soft voice that whispered in her head, a face dimly seen through wavering mists. Once, she recalled, there was a machine that clicked and hummed, and little lights flashing and spinning in darkness. Her memory was stirred, roiled like a quiet pool things she had forgotten through most of her life floated to the surface. It seemed as if her mother was beside her.

In the vague foggy dawn, he let her go. There was a deep unhuman calm in her, she looked at him with something of a sleepwalker's empty stare and her voice was flat. It would pass, she would soon become normal again, but Joel Weatherfield would be a memory with little emotional colour, a ghost somewhere in the back of her mind.

A ghost. He felt utterly tired, drained of strength and will. He didn't belong here, he was a shadow that should have been flitting between the stars, the sunlight of Earth erased him.

'Good-bye, Peggy,' he said. 'Keep my secret. Don't let anyone know where I am. And good luck go with you all your days.'

'Joel –' She paused on the doorstep, a puzzled frown crossing her features. 'Joel, if you can think at me that way, can't your people do the same?'

'Of course. What of it?' For the first time, he didn't know what was coming, he had changed her too much for prediction.

'Just that – why should they bother with gadgets like your ultrawave for talking to each other? They should be able to think between the stars.'

He blinked. It had occurred to him, but he had not thought much beyond it, he had been too preoccupied with his work.

'Good-bye, Joel.' She turned and walked away through the dripping grey fog. An early sunbeam struck through a chance rift and glanced off her hair. He stood in the doorway until she was gone.

He slept through most of the day. Awakening, he began to think over what had been said.

By all that was holy, Peggy was right! He had immersed himself too deeply in the purely technical problems of the ultrawave, and since then in mathematical research which passed the time of waiting, to stand off and consider the basic logic of the situation. But this – it made sense.

He had only the vaguest notion of the inherent powers of his own mind. Physical science had offered too easy an outlet for him. Nor could he, unaided, hope to get far in such studies. A human feral child might have the heredity of a mathematical genius, but unless he was found and taught by his own kind he would never comprehend the elements of arithmetic – or of speech or sociability or any of the activities which set man off from the other animals. There was just too long a heritage of prehuman and early human development for one man, alone, to recapitulate in a lifetime, when his environment held no indication of the particular road his ancestors had taken.

But those idle nerves and brain centres must be for something. He suspected that they were means of direct control over the most basic forces in the universe. Telepathy, telekinesis, precognition – what godlike heritage had been denied him?

At any rate, it did seem that his race had gone beyond the need of physical mechanisms. With complete understanding of the structure of the space-time-energy continuum, with control by direct will of its underlying processes, they would project themselves or their thoughts from star to star, create what they needed by sheer thought – and pay no attention to the gibberings of lesser races.

Fantastic, dizzying prospect! He stood breathless before the great shining vision that opened to his eyes.

He shook himself back to reality. The immediate problem was getting in touch with his race. That meant a study of the telepathic energies he had hitherto almost ignored.

He plunged into a fever of work. Time became meaningless, a succession of days and nights, waning light and drifting snow and the slow return of spring. He had never had much except his work to live for, now it devoured the last of his thoughts. Even during the periods of rest and exercise he forced himself to take, his mind was still at the problem, gnawing at it like a dog with a bone. And slowly, slowly, knowledge grew.

Telepathy was not directly related to the brain pulses measured by encephalography. Those were feeble, short-range by-products of neuronic activity. Telepathy, properly controlled, leaped over an intervening space with an arrogant ignoring of time. It was, he decided, another part of what he had labelled the ultrawave spectrum, which was related to gravitation as an effect of the geometry of space-time. But, while gravitational effects were produced by the presence of matter, ultrawave effects came into being when certain energy fields vibrated.

However, they did not appear unless there was a properly tuned receiver somewhere. They seemed somehow 'aware' of a listener even before they came into existence. That suggested fascinating speculations about the nature of time, but he turned away from it. His people would know more about it than he could ever find out alone.

But the concept of waves was hardly applicable to something that travelled with an 'infinite velocity' – a poor term semantically, but convenient. He could assign an ultrawave a frequency, that of the generating energy fields, but then the wavelength would be infinite. Better to think of it in terms of tensors, and drop all pictorial analogies.

His nervous system did not itself contain the ultra-energies. Those were omnipresent, inherent in the very structure of the cosmos. But his telepathy centres, properly trained, were somehow coupled to that great underlying flow, they could impose the desired vibrations on it. Similarly, he supposed, his other centres could control those forces to create or destroy or move matter, to cross space, to scan the past and future probability-worlds, to. . . .

He couldn't do it himself. He just couldn't find out enough in even his lifetime. Were he literally immortal, he might still never learn what he had to know; his mind had been trained into human thought patterns, and this was something that lay beyond man's power of comprehension.

But all I need is to send one clear call . . .

He struggled with it. Through the endless winter nights he sat in the cabin and fought to master his brain. How did you send a shout to the stars?

Tell me, feral child, how do you solve a partial differential equation?

Perhaps some of the answer lay in his own mind. The brain has two types of memory, the 'permanent' and the 'circulating,' and apparently the former kind is never lost. It recedes into the subconscious, but it is still there, and it can be brought out again. As a child, a baby, he would have observed things, remembered sights of apparatus and feelings of vibration, which his more mature mind could now analyze.

He practiced autohypnosis, using a machine he devised to help him, and the memories came back, memories of warmth and light and great pulsing forces. Yes – yes, there was an engine of some sort, he could see it thrumming and flickering before him. It took a while before he could translate the infant's alien impressions into his present sensory evaluations, but when that job was done he had a clear picture of – something.

That helped, just a little. It suggested certain types of hookup, empirical patterns which had not occurred to him before. And now slowly, slowly, he began to make progress.

An ultrawave demands a receiver for its very existence. So he could not flash a thought to any of his people unless one of them happened to be listening on that particular 'wave' – its pattern of frequency, modulation, and other physical characteristics. And his untrained mind simply did not send on that 'band'. He couldn't do it, he couldn't imagine the wave-form of his race's normal thought. He was faced with a problem similar to that of a man in a foreign country who must invent its language for himself before he can communicate – without even being allowed to listen to it and knowing only that its phonetic, grammatical, and semantic values are entirely different from those of his native speech.

Insoluble? No, maybe not. His mind lacked the power to send a call out through the stars, lacked the ability to make itself intelligible. But a machine has no such limitations.

He could modify his ultrawave; it already had the power, and he could give it the coherence. For he could insert a random factor in it, a device which would vary the basic wave-form in every conceivable permutation of characteristics, running through millions or billions of tries in a second – and the random wave could be modulated too, his own thoughts could be superimposed. Whenever the machine found resonance with anything that could receive – anything, literally, for millions of light-years – an ultrawave would be generated and the random element cut off. Joel could stay on that band then, examining it at his leisure.

Sooner or later, one of the bands he hit would be that of his race. And he would know it.

The device, when he finished, was crude and ugly, a great ungainly thing of tangled wires and gleaming tubes and swirling cosmic energies. One lead from it connected to a metal band around his own head, imposing his basic ultrawave pattern on the random factor and feeding back whatever was received into his brain. He lay on his bunk, with a control panel beside him, and started the machine working.

Vague mutterings, sliding shadows, strangeness rising out of the roiled depths of his mind. . . . He grinned thinly, battling down the cold apprehension which rose in his abused nerves, and began experimenting with the machine. He wasn't too sure of all its characteristics himself, and it would take a while too before he had full control of his thought-pattern.

Silence, darkness, and now and then a glimpse, a brief blinding instant when the random gropings struck some basic resonance and a wave sprang into being and talked to his brain. Once he looked through Margaret's eyes, across a table to Langtree's face. There was candlelight, he remembered afterward, and a small string orchestra was playing in the background. Once he saw the ragged outlines of a city men had never built, rising up toward a cloudy sky while a strangely slow and heavy sea leaped against its walls.

Once, too, he did catch a thought flashing between the stars. But it was no thought of his kind, it was a great white blaze like a sun exploding in his head, and cold, cold. He screamed aloud, and for a week afterward dared not resume his experiments.

In the springtime dusk, he found his answer.

The first time, the shock was so great that he lost contact again. He lay shaking, forcing calm on himself, trying to reproduce the exact pattern his own brain, as well as the machine, had been sending. Easy, easy – The baby's mind had been drifting in a mist of dreams, *thus* . . .

The baby. For his groping, uncontrollable brain could not resonate with any of the superbly trained adult minds of his people.

But a baby has no spoken language. Its mind slides amorphously from one pattern to another, there are no habits as yet to fix it, and one tongue is as good as any other. By the laws of randomness, Joel had struck the pattern which an infant of his race happened to be giving out at the moment.

He found it again, and the tingling warmth of contact flowed into him, deliciously, marvellously, a river in a dusty desert, a sun warming the chill of the solipsistic loneliness in which humans wandered from their births to the end of their brief meaningless lives. He fitted his mind to the baby's, let the two streams of consciousness flow into one, a river running toward the mighty sea of the race.

The feral child crept out of the forest. Wolves howled at his back, the hairy four-footed brothers of cave and chase and darkness, but he heard them not. He bent over the baby's cradle, the tangled hair falling past his gaunt witless face, and looked with a dim stirring of awe and wonder. The baby spread its hand, a little soft starfish, and his own gnarled fingers stole toward it, trembling at the knowledge that this was a paw like his own.

Now he had only to wait until some adult looked into the child's mind. It shouldn't be long, and meanwhile he rested in the timeless drowsy peace of the very young.

Somewhere in the outer cosmos, perhaps on a planet swinging about a sun no one of Earth would ever see, the baby rested in a cradle of warm, pulsing forces. He did not have a room around him, there was a shadowiness which no human could ever quite comprehend, lit by flashes of the energy that created the stars.

The baby sensed the nearing of something that meant warmth and softness, sweetness in his mouth and murmuring in his mind. He cooed with delight, reaching his hands out into the shaking twilight of the room. His mother's mind ran ahead of her, folding about the little one.

A scream!

Frantically, Joel reached for her mind, flashing and flashing the pattern of location-pulses through the baby's brain into hers. He lost her, his mind fell sickeningly in on itself – no, no, someone else was reaching for him now, analyzing the pattern of the machine and his own wild oscillations and fitting smoothly into them.

A deep, strong voice in his brain, somehow unmistakably male – Joel relaxed, letting the other mind control his, simply emitting his signals.

It would take – them – a little while to analyze the meaning of his call. Joel lay in a half-conscious state, aware of one small part of the being's mind maintaining a thread of contact with him while the rest reached out, summoning others across the universe, calling for help and information.

So he had won. Joel thought of Earth, dreamily and somehow wistfully. Odd that in this moment of triumph his mind should dwell on the litle things he was leaving behind – an Arizona sunset, a nightingale under the moon, Peggy's flushed face bent over an instrument beside his. Beer and music and windy pines.

But O my people! Never more to be lonely . . .

Decision. A sensation of falling, rushing down a vortex of stars toward Sol – approach!

The being would have to locate him on Earth. Joel tried to picture a map, though the thought-patterns that corresponded in his brain to a particular visualization would not make sense to the other. But in some obscure way, it might help.

Maybe it did. Suddenly the telepathic band snapped, but there was a rush of other impulses, life forces like flame, the nearness of a god. Joel stumbled gasping to his feet and flung open the door.

The moon was rising above the dark hills, a hazy light over trees and patches of snow and the wet ground. The air was chill and damp, sharp in his lungs.

The being who stood there, outlined in the radiance of his garments, was taller than Joel, an adult. His grave eyes were too brilliant to meet, it was as if the life within him were incandescent. And when the full force of his mind reached out, flowing over and into Joel, running along every nerve and cell of him . . .

He cried out with the pain of it and fell to his hands and knees. The intolerable force lightened, faded to a thrumming in his brain that shook every fibre of it. He was being studied, analyzed, no tiniest part of him was hidden from those terrible eyes and from the logic that recreated more of him than he knew himself. His own distorted telepathic language was at once intelligible to the watcher, and he croaked his appeal.

The answer held pity, but it was as remote and inexorable as the thunders on Olympus.

Child, it is too late. Your mother must have been caught in a – ? – energy vortex and caused to – ? – on Earth, and now you have been raised by the animals.

Think, child. Think of the feral children of this native race. When they were restored to their own kind, did they become human? No, it was too late. The basic personality traits are determined in the first years of childhood, and their specifically human attributes, unused, had atrophied.

It is too late, too late. Your mind has become too fixed in rigid and limited patterns. Your body has made a different adjustment from that which is necessary to sense and control the forces we use. You even need a machine to speak.

You no longer belong to our race.

Joel lay huddled on the ground, shaking, not thinking or daring to think.

The thunders rolled through his head: *We cannot have you interfering with the proper mental training of our children. And since you can never rejoin your kind, but must make the best adaptation you can to the race you live with, the kindest as well as the wisest thing for us to do is to make certain changes. Your memory and that of others, your body, the work you are doing and have done –*

There were others filling the night, the gods come to Earth, shining and terrible beings who lifted each fragment of experience he had ever had out of him and made their judgments on it. Darkness closed over him, and he fell endlessly into oblivion.

He awoke in his bed, wondering why he should be so tired.

Well, the cosmic-ray research had been a hard and lonely grind. Thank heaven and his lucky stars it was over! He'd take a well-earned vacation at home now. It'd be good to see his friends again – and Peggy.

Dr Joel Weatherfield, eminent young physicist, rose cheerfully and began making ready to go home.

They Fly So High

BY ROSS ROCKLYNNE

from *Amazing Stories*, June 1952

When the April 1968 *Galaxy* carried Ross Rocklynne's 'Touch of the Moon', a story about the relationship between men living on the Moon and those on Earth, many readers may have thought it was the work of a new author. Nothing could be further from the truth. Rocklynne had been a prominent sf writer since the mid-1930s, but left science fiction during the 1950s to pursue other avenues.

Ross L. Rocklin was born on Friday 21 February 1913. His first sale was to F. Orlin Tremaine, 'Man of Iron', about a man who could walk through solid metal. It appeared in the August 1935 *Astounding*. Shortly thereafter he began his memorable series about Lieutenant Colbie and master criminal Edward Deveral. These stories fall into the category of scientific problems, wherein some apparently insoluble difficulty is overcome by strict application of one or more scientific rules. Three stories appeared in this series in which the protagonists are duly trapped in the hollow centre of the hypothetical planet Vulcan; trapped deep in a pit on Jupiter, and finally sliding to-and-fro on an almost frictionless concave mirror-surface miles across.

This made Rocklynne's name, and a later series, which began with 'Into the Darkness' (*Astonishing*, June 1940) wherein the hero was a spiral nebula (!), cemented his position. Alas, he succumbed for a while to writing potboilers for Ray Palmer's magazines, but in the early 1950s he was back to his old form. 'They Fly So High', which follows, in effect revived the Colbie-Deverel series but with new characters. He discontinued the format when he left the sf field.

Today, Rocklynne is writing regularly again.

Dornley, seated in the galley of the galloping spaceship with his prisoner, was struck with a queer impression. Actually, Dr Waldo Skutch was not worried that he had been ousted at point of gun from Callisto.

'I could vacuum out another cup of coffee for you, sir' – Dornley had been taught to be polite at the Space Academy, even to dangerous criminals – 'but then you *don't* seem to be nervous or worried, do you?' The best way to get at the subject.

Besides, August Dornley felt he *did* have an inquiring mind. Skutch the authorities said, was planning the overthrow of the entire human race. Why? Where was his criminal base located? What was the nature of the secret arsenal of new weapons he was making? Good questions. Find the answers. Get into Skutch's confidence.

'Nervous?' boomed Skutch, transfixing Dornley with his pale strange eyes over which the cliffs of gray hair hung. 'Worried? My dear young Lieutenant Dornley, worry is a special affection of the human race, an unnecessary evil of the mind for which they have great love. Worry is of the future; I, Skutch, am of the present.' He touched his barrel-chest with a large, curved thumb.

'You don't consider yourself of the human race, sir?' This certainly was a question some clever interrogator would ask Skutch when he faced trial.

'I am of the human race; my physical body proves it, unfortunately. But as long as my mind functions, my chances of becoming unhuman are excellent, most excellent!' Skutch let go of his coffee cup to tap his great forehead, over which the disheveled coarse gray hair hung. 'Brains, young man, brains. You are of the human race, and no doubt proud of it. But what have you done with your brains?'

Dornley would not let himself be irritated by this old man with the strange eyes. He smiled. 'I got through the Space Academy in record time with top honors,' he said. 'If I hadn't had some kind of unusual merit, I would have been sent to the front lines in one of the warships. Instead, I was ranked up to Special Duty.'

'And of that use of your brains you are proud!'

'Well, let's see,' said Dornley, touched off a little. 'I tracked you down to Callisto. I fooled you into leaving your ship. Then

I set up a random-firing booby-gun, and caught you from be-hind. When it comes to a question of brains –'

Skutch threw back his great tattered head and laughed. His laughs were muted, gleeful squeals. Finally he stopped.

'Don't you think I knew I could not escape capture?' he demanded. 'Now, let me ask you what happened to *your* ship.'

Dornley's healthy tanned face showed a flush. 'You blasted it,' he admitted. 'So what's the difference? We're using yours.'

Skutch abruptly leaned across the table on his elbows, staring intently at Dornley. 'You do have brains,' he said in the gentlest tone he had used so far. 'But you have not been taught to think. *Think*, young man, *think*. I, Skutch, do not worry about the future. But that does not mean that I do not consider the pos-sibilities and the probabilities of the future. Now, can you *think*?'

Dornley was nettled at first. Then he felt distinct alarm. His training made him sit quietly, but it also made his hand inevit-ably grip the handle of his Biow thermo-gun.

'I'll make a guess,' he said steadily. 'The ship itself is a booby trap.'

Suddenly he did get up, leaning his lank body over his chair to reach the galley vision disks. Jupiter showed one sweeping section of its baleful perimeter. He widened the aperture. Jupiter jumped back, showing itself in its entirety as a bulky, mottled orange. Around it stars lay thickly. Dornley rotated the pickup through one hundred and eighty degrees of all three co-ordinates. Japetus lay twenty minutes behind. The other satel-lites shone dimly.

Along the bottom of the disks, no pips of brilliance showed. There were no other ships in the area. Attack was ruled out, but so was the possibility of rescue.

He shut off the mechanism, faced Skutch quietly.

'So it's in the ship. Probably an explosive that you rigged into the fuel beforehand, primed to trigger off after a certain interval – unless you were free to unrig it.' He could feel sweat trickling down his armpits. 'I can also assume that there's nothing to be done about it at this late date, otherwise you wouldn't have tipped me off.'

'Now,' said Skutch, grinning widely, 'you are thinking. But not enough. You really don't think I would arrange my own death. Actually, I would. My work is well on its way. It is left in capable hands. I wouldn't be missed for long. So I am prepared to let the ship blow up with us in it if you do not move quickly.'

Count to ten. Dornley said evenly, 'You virtually admit you are conspiring against humanity. This doesn't sound very much like the idealized picture of yourself, Dr Skutch, as a superior human. Earth uses science to make war, a war that is inevitable and must be fought. You plan to use superior science to overcome both victor and loser. Is that correct? Am I *thinking*?' He tossed the last out with bitter sarcasm, then turned on his long legs and went aft fast. He came back with two boxed pressure-suits, the supra-lux type that would withstand, if necessary, fifteen thousand atmospheric pressures.

'You are thinking,' said Skutch, frowning heavily at him as he ripped open the boxes, 'with the lower half of your body.'

Dornley, thin-lipped, ignored him utterly. Skutch rumbled on: 'Science! Pah!' He almost spat. 'Science is a toy, a plaything. And I am a criminal because I desert my enforced task as toymaker. I am tracked down because it is feared I am conspiring against authority. I am to be tried and sentenced and forced to conceive of more ingenious toys. Tried by men who are unconscious automatons, men who think with the thoughts of others.' He fell silent.

The boxes opened up; the pressure-suits came out, fat dull things looking like blown-up corpses.

Skutch surveyed them interestedly. 'Perhaps we do not have enough time,' he said gravely. 'Will five minutes do?'

Dornley worked twice as fast, sweating, checking air vents and controls, examining the pins of the gravity units, making sure the food and water units were full and operating. Skutch observed this thoroughness with great approval.

'You can think,' he said, nodding his great gray head. 'But, here without a spirit of revenge motivating me, perhaps you have here an excellent example of how the free individual can manipulate the Universe. I, Skutch, am manipulating you, am manipulating this ship, am manipulating events – even though I am chained to this table. Wouldn't you give much for such an accomplishment?'

'I'd give much if you'd shut up, Dr Skutch,' Dornley said firmly. Skutch shrugged his heavy old shoulders. 'Now, get into this suit.'

Dornley unchained him and helped him in, bolting down the solid, transparent supra-lux visor. Skutch choked a little.

Dornley readjusted the intake of oxygen. Thirty-nine seconds later they shot out from the air-lock and Skutch, handcuffed to Dornley, was dryly complimenting him for a fast piece of work. Ten seconds later, several large cracks abruptly appeared in the slim black ship's hull. Through these cracks, and through the shattered ports, was seen a glow of fuming violence. Bilious yellow gases escaped under pressure, swiftly expanded to the point of invisibility. The numerous cracks in the hull became a little larger, that was all. They began moving, under their own velocity, farther and farther away until the derelict was gone.

Dornley was depressed and silent. Actually, he could blame himself and a certain amount of inexperience for having fallen into a trap. Skutch was a wise old bear; and, it appeared, he understood human nature. Looking down at giant Jupiter – that immense planet did determine where *down* was – he was almost sure it would have been better to take a quick death in the ship.

'Jupiter,' mused Skutch. His voice came through the radio receiver with its booming quality strained out. 'Jupiter, giant of the system, a mighty creature, an aged old man. Jupiter, my friend, I salute you. Soon we shall meet.'

Dornley said nothing. Skutch said, 'You did not know, I suppose, that Jupiter is alive?'

Dornley turned his head until his face was against Skutch's. He was sure he was looking at a crazy old man. But Skutch grinned hugely, his gray whiskers protruding around his mouth like those of a tiger.

'I have trapped you, young man. You are, it would appear, much worse off than I expected. You would make the statement, flatly, that Jupiter does *not* live. Your mind is fettered. You are chained to dogma. Other minds tell you what to think. Perhaps I should discard you.' He sighed heavily, but calculatingly.

Dornley said flatly, 'Jupiter is *not* alive.'

'You see?' Skutch's free arm appealed to the cold stars. 'If only he had said "I do not have sufficient material on which to base an opinion. Jupiter *may* be alive." '

Dornley smiled wanly. 'Men have landed on Jupiter. They've built Jupiter City up near the Red Spot. They haven't detected a heartbeat, or breathing. But I'll grant you the point. He might be alive in other ways.'

'Good, good,' applauded Skutch. 'You are showing signs of improvement. Understand me, young man. Sometimes I make flat statements which I do not know to be true. But these are merely for testing people.'

'Which people?'

'*All* people,' said Skutch solemnly. 'I have my life work which you do not yet know about. I am, you would say at your present level of understanding, creating an ultimate weapon, a weapon so powerful that none will stand against it. For this I would be damned, sentenced to death if the Terrestrial Court ever got hold of me, which they shall not. We are falling now.'

They were indeed falling. The planet's powerful drag had finally overcome their momentum outward; the meter in the wrist of Dornley's pressure-suit, accurately judging the changing shifts of satellite and planetary gravities, gave them an accelerating velocity. They would, at this rate, hit the planet's atmosphere in eight hours. No good. Every hour, at least, they would have to adjust the gravity units built into the suits to cut their speed down.

Dornley, attached to his strange companion, stared down at that broad orange, yellow, and red monster of the sky. Vagrant fear-thoughts floated to the surface of his mind. He knew he should be screaming with terror. They were alone out here, detached from things, living with a finality equal to death. His heart beat a little faster; his breathing stepped up. He began to think of himself as still a young punk, with a long and satisfactory life not yet ready to be cut short. He sweated.

'Dr Skutch,' he said hoarsely, 'how do you do it? Why aren't you afraid?'

'Afraid?' Skutch's voice was astonished. Then it became very soft and gentle. 'I understand, young man,' he said. 'You are worried. You think we will not live. And why is this?'

The question was gently probing.

Dornley bit his lip. 'It's obvious. Jupiter has caught people before. Ships unable to fight free of the gravity. They've sent distress signals that were picked up. No rescue ship could get to them in time. And we don't even have sending equipment.'

'Aha!' Skutch's teeth clicked triumphantly. 'We come to the core of mankind's woes. Man looks back on past occurrences, and plans the future accordingly. The future therefore is thought of as a carbon copy of the past. This is definitely not so, young man. Your no doubt excellent brain is using identity thought. What a dangerous thing! Understand this: *no one* event is identical with another. What is happening to us now

has no relationship whatever with anything that ever happened
to anybody else. This is a new situation. We can make of it what
we will without letting past events dictate to us. Do you understand?'

'It makes sense,' Dornley said wearily. 'But it still scares the
living daylights out of me.'

'My dear Lieutenant Dornley,' Skutch snapped with asperity,
'that is because you are, if I may say it, not alive. You are not
being. Look around you!' He made a great, enthusiastic, sweeping arc with his free arm. 'Would you be dead like most of mankind? Here you have beauty! Here you have majesty! Here
you have depth and mystery and awesome ideas to contend
with! There is joy out here, not terror. Young man, I command
you *to be!*'

If there had been anything to sit on, Dornley would have
sat up at the sternness in Skutch's voice. At any rate, he felt
some kind of bells ringing in his head, and he did look around.
It was beautiful, he decided forlornly – if you didn't worry.

Skutch was looking through Dornley's visor at him. He grinned widely. 'That's better. Young man, I have a suggestion. Go
to sleep. I shall be sure to adjust our falling speed so that we
shall not strike the atmosphere fast enough to create heat.'

Dornley did go to sleep, as if Skutch had used positive suggestion. He slept long, solidly, and potently. When he awoke, it
was because he and Skutch were pinwheeling through a thicken-
ing atmosphere. Skutch muttered something about not knowing
where the stabilizer controls were. Dornley found them for him;
soon, the tiny gyroscopes whirring, they were falling feet first.

There was little light. Starlight could not penetrate this incredibly thick skin of gases that covered Jupiter. A red glow,
originating from the reflection of the Great Red Spot halfway
around the planet, afforded hardly any illumination. Dornley
turned on the search-beam unit in the breast of his suit to read
his meters. Twelve hundred miles to go to get to the surface.
He spoke to Skutch. Skutch muttered groggily. Dornley said
nothing more, and let Skutch fall asleep.

The vigil could have been full of terror, but Dornley reflected
that some of Skutch's strange philosophy had gotten through
to him, and no doubt would keep him pepped up for a while.
He frowned. A strange experience, a strange man, who *was*
working on an ultimate weapon, and *did* have conspirators
working with him, by his own admission.

Something didn't jibe. What? No answer.

They fell. Dornley thought, so this was a new situation? Hm-m-m. But it was the same deadly planet. But maybe not. Old Man Jupiter was a guy with many faces, many mysteries, ninety-nine percent unknown.

Two and a half times Earth gravity; fifteen thousand times Earth's atmospheric pressure!

Dornley grimaced down through heaving blackness. 'Jupiter, old man,' he prayed as an experiment, 'let us down easy. And if we get away free, and I get Skutch where he belongs, I promise . . ." *Could go to church every Sunday; but Jupiter doesn't care.*

Five hundred miles. Dornley didn't dare take his eyes away from the set of meters. One hundred miles. He kept his eyes glued to them. Ten miles. He tried to wake up Skutch. Two miles. Skutch would not waken. One thousand feet.

'Skutch!' screamed Dornley. Three hundred feet. But fractional readings didn't work. Twenty-five feet below his search-beam glanced off a liquid, gleaming surface. Dornley, robbed of the time to do things properly, wasn't able to throw Skutch's gravity reactor over; he could only shove over his own. Result, not enough gravity decrease. They hit hard and went under.

Under.

Thank you, Old Man Jupiter.

Skutch was muttering as they floated up. Floated up was not the best description of the process. They were being carried up. Nor did they break surface. The surface was under them.

In any event, the movement ceased. Dornley's chest-beam was still on. It illuminated what at first glance seemed to be a smooth circular cavern exuding a greenish, a gorgeous radiance. The radiance was, of course, the dispersed radiance of the beam.

Skutch muttered again. Dornley tried to move. He was flat on his back, locked tight against Skutch. Like a vise. His helmet was held down; he could barely move his head inside it. One arm was lying free against his chest; he carefully kept it that way. His legs were clamped together, and in turn locked to Skutch's. His other arm was squeezed in tight to Skutch's. Strange.

Silence. Skutch spoke. 'Well, young man? You are thinking?'

Dornley *was* thinking – rather detachedly. He was thinking of two men alone on an uninhabited planet – uninhabited except for an inaccessible domed city halfway around the planet. Two men thinking of impossibilities, in terms of hope and escape and rescue.

So he should think. What he should do was reach over with his free arm and tune the great Dr Waldo Skutch's oxygen intake to zero.

Skutch's sigh came. 'I am disappointed in you, Lieutenant. An unchained mind already would have diagnosed the situation and be devising solutions. The free man manipulates the world; the world manipulates the slave. Are you slave to your own pessimism? That is the important problem, not whether you will continue to live.

'However, I shall start your enslaved mind to working. The "cave," as you have already misnomered it, is not a cave. Listen to the Jupiter wind.' A wind did sound, outside somewhere, a whining, gusty thunder that rose, fell, augmented, diminished. The gorgeously green 'cave' expanded and contracted correspondingly, sometimes as much as two or three feet.

'You see?' Skutch chuckled. 'Jupiter is breathing. We have fallen into his mouth and are enveloped in a bubble of spit! One's imagination could make much of this. But let us stick to fact, fact at least as the mind of man knows it.

'Fifteen thousand atmospheres press on a lake of strange liquid metal. A unique distortion occurs on the surface of the lake. One could say that a surface tension thousands of times one would think possible is almost certain to be created. *Now* you are thinking?' Skutch's voice was hopeful; he was like a man who has primed a pump and is sure water must come out.

'Hell,' muttered Dornley rebelliously. He was thinking of two needles locked together on a surface film of water. So how does one free the two needles so they can eddy around for a while with a certain amount of freedom? Stir up the water around them, maybe. Not that exactly. . . .

'Don't worry, I'm not exactly dead,' he told Skutch. 'I've got a free arm. I've also got an idea.'

He could reach Skutch's gravity unit rheostat with some effort; his own was easy. He turned both rheostats on full; instantly, their weights increased and they sagged below the surface of the liquid stuff, lying in a sort of deep hollow.

'Get set,' he told Skutch. He turned both rheostats suddenly back to the zero mark, which equaled one-half a gravity. Dornley's breath whooshed out as the sag in the surface of the lake bounced back in place, snapping the two men a half dozen feet into the air.

There was a breaking sound. When Dornley came to, he was sitting cross-legged a half dozen feet from Skutch. Skutch had fallen on his back, helpless again, arms and legs forced together. But he was chuckling delightedly, and told Dornley that when he came this way, he could pull Skutch to a sitting position too.

Dornley was about to demonstrate that he intended to stay where he was when he noticed that inevitably the strengthened surface between them was drawing them together. Well, anyway, the handcuffs, brittle in the subzero cold, had snapped, and Dornley was arm-free, so there was that much gained.

A moment later, the two men were sitting knee to knee.

Dornley now looked around with greater interest.

'It's a bubble, all right,' he admitted. 'Big babies. There's a gas seepage in the bed of the lake, I'd say. The wind causes change in pressure outside. That's a good aerodynamic principle that works on any planet. The bubble gets bigger or smaller accordingly.'

One section of the bubble became a flat wall.

'Interesting,' commented Dornley, so fascinated he didn't know his worry about the future had momentarily slipped away. 'Another bigger bubble bumped into it.'

Skutch surveyed him with an extremely friendly smile, but he said nothing, being speechless for the first time.

Dornley tentatively tugged his Biow thermo-gun from its holster, and after some hesitation took a potshot at the two bubbles' connecting skin. It turned a brighter green in one spot, but didn't break, so Dornley turned the temperature up a little. This time there was a crack of thunder, and things happened. Dornley and Skutch were tossed around, and when things quieted down, they were again being forced together, and a bubble four times as big arched over them. The two bubbles apparently had merged.

Dornley grinned, and Skutch grinned back.

'You see?' Skutch spread his hands as if life itself had been explained. 'One plays with toys, but one does not allow toys to play with him – unless he wants them to. In this way, free men master all that is within and without them. Now, my dear Lieutenant, I am sure you have determined our next step, the means of securing escape from this lake?' His shaggy brows went up.

Dornley surveyed him thoughtfully. He was beginning to get

certain ideas, very strong and intuitive ideas.

'I have not determined it,' he stated.

The shaggy face behind the visor smiled broadly. Skutch reached out a hand. 'Let me have your gun, young man,' he commanded.

Instead of doing that, Dornley brought the gun up and centered it on the chest of Skutch's pressure-suit.

He said conversationally, 'Dr Skutch, if I were to turn the heat intensity on this thermal weapon up, to full blast, it would take me five minutes to burn a hole in your suit and let fifteen thousand atmospheric pressures in.'

Skutch's face was wrenched with a bitter surprise. He snarled. '*Why?*'

'I've been a good boy, Dr Skutch. I didn't lose my temper when you began . . . uh . . . manipulating me. I treated you like a prisoner of war, with courtesy, with great courtesy. Believe me, I shall continue to be courteous. But I am still a member of the Service, and I have my duty. We are *not* friends.'

Skutch relaxed visibly, his tiger-look vanishing. 'Oh, that.' He shrugged contemptuously. 'Duty. Courtesy. Catchwords. Other men's thoughts again. They mean nothing.'

'That's not all,' said Dornley determinedly. 'I have certain beliefs regarding you. One is that you *are* conspiring to overthrow not only the Earth government, but the governments, eventually, of the other planets as well. The enemy planets.'

'Enemy!' Skutch raised his hands to invisible gods. 'There he goes again! Whose enemy? Not his enemy. The enemy of the higher-ups who think for him. You have learned nothing from me, young man, *nothing?*'

Dornley felt his thinking apparatus going haywire.

'Furthermore,' he went on distractedly, 'you *do* have a base, a headquarters, and you have many men under you. This has been suspected too. But not until now has anyone been convinced of its location. That base, I am convinced, is on this planet. And not too far from here! Else, *why* are you so optimistic?

'Again, by your own admission to me, you, a genius in the field of science, are working with your men on a weapon so powerful that it could not be withstood by any power. Of this I believe you are capable.

'Dr Skutch, I can be optimistic too, under certain conditions, but I *know* we can't reach Jupiter City. And I cannot allow you the possibility of escape to your headquarters, even if I die.

'I am sure I should kill you now.'

Skutch grunted. 'Why don't you?'

Dornley sweated. Skutch grunted again, almost disinterestedly. 'You don't believe half of what you're saying, Lieutenant. That's why. You're waiting for proof from me. I'll give you proof. My base *is* near here – only three thousand miles. You do think. And I do have many men – and women – and children – under me. And I am creating a super-weapon that is intended to destroy! Tell me, Lieutenant, how would you like to see that super-weapon in operation?'

Dornley clamped his teeth together. 'I would, but –'

'Excellent!' Some of Skutch's ebullience came back. Then his stare became bright and penetrating.

'Lieutenant, what possessions do you have?'

The direction of the conversation was going out of control. Dornley felt loggy. 'None,' he said wearily. 'I'm in the Service. A few papers, old letters, some civilian clothes, a number of books. That's all. Why?'

'You're not married? You have no children? You have no relatives you are tied to?' At Dornley's lack of replies in the affirmative, he cried, 'Excellent, excellent, excellent! Lieutenant, how would you like to take a trip to my base, my so-called militant headquarters, and watch the rays of my deadly weapon at work?'

Dornley felt himself crumbling. He suspected some kind of equivocation here that would put him in a still worse position. But worse from whose viewpoint? He was tired of thinking. Well, answer the question. From the viewpoint of duty, from the viewpoint of oaths, from the viewpoint of the men who bossed the men who bossed the men who bossed the men, who in turn got their ideas and their convictions from official papers written by the last generation, or men ten generations dead, who had written books and conceived traditions and rules . . . A tanglework of convention and protocol and axiomatic falsehoods that had a bad beginning. War, poverty, pain, violence, science, more science, better science, super-science, war, poverty . . . Super-dooper science . . .

Pensively he looked beyond Skutch. Life was wrong. Yes, drastically wrong somehow. He was in a position where he should kill Skutch – but he couldn't. What then? He had to go with Skutch. That too was being forced on him. Go with

Skutch! Find out, at least, what he was up to. Get a look at this so-called super-weapon, at his base, at the people he worked with. And then –

He shook his head regretfully. 'I can't kill you, Doctor. I'll go with you, if we can make it. If I don't like what I see, I promise I'll leave and won't say anything. That goes against my oath, but that's the way I'll stand.'

'But if you do like it?' The question was probing.

'You'd want me to stay? Give up Earth?'

'Bah!' Skutch rocked back. 'You never had Earth. Earth had you. No, no, young man. You'd go back. Someday we'll all go back – if we want to. But not for long.'

Dornley gave him a fleeting, worn smile, said nothing. Skutch's breath came out in a long, sustained sigh.

Dornley looked at his gun. 'As for getting to "dry" land,' he mused, 'that should be easy. A spot heat should reduce the tension and give us a pull in the opposite direction.'

He destroyed the gently vibrating bubble with a single blast. It disappeared in thunder, though for a second great drops of it rained down. Dornley waited until he and Skutch once more swung together, waited until he had accustomed himself to winds that had the push of undersea currents. He then adjusted the gun to maximum aperture. This gave him a fanning beam, which he played on the surface film to his left, adequately lessening its tension.

The surface forces to Dornley's right being greater, they contracted continuously, pulling him and Skutch smoothly away from the heated surface. Dornley, wanting to be sure they did not move in a circle, turned up the stabilizers.

After an hour, what would roughly be described as a 'beach' appeared. Strong cohesive forces, however, caused the lake edge to sweep upward in a sharp curve, a dozen feet high. Dornley surveyed that obstacle distrustfully, but apparently the strength of the contracting film was enough to overcome gravitational pull. They swooped up, poised. Skutch clawed at the rocky ledge of the beach and got free. Dornley was poised on the lip. Skutch got him under the armpits and heaved him out.

Dornley looked questioningly at Skutch as they stood free with ammonia-methane winds moving sluggishly around them. Skutch motioned him to sit down.

'They'll come for us,' he said complacently.

'They know we're here?' Dornley was incredulous.

Skutch grinned hugely. 'Why not? Science is not an end, but it is a tool.' He picked up two slate-colored rocks, knocked them together. 'Sounds travel, and do not stop. Instruments pick up vibrations. They'll be here. We do have ways to move about the planet.'

There was silence. Then Dornley saw that Skutch was looking at him, intently, purposefully.

'You will live with us,' Skutch said slowly. 'You will learn. There will be girls there. There will be girls who will fall in love with you – if they want to. You will lack for nothing. But you must learn.

'When I say Jupiter is alive, you will say maybe it is alive, and try to find out why I think it is alive. When I say apple trees will thrive in a glass of water, you will question the concept. You will re-examine every tradition, every convention, every idea that has been thrust at you and which you have been forced to accept. You will ask why you *must* do such and such. Who said so? You will begin throwing out hundreds of false ideas, but *you* will use *them*, they will not use you. You will examine your fears, your guilts, your jealousies, your envies. Eventually, you will compel them, they will not compel you. No thing, no one, no idea, will ever use you again. Unless you want it to.'

He rocked back on his haunches, hands on his spread knees, grinning his tiger's grin.

'The prospect frightens you? Do not let it, young man. Already I have used my secret weapon on you. Its rays are deeply imbedded in your body. Already you see how easily one's own personal bubbles can burst. You will never be the same.

'But not for a thousand years will we, or those who come after us, be ready for humanity itself.'

The winds moved sluggishly. Time passed. Dornley sat stricken, wondering what he could discard, wondering what he could keep.

The Last Day

BY RICHARD MATHESON

from *Amazing Stories*, April–May 1953

During Palmer's reign *Amazing* had become labelled with the stigma of a potboiler publication. Howard Browne had much to live down when he assumed control, and despite the quality of the fiction, as evidenced by the previous story, his first few years were sorely marred. The chance for a major change came when Ziff-Davis agreed to switch to digest size. With an increased budget, Browne acquired first-class stories and produced a superb quality magazine that ranks among one of the best produced of any sf publication. Without a doubt the most startling and absorbing story in that first digest was the following, 'The Last Day' by Richard Matheson.

Today Matheson is more generally known as an author of horror stories, and as a Hollywood scriptwriter, particularly with the Roger Corman-directed Poe films. But Matheson is truly a product of the science fiction world, having made a terrific impact with his brief story, 'Born of Man and Woman', in the Summer 1950 *F & SF*, with its first person recount by a mutant. Matheson who was born in 1926, had grown up in Brooklyn intending to become an engineer. Following the sale and reception of his first story, he concentrated on writing, and remained professional ever since. In the sf field, stories like 'Brother to the Machine' (*If*, November 1952) about the psychology of robots, and 'The Foodlegger' (*Thrilling Wonder*, April 1952) where in the future food is a dirty word, soon earned him a solid reputation. He has a talent for creating a pitch of suspense in his horror works, especially the noted *I Am Legend*, and the more recent *Hell-House*. With the successful adaptation of his novel, *The Incredible Shrinking Man*, to the screen, Matheson concentrated more on scripting, but he never ignored the prose field. A straight story, 'The Distributor', won him *Playboy's* annual $1000 fiction award in 1958, and his novel, *The Beardless Warriors*, about teenagers in World War II, based on his own experiences, received high critical acclaim.

His appearances in sf are regrettably rare today, but in the early 1950s it was hard to avoid him. With stories like 'The Last Day' however it was a delight to have him around.

He woke up and the first thing he thought was: *the last night is gone*.

He had slept through half of it.

He lay there on the floor and looked up at the ceiling. The walls still glowed reddish from the outside light. There was no sound in the living-room but that of snoring.

He looked around. There were bodies sprawled all over the room. On the couch, slumped on chairs, curled up on the floor.

He raised up on one elbow and winced at the shooting pains in his head. He closed his eyes and held them tightly shut for a moment. Then he opened them again. He ran his tongue over the inside of his dry mouth. There was still a stale taste of liquor and food in his mouth.

He rested on his elbow as he looked around the room again, his mind slowly registering the scene.

Nancy and Bill lying in each other's arms, both naked. Norman curled up in an armchair, his thin face taut as he slept. Mort and Mel lying on the floor, covered with dirty throw rugs. Both snoring. Others on the floor.

Outside the red glow.

He looked at the window and his throat moved. He blinked He looked down over his long body. He swallowed again.

I'm alive, he thought, and it's all true.

He rubbed his eyes. He took a deep breath of the dead air in the apartment.

He knocked over a glass as he struggled to his feet. The liquor and soda sloshed over the rug and soaked into the dark blue weave.

He looked around at the other glasses, broken, kicked over, hurled against the wall. He looked at the bottles all over, all empty.

He stood staring around the room. He looked at the record player overturned, the albums all strewn around, jagged pieces of records in crazy patterns on the rug.

He remembered.

It was Mort who had started it the night before. Mort who had suddenly rushed to the playing record machine and shouted drunkenly, 'What the hell is music any more! Just a lot of noise!'

And he had driven the point of his shoe against the front of the record player and knocked it against the wall. He had lurched over and down on his knees. He had struggled up with the player in his beefy arms and heaved the entire thing over on its back and kicked it again.

'The hell with music!' Mort had yelled. 'I hate the crap anyway!'

Then he'd started to drag records out of their albums and their envelopes and snap them over his kneecap.

'Come on!' he'd yelled to everybody. 'Come on!'

And it had caught on. The way all crazy ideas had caught on in those last few days.

Mel had jumped up from making love to a girl. He had flung records out the windows, scaling them far across the street. And Charlie had put aside his gun for a moment to stand at the windows too and try to hit people in the street with the records.

Richard had watched the dark saucers bounce and shatter on the sidewalks below. He'd even thrown one himself. Then he'd just turned away and let the others rage. He'd taken Mel's girl into the bedroom and for a few moments they forgot what was happening to their world.

He thought about that as he stood waveringly in the reddish light of the room.

He closed his eyes a moment.

Then he looked at Nancy and remembered taking her too sometime in the jumble of wild hours that had been yesterday and last night.

She looked vile now, he thought. She'd always been an animal. Before, though, she'd had to veil it. Now, in the final twilight of everything, she could revel in the only thing she'd ever really cared about.

He wondered if there were any people left in the world with

real dignity. The kind that was still there when it no longer was necessary to impress people with it.

He stepped over the body of a sleeping girl. She had on only a slip. He looked down at her tangled hair, at her smeared red lips, at the tight, unhappy frown printed on her face.

He glanced into the bedroom as he passed it. There were three girls and two men in the bed.

He found the body in the bathroom.

It was thrown carelessly in the tub and the shower curtain torn down to cover it. Only the legs showed, dangling ridiculously over the front rim of the tub.

He drew back the curtain and looked at the blood-soaked shirt, at the white, still face.

Charlie.

He shook his head, then turned away and washed his face and hands at the sink. It didn't matter. Nothing mattered. As a matter of fact, Charlie was one of the lucky ones now. A member of the legion who had put their heads into ovens, or cut their wrists or taken pills or done away with themselves in the accepted fashions of suicide.

As he looked at his tired face in the mirror he thought of cutting his wrists. But he knew he couldn't. Because it took more than just despair to incite self-destruction.

He took a drink of water. Lucky, he thought, there's still water running. He didn't suppose there was a soul left to run the water system. Or the electric system or the gas system or the telephone system or any system for that matter.

What fool would work on the last day of the world?

Spencer was in the kitchen when Richard went in.

He was sitting in his shorts at the table looking at his hands. On the stove some eggs were frying. The gas must still be working then too, Richard thought.

'Hello,' he said to Spencer.

Spencer grunted without looking up. He stared at his hands. Richard let it go. He turned the gas down a little. He took bread out of the cupboard and put it in the electric toaster. But the toaster didn't work. He shrugged and forgot about it.

'What time is it?' Spencer was looking at him with the question.

Richard looked at his watch. 'It stopped,' he said.

They looked at each other.

'Oh,' Spencer said. Then he asked, 'What day is it?'

Richard thought. 'Sunday, I think,' he said.

'I wonder if people are at church,' Spencer said.

'Who cares?'

Richard opened the refrigerator.

'There aren't any more eggs,' Spencer said.

Richard shut the door. 'No more eggs,' he said dully, 'No more chickens. No more anything.'

He leaned against the wall with a shuddering breath and looked out the window at the red sky.

Mary, he thought. Mary, who I should have married. Who I let go. He wondered where she was. He wondered if she were thinking about him at all.

Norman came trudging in, groggy with sleep and hangover. His mouth hung open. He looked dazed.

'Morning,' he slurred.

'Good morning, merry sunshine,' Richard said, without mirth.

Norman looked at him blankly. Then he went over to the sink and washed out his mouth. He spit the water down the drain.

'Charlie's dead,' he said.

'I know,' Richard said.

'Oh. When did it happen?'

'Last night,' Richard told him. 'You were unconscious. You remember how he kept saying he was going to shoot us all? Put us out of our misery?'

'Yeah,' Norman said. 'He put the muzzle against my head. He said "feel how cool it is".'

'Well, he got in a fight with Mort,' Richard said. 'The gun went off.' He shrugged. 'That was it.'

They looked at each other without expression.

Then Norman turned his head and looked out the window. 'It's still up there,' he muttered.

They looked up at the great flaming ball in the sky that crowded out the sun, the moon, the stars.

Norman turned away, his throat moving. His lips trembled and he clamped them together. 'Jesus,' he said. 'It's *today*.'

He looked up at the sky again. 'Today,' he repeated. '*Everything*.'

'Everything,' said Richard.

Spencer got up and turned off the gas. He looked down at

the eggs for a moment. Then he said, 'What the hell did I fry these for?'

He dumped them into the sink and they slid greasily over the white surface. The yolks burst and spurted smoking, yellow fluid over the enamel.

Spencer bit his lips. His face grew hard. 'I'm taking her again,' he said suddenly.

He pushed past Richard and dropped his shorts off as he turned the corner into the hallway.

'There goes Spencer,' Richard said.

Norman sat down at the table. Richard stayed at the wall.

In the living room they heard Nancy suddenly call out at the top of her strident voice: 'Hey, wake up, everybody! Watch me do it! Watch me, everybody, *watch me!*'

Norman looked at the kitchen doorway for a moment. Then something gave inside of him and he slumped his head forward on his arms on the table. His thin shoulders shook.

'I did it too,' he said brokenly. 'I did it too. Oh God, what did I come here for?'

'Sex,' Richard said. 'Like all the rest of us. You thought you could end your life in carnal, drunken bliss.'

Norman's voice was muffled. 'I can't die like that,' he sobbed. 'I can't.'

'A couple of billion people are doing it,' Richard said. 'When the sun hits us, they'll still be at it. What a sight.'

The thought of a world's people indulging themselves in one last orgy of animalism made him shudder. He closed his eyes and pressed his forehead against the wall and tried to forget.

But the wall was warm.

Norman looked up from the table. 'Let's go home,' he said.

Richard looked at him. 'Home?' he said.

'To our parents. My mother and father. Your mother.'

Richard shook his head. 'I don't want to,' he said.

'But I can't go alone.'

'Why?'

'Because . . . I can't. You know how the streets are full of guys just *killing* everybody they meet.'

Richard shrugged.

'Why won't you?' Norman asked.

'I don't want to see her.'

'Your *mother?*'

'Yes.'

'You're crazy,' Norman said. 'Who else is there to . . . '

'No.'

He thought of his mother at home waiting for him. Waiting for him on the last day. And it made him ill to think of delaying, of maybe never seeing her again.

But he kept thinking: how can I go home and have her try to make me pray? Try to make me read from the Bible, spend these last hours in a muddle of religious absorption?

He said it again for himself. '*No.*'

Norman looked lost. His chest shook with a swallowed sob. 'I want to see my mother,' he said.

'Go ahead,' Richard said casually.

But his insides were twisting themselves into knots. To never see her again. Or his sister and her husband and her daughter.

Never to see any of them again.

He sighed. It was no use fighting it. In spite of everything, Norman was right. Who else was there in the world to turn to? In a wide world about to be burned, was there any other person who loved him above all others?

'Oh . . . all right,' he said. 'Come on. Anything to get out of this place.'

The apartment house hall smelled of vomit. They found the janitor dead drunk on the stairs. They found a dog in the foyer with its head kicked in.

They stopped as they came out the entrance of the building.

Instinctively, they looked up.

At the red sky, like molten slag. At the fiery wisps that fell like hot rain drops through the atmosphere. At the gigantic ball of flame that kept coming closer and closer, that blotted out the universe.

They lowered their watering eyes. It hurt to look. They started walking along the street. It was very warm.

'December,' Richard said. 'It's like the tropics.'

As they walked along in silence he thought of the tropics, of the poles, of all the world's countries he would never see. Of all the things he would never do.

Like hold Mary in his arms and tell her, as the world was ending, that he loved her very much and was not afraid.

'*Never*,' he said, feeling himself go rigid with frustration.

'What?' Norman said.

'Nothing. Nothing.'

As they walked Richard felt something heavy in his jacket pocket. It bumped against his side. He reached in and drew out the object.

'What's that?' Norman asked.

'Charlie's gun,' Richard said. 'I took it last night so nobody else would get hurt.'

His laughter was harsh. 'So nobody else would get hurt,' he said bitterly. 'Jesus, I ought to be on the stage.'

He was about to throw it away when he changed his mind. He slid it back into his pocket.

'I may need it,' he said.

Norman wasn't listening. 'Thank God nobody stole my car. Oh – !'

Somebody had thrown a rock through the windshield.

'What's the difference?' Richard said.

'I . . . none, I suppose.'

They got into the front seat and brushed the glass off the cushion. It was stuffy in the car. Richard pulled off his jacket and threw it out. He put the gun in his side pants pocket.

As Norman drove downtown they passed people in the street.

Some were running around wildly, as if they were searching for something. Others were fighting. Strewn all over the sidewalks were bodies of people who had leaped from windows and been struck down by speeding cars. Buildings were on fire, windows shattered from the explosions of unlit gas jets.

There were people looting stores.

'What's the *matter* with them?' Norman asked miserably. 'Is that how they want to spend their last day?'

'Maybe that's how they spent their whole life,' Richard answered.

He leaned against the door and gazed at the people they passed. Some of them waved at him. Some cursed and spat. A few threw things at the speeding car.

'People die the way they lived,' he said. 'Some good, some bad.'

'*Look out!*' Norman cried out as a car came careening down the street on the wrong side. Men and women hung out of the window shouting and singing and waving bottles.

Norman twisted the wheel violently and they missed the car by inches.

'Are they crazy?' he said.

Richard looked out through the back window. He saw the car skid, saw it get out of control and go crashing over on its side, the wheels spinning crazily.

He turned back without speaking. Norman kept looking ahead grimly, his hands on the wheel, white and tense.

Another intersection.

A car came speeding across their path. Norman jammed on the brakes with a gasp. They crashed against the dashboard, getting their breath knocked out.

Then, before Norman could get the car started again, a gang of teenage boys with knives and clubs came dashing into the intersection. They'd been chasing the other car. Now they changed direction and flung themselves at the car that held Norman and Richard.

Norman threw the car into first and gunned across the street.

A boy jumped on the back of the car. Another tried for the running board, missed and went spinning over the street. Another jumped on the running board and grabbed the door handle. He slashed at Richard with a knife.

'Gonna kill ya bastids!' yelled the boy. 'Sonsabitches!'

He slashed again and tore open the back of the seat as Richard jerked his shoulder to the side.

'Get out of here!' Norman screamed, trying to watch the boy and the street ahead at the same time.

The boy tried to open the door as the car wove wildly down Broadway. He slashed again but the car's motion made him miss.

'I'll *get* ya!' he screamed in a fury of brainless hate.

Richard tried to open the door and knock the boy off, but he couldn't. The boy's twisted white face thrust in through the window. He raised his knife.

Richard had the gun now. He shot the boy in the face.

The boy flung back from the car with a dying howl and landed like a sack of rocks. He bounced once, his left leg kicked and then he lay still.

Richard twisted around.

The boy on the back was still hanging on, his crazed face pressed against the back window. Richard saw his mouth moving as the boy cursed.

'Shake him off!' he said.

Norman headed for the sidewalk, then suddenly veered back into the street. The boy hung on. Norman did it again. The boy still clung to the back.

Then on the third time he lost his grip and went off. He tried to run along the street but his momentum was too great and he went leaping over the curb and crashing into a plate glass window, arms stuck up in front of him to ward off the blow.

They sat in the car, breathing heavily. They didn't talk for a long while. Richard flung the gun out the window and watched it clatter on the concrete and bounce off a hydrant. Norman started to say something about it, then stopped.

The car turned into Fifth Avenue and started downtown at sixty miles an hour. There weren't many cars.

They passed churches. People were packed inside them. They overflowed out onto the steps.

'Poor fools,' Richard muttered, his hands still shaking.

Norman took a deep breath. 'I wish I was a poor fool,' he said. 'A poor fool who could believe in something.'

'Maybe,' Richard said. Then he added, 'I'd rather spend the last day believing what I think is true.'

'The last day,' Norman said. 'I . . .' He shook his head. "I can't believe it,' he said. 'I read the papers. I see that . . . that *thing* up there. I know it's going to happen. But God! The *end?*'

He looked at Richard for a split second. 'Nothing afterward?'

Richard said, 'I don't know.'

At 14th Street Norman drove to the East side, then sped across the Manhattan Bridge. He didn't stop for anything, driving around bodies and wrecked cars. Once he drove over a body and Richard saw his face twitch as the wheel rolled over the dead man's leg.

'They're all lucky,' Richard said. 'Luckier than we are.'

They stopped in front of Norman's house in Brooklyn. Some kids were playing ball in the street. They didn't seem to realize what was happening. Their shouts sounded very loud in the silent street. Richard wondered if their parents knew where the children were. Or cared.

Norman was looking at him. 'Well . . . ?' he started to say.

Richard felt his stomach muscles tightening. He couldn't answer.

'Would you . . . like to come in for a minute?' Norman asked.

Richard shook his head. 'No,' he said. 'I better get home. I . . . should see her. My mother, I mean.'

'Oh.' Norman nodded. Then he straightened up. He forced a momentary calm over himself. 'For what it's worth, Dick,' he said, 'I consider you my best friend and . . .'

He faltered. He reached out and gripped Richard's hand. Then he pushed out of the car, leaving the keys in the ignition.

'So long,' he said hurriedly.

Richard watched his friend run around the car and move for the apartment house. When he had almost reached the door, Richard called out: 'Norm!'

Norman stopped and turned. The two of them looked at each other. All the years they had known each other seemed to flicker between them.

Then Richard managed to smile. He touched his forehead in a last salute.

'So long, Norm,' he said.

Norman didn't smile. He pushed through the door and was gone.

Richard looked at the door for a long time. He started the motor. Then he turned it off again thinking that Norman's parents might not be home.

After a while he started it again and began the trip home.

As he drove he kept thinking.

The closer he got to the end, the less he wanted to face it. He wanted to end it now. Before the hysterics started.

Sleeping pills, he decided. It was the best way. He had some at home. He hoped there were enough left. There might not be any left in the corner drug store. There'd been a rush for sleeping pills during those last few days. Entire families took them together.

He reached the house without event. Overhead the sky was an incandescent crimson. He felt the heat on his face like waves from a distant oven. He breathed in the heated air, his lungs cringing.

He unlocked the front door and walked in slowly.

I'll probably find her in the front room, he thought. Surrounded by her books, praying, exhorting invisible powers to succor her as the world prepared to fry itself.

She wasn't in the front room.

He searched the house. And, as he did, his heart began to

beat quickly, and when he knew she really wasn't there he felt a great hollow feeling in his stomach. He knew that his talk about not wanting to see her had been just talk. He loved her. And she was the only one left now.

He searched for a note in her room, in his, in the living-room.

'Mom,' he said. 'Mom, where are you?'

He found the note in the kitchen. He picked it up from the table:

> *Richard darling,*
> *I'm at your sister's house. Please come there. Don't make me spend the last day without you. Don't make me leave this world without seeing your dear face again. Please.*

The last day.

There it was in black and white. And, of all people, it had been his mother to write down the words. She who had always been so skeptical of his taste for material science. Now admitting the reality of science's last prediction.

Because she couldn't doubt any more. Because the sky was filled with flaming evidence and no one could doubt any more.

The whole world going. The staggering detail of evolutions and revolutions, of strifes and clashes, of endless continuities of centuries streaming back into the clouded past, of rocks and trees and animals and men. All to pass. In a flash, in a moment. The pride, the vanity of man's world incinerated by a freak of astronomical disorder.

What point was there to all of it, then? None, none at all. Because it was all ending.

He got sleeping pills from the medicine cabinet and left. He drove to his sister's house thinking about his mother as he passed through the streets littered with everything from empty bottles to dead people.

If only he didn't dread the thought of arguing with his mother on this last day. Of disputing with her about her God and her conviction.

He made up his mind not to argue. He'd force himself to make their last day a peaceful one. He would accept her simple devotion and not hack at her faith any more.

The front door was locked at Grace's house. He rang the bell and, after a moment, heard hurried steps inside.

He heard Ray shout inside, 'Don't open it, Mom! It may be

that gang again!'

'It's Richard, I know it is!' his mother called back.

Then the door was open and she was embracing him and crying happily.

He didn't speak at first. Finally he said softly, 'Hello, Mom.'

His niece Doris played all afternoon in the front room while Grace and Ray sat motionless in the living-room looking at her.

If I were with Mary, Richard kept thinking. If only we were together today. Then he thought that they might have had children. And he would have had to sit like Grace and know that the few years his child had lived would be its only years.

The sky grew brighter as evening approached. It flowed with violent crimson currents. Doris stood quietly at the window and looked at it. She hadn't laughed all day or cried. And Richard thought to himself, she *knows*.

And thought too that at any moment his mother would ask them all to pray together. To sit and read the Bible and hope for divine charity.

But she didn't say anything. She smiled. She made supper. Richard stood with her in the kitchen as she made supper.

'I may not wait,' he told her. 'I . . . may take sleeping pills.'

'Are you afraid, son?' she asked.

'Everybody is afraid,' he said.

She shook her head. 'Not everybody,' she said.

Now, he thought, it's coming. That smug look, the opening line.

She gave him a dish with the vegetable and they all sat down to eat.

During supper none of them spoke except to ask for food. Doris never spoke once. Richard sat looking at her from across the table.

He thought about the night before. The crazy drinking, the fighting, the carnal abuses. He thought of Charlie dead in the bathtub. Of the apartment in Manhattan. Of Spencer driving himself into a frenzy of lust as the climax to his life. Of the boy lying dead in the New York gutter with a bullet in his brain.

They all seemed very far away. He could almost believe it had all never happened. Could almost believe that this was just another evening meal with his family.

Except for the cherry glow that filled the sky and flooded in through the windows like an aura from some fantastic fireplace.

Near the end of the meal Grace went and got a box. She sat down at the table with it and opened it. She took out white pills. Doris looked at her, her large eyes searching.

'This is dessert,' Grace told her. 'We're all going to have white candy for dessert.'

'Is it peppermint?' Doris asked quietly.

'Yes,' Grace said. 'It's peppermint.'

Richard felt his scalp crawling as Grace put pills in front of Doris. In front of Ray.

'We haven't enough for all of us,' she said to Richard.

'I have my own,' he said.

'Have you enough for Mom?' she asked.

'I won't need any,' her mother said.

In his tenseness Richard almost shouted at her. Shouted stop being damned noble! But he held himself. He stared in fascinated horror at Doris holding the pills in her small hand.

'This isn't peppermint,' she said. 'Momma, this isn't –'

'*Yes it is.*' Grace took a deep breath. 'Eat it, darling.'

Doris put one in her mouth. She made a face. Then she spit it into her palm. 'It *isn't* peppermint,' she said, upset.

Grace threw up her hand and dug her teeth in the white knuckles. Her eyes moved frantically to Ray.

'Eat it, Doris,' Ray said. 'Eat it, it's good.'

Doris started to cry. 'No, I don't like it.'

'*Eat it!*'

Ray turned away suddenly, his body shaking. Richard tried to think of some way to make her eat the pills, but he couldn't.

Then his mother spoke. 'We'll play a game, Doris,' she said. 'We'll see if you can swallow all the candy before I count ten. If you do, I'll give you a dollar.'

Doris sniffed. 'A dollar?' she said.

Richard's mother nodded. 'One,' she said.

Doris didn't move.

'Two,' said Richard's mother. 'A dollar . . .'

Doris brushed aside a tear. 'A . . . whole dollar?'

'Yes, darling. Three, four, hurry up.'

Doris reached for the pills.

'Five . . . six . . . seven . . .'

Grace had her eyes shut tightly Her cheeks were white.

'Nine . . . ten . . .'

Richard's mother smiled, but her lips trembled and there was a glistening in her eyes. 'There,' she said cheerfully. 'You've won the game.'

Grace suddenly put pills into her mouth and swallowed them in fast succession. She looked at Ray. He reached out one trembling hand and swallowed his pills. Richard put his hand in his pocket for his pills but took it out again. He didn't want his mother to watch him take them.

Doris got sleepy almost immediately. She yawned and couldn't keep her eyes open. Ray picked her up and she rested against his shoulder, her small arms around his neck. Grace got up and the three of them went back into the bedroom.

Richard sat there while his mother went back and said good-bye to them. He sat staring at the white tablecloth, at the remains of food.

When his mother came back she smiled at him. 'Help me with the dishes,' she said.

'The . . . ?' he started. Then he stopped. What difference did it make what they did?

He stood with her in the red-lit kitchen feeling a sense of sharp unreality as he dried the dishes they would never use again and put them in the closet that would be no more in a matter of hours.

He kept thinking about Ray and Grace in the bedroom. Finally he left the kitchen without a word and went back. He opened the door and looked in. He looked at the three of them for a long time. Then he shut the door again and walked slowly back to the kitchen. He stared at his mother.

'They're . . .'

'All right,' his mother said.

'Why didn't you say anything to them?' he asked her. 'How come you let them do it without saying anything?'

'Richard,' she said, 'everyone has to make his own way on this day. No one can tell others what to do. Doris was *their* child.'

'And I'm yours. . . .'

'You're not a child any longer,' she said.

He finished up the dishes, his fingers numb and shaking. 'Mom, about last night . . .' he started.

'I don't care about it.'

'But . . .'

'It doesn't matter,' she said. 'This part is ending.'

Now, he thought, almost with pain. *This* part. Now she

would talk about afterlife and heaven and reward for the just and eternal penitence for the sinning.

She said, 'Let's go out and sit on the porch.'

He didn't understand. He walked through the quiet house with her. He sat next to her on the porch steps and thought: I'll never see Grace again. Or Doris. Or Norman or Spencer or Mary.

He couldn't take it all in. It was too much. All he could do was sit there woodenly and look at the red sky and the huge sun about to swallow them. He couldn't even feel nervous any more. Fears were blunted by endless repetition.

'Mom,' he said after a while, 'why . . . why haven't you spoken about religion to me? I know you must want to.'

She looked at him and her face was very gentle in the red glow. 'I don't have to, darling,' she said. 'I know we'll be together when this is over. You don't have to believe it. I'll believe for both of us.'

And that was all. He looked at her, wordless before her confidence.

'If you want to take those pills now,' she said, 'it's all right. You can go to sleep in my lap.'

He felt himself tremble. 'You wouldn't mind?'

'I want you to do what you think is best.'

He didn't know what to do until he thought of her sitting there alone when the world ended.

'I'll stay with you,' he said.

She smiled. 'If you change your mind,' she said, 'you can tell me.'

They were quiet for a while. Then she said, 'It *is* pretty.'

'*Pretty*?' he asked.

'Yes,' she said. 'God closes a bright curtain on our play.'

He didn't know. But he put his arm around her shoulders and she leaned against him. And he did know *one* thing.

They sat there in the evening of the last day. And, though there was no actual point to it, they loved each other.

Hands Off

BY ROBERT SHECKLEY

from *Galaxy Science Fiction*, April 1954

One of *Galaxy's* mainstays during its early life was the astonishingly prolific Robert Sheckley who brought considerable verve and sparkle to sf. Many critics claim that the genre was quite humourless, but writers like Eric Frank Russell, Harry Harrison and Robert Sheckley can prove that statement ridiculously false.

Robert Sheckley was born in Brooklyn on Monday 16 July 1928 and grew up in New Jersey. He majored in English at New York University, and had a thorough grounding in all aspects of English literature. He has admitted that his favourite science fiction writer was Henry Kuttner, so it is doubly appropriate that both writers appear within this volume.

To support himself Sheckley began by writing anything and everything, placing two short stories with the college magazine. Then he sold a short fantasy 'Final Examination' to *Imagination* (May 1952) and followed this almost instantaneously with a fantasy sale *outside* the field: 'Fear in the Night' to *Today's Woman*. A simple story, it tells how a husband plays on his wife's fear of snakes by tormenting her while she is asleep. Imagine my surprise long afterwards to read a story, 'The Web' by Dick Harrington, in the September 1969 issue of *London Mystery Magazine* which is an exact copy of that story apart from the substitution of spiders! Sheckley's influence is far and wide.

By sf's boom year, 1953, Sheckley was appearing almost everywhere, and he soon gave up outside jobs to write full-time. Nevertheless, Sheckley's wanderlust has caused him to travel incessantly, and editors frequently lose track of him. Throughout the 1950s Sheckley maintained steady sales of solid, well-plotted sf, branching out later into the suspense and thriller field as well. He was one of the first writers to sell sf regularly to *Playboy*, which helped build his career.

Now Sheckley is one of the most respected names in sf, although his appearances are rare today. What better then than to revive one of his early classics as emphasis of Sheckley's contribution to science fiction?

The ship's mass detector flared pink, then red. Agee had been dozing at the controls, waiting for Victor to finish making dinner. Now he looked up quickly. 'Planet coming,' he called, over the hiss of escaping air.

Captain Barnett nodded. He finished shaping a hot patch, and slapped it on *Endeavour's* worn hull. The whistle of escaping air dropped to a low moan, but was not entirely stopped. It never was.

When Barnett came over, the planet was just visible beyond the rim of a little red sun. It glowed green against the black night of space and gave both men an identical thought.

Barnett put the thought into words. 'Wonder if there's anything on it worth taking,' he said, frowning.

Agee lifted a white eyebrow hopefully. They watched as the dials began to register.

They would never have spotted the planet if they had taken *Endeavor* along the South Galactic Trades. But the Confederacy police were becoming increasingly numerous along that route and Barnett preferred to give them a wide berth.

The *Endeavor* was listed as a trader – but the only cargo she carried consisted of several bottles of an extremely powerful acid used in opening safes, and three medium-sized atomic bombs. The authorities looked with disfavor upon such goods and they were always trying to haul in the crew on some old charge – a murder on Luna, larceny on Omega, breaking and entering on Samia II. Old, almost forgotten crimes that the police drearily insisted on raking up.

To make matters worse, *Endeavour* was outgunned by the newer police cruisers. So they had taken an outside route to New Athens, where a big uranium strike had opened.

'Don't look like much,' Agee commented, inspecting the dials critically.

'Might as well pass it by,' Barnett said.

The readings were uninteresting. They showed a planet smaller than Earth, uncharted, and with no commercial value other than oxygen atmosphere.

As they swung past, their heavy metals detector came to life.

'There's stuff down there' Agee said, quickly interpreting the multiple readings. 'Pure. *Very* pure – and on the surface!'

He looked at Barnett, who nodded. The ship swung toward the planet.

Victor came from the rear, wearing a tiny wool cap crammed on his big shaven head. He stared over Barnett's shoulder as Agee brought the ship down in a tight spiral. Within half a mile of the surface, they saw their deposit of heavy metal.

It was a spaceship, resting on its tail in a natural clearing.

'Now *this* is interesting,' Barnett said. He motioned Agee to make a closer approach.

Agee brought the ship down with deft skill. He was well past the compulsory retirement limit for master pilots, but it didn't affect his coordination. Barnett, who had found him stranded and penniless, had signed him on. The captain was always glad to help another human, if it was convenient and likely to be profitable. The two men shared the same attitude toward private property, but sometimes disagreed on ways of acquiring it. Agee preferred a sure thing. Barnett, on the other hand, had more courage than was good for a member of a relatively frail species like *Homo sapiens*.

Near the surface of the planet, they saw that the strange ship was larger than *Endeavour* and bright, shining new. The hull shape was unfamiliar, as were the markings.

'Ever see anything like it?' Barnett asked.

Agee searched his capacious memory. 'Looks a bit like a Cephean job, only they don't build 'em so squat. We're pretty far out, you know. That ship might not even be from the Confederacy.'

Victor stared at the ship, his big lips parted in wonder. He sighed noisily. 'We could sure use a ship like that, huh, Captain?'

Barnett's sudden smile was like a crack appearing in granite. 'Victor,' he said, 'in your simplicity, you have gone to the heart of the matter. We *could* use a ship like that. Let's go down and talk with its skipper.'

Before strapping in, Victor made sure the freeze-blasters were on full charge.

On the ground, they sent up an orange and green parley flare, but there was no answer from the alien ship. The planet's atmosphere tested breathable, with a temperature of 72 degrees Fahrenheit. After waiting a few minutes, they marched out, freeze-blasters ready under their jumpers.

All three men wore studiously pleasant smiles as they walked the fifty yards between ships.

Up close, the ship was magnificent. Its glistening silver-gray hide had hardly been touched by meteor strikes. The airlock was open and a low hum told them that the generators were recharging.

'Anyone home?' Victor shouted into the airlock. His voice echoed hollowly through the ship. There was no answer – only the soft hum of the generators and the rustle of grass on the plain.

'Where do you suppose they went?' Agee asked.

'For a breath of air, probably,' Barnett said. 'I don't suppose they'd expect any visitors.'

Victor placidly sat down on the ground. Barnett and Agee prowled around the base of the ship, admiring its great drive ports.

'Think you can handle it?' Barnett asked.

'I don't see why not,' Agee said. 'For one thing, it's conventional drive. The servos don't matter – oxygen-breathers use similar drive-control systems. It's just a matter of time until I figure it out.'

'Someone coming,' Victor called.

They hurried back to the airlock. Three hundred yards from the ship was a ragged forest. A figure had just emerged from among the trees, and was walking toward them.

Agee and Victor drew their blasters simultaneously.

Barnett's binoculars resolved the tiny figure into a rectangular shape, about two feet high by a foot wide. The alien was less than two inches thick and had no head.

Barnett frowned. He had never seen a rectangle floating above tall grass.

Adjusting the binoculars, he saw that the alien was roughly humanoid. That is, it had four limbs. Two, almost hidden by the grass, were being used for walking, and the other two jutted stiffly into the air. In its middle, Barnett could just make out two tiny eyes and a mouth. The creature was not wearing any sort of suit or helmet.

'Queer-looking,' Agee muttered, adjusting the aperture of his blaster. 'Suppose he's all there is?'

'Hope so,' Barnett said, drawing his own blaster.

'Range about two hundred yards.' Agee leveled his weapon, then looked up. 'Did you want to talk to him first, Captain?'

'What's there to say?' Barnett asked, smiling lazily. 'Let him get a little closer, though. We don't want to miss.'

Agee nodded and kept the alien steadily in his sights.

Kalen had stopped at this deserted little world hoping to blast out a few tons of erol, a mineral highly prized by the Mabogian people. He had had no luck. The unused thetnite bomb was still lodged in his body pouch, next to a stray kerla nut. He would have to return to Mabog with ballast instead of cargo.

Well, he thought, emerging from the forest, better luck next –

He was shocked to see a thin, strangely tapered spaceship near his own. He had never expected to find anyone else on this deadly little world.

And the inhabitants were waiting in front of his own airlock! Kalen saw at once they were roughly Mabogian in form. There was a race much like them in the Mabogian Union, but their spaceships were completely different. Intuition suggested that these aliens might well be representative of that great civilization rumored to be on the periphery of the Galaxy.

He advanced eagerly to meet them.

Strange, the aliens were not moving. Why didn't they come forward to meet him? He knew that they saw him, because all three were pointing at him.

He walked faster, realizing that he knew nothing of their customs. He only hoped that they didn't run to long-drawn-out ceremonies. Even an hour on this inimical world had tired him. He was hungry, badly in need of a shower. . . .

Something intensely cold jarred him backward. He looked around apprehensively. Was this some unknown property of the planet?

He moved forward again. Another bolt lanced into him, frosting the outer layer of his hide.

This was serious. Mabogians were among the toughest life-forms in the Galaxy, but they had their limits. Kalen looked around for the source of the trouble.

The aliens were *shooting* at him!

For a moment, his thinking centers refused to accept the evidence of his senses. Kalen knew what murder was. He had observed this perversity with stunned horror among certain debased animal forms. And, of course, there were the abnormal psychology books, which documented every case of premeditated murder that had occurred in the history of Mabog.

But to have such a thing actually happen to *him*! Kalen was unable to believe it.

Another bolt lanced into him. Kalen stood still, trying to convince himself that this was really happening. He couldn't understand how creatures with sufficient sense of cooperation to run a spaceship could be capable of *murder*.

Besides, they didn't even know him!

Almost too late, Kalen whirled and ran toward the forest. All three aliens were firing now and the grass around him was crackling white with frost. His skin surface was completely frosted over. Cold was something the Mabogian constitution was not designed for and the chill was creeping into his internal organs.

But he could still hardly believe it.

Kalen reached the forest and a double blast caught him as he slid behind a tree. He could feel his internal system laboring desperately to restore warmth to his body and, with profound regret, he allowed the darkness to take him.

'Stupid kind of alien,' Agee observed, holstering his blaster.

'Stupid and strong,' Barnett said. 'But no oxygen-breather can take much of that.' He grinned proudly and slapped the silver-gray side of the ship. 'We'll christen her *Endeavour II*.'

'Three cheers for the captain!' Victor cried enthusiastically.

'Save your breath,' Barnett said. 'You'll need it.' He glanced overhead. 'We've got about four hours of light left. Victor, transfer the food, oxygen and tools from *Endeavour I* and disarm her piles. We'll come back and salvage the old girl some day. But I want to blast off by sundown.'

Victor hurried off. Barnett and Agee entered the ship.

The rear half of *Endeavour II* was filled with generators, engines, converters, servos, fuel and air tanks. Past that was an enormous cargo hold, occupying almost another half of the ship. It was filled with nuts of all shapes and colors, ranging in size from two inches in diameter to some twice the size of a man's head. That left only two compartments in the bow of the ship.

The first should have been a crew room, since it was the only available living space. But it was completely bare. There were no deceleration cots, no tables or chairs – nothing but polished metal floor. In the walls and ceiling were several small openings, but their purpose was not readily apparent.

Connected to this room was the pilot's compartment. It was very small, barely large enough for one man, and the panel under the observation blister was packed solidly with instruments.

'It's all yours,' Barnett said. 'Let's see what you can do.'

Agee nodded, looked for a chair, then squatted in front of the panel. He began to study the layout.

In several hours, Victor had transferred all their stores to *Endeavour II*. Agee still had not touched anything. He was trying to figure out what controlled what, from the size, color, shape and location of the instruments. It wasn't easy, even accepting similar nervous systems and patterns of thought. Did the auxiliary step-up system run from left to right? If not, he would have to unlearn his previous flight coordination. Did red signify danger to the designers of this ship? If it did, that big switch could be for dumping fuel. But red could also mean hot fuel, in which case the switch might control coarse energy flow.

For all he knew, its purpose was to overload the piles in case of enemy attack.

Agee kept all this in mind as he studied the controls. He wasn't too worried. For one thing, spaceships were tough beasts, practically indestructible from the inside. For another, he believed he had caught onto the pattern.

Barnett stuck his head in the doorway, with Victor close behind him. 'You ready?'

Agee looked over the panel. 'Guess so.' He touched a dial lightly. 'This *should* control the airlocks.'

He turned it. Victor and Barnett waited, perspiring, in the chilly room.

They heard the smooth flow of lubricated metal. The airlocks had closed.

Agee grinned and blew on his fingertips for luck. 'Here's the air-control system.' He closed a switch.

Out of the ceiling, a yellow smoke began to trickle.

'Impurities in the system,' Agee muttered, adjusting a dial. Victor began to cough.

'Turn it off,' Barnett said.

The smoke poured out in thick streams, filling the two rooms almost instantly.

'Turn it off!'

'I can't see it!' Agee thrust at the switch, missed and struck a button under it. Immediately the generators began to whine angrily. Blue sparks danced along the panel and jumped to the wall.

Agee staggered back from the panel and collapsed. Victor was already at the door to the cargo hold, trying to hammer it down with his fists. Barnett covered his mouth with one hand and rushed to the panel. He fumbled blindly for the switch, feeling the ship revolve giddily around him.

Victor fell to the deck, still beating feebly at the door.

Barnett jabbed blindly at the panel.

Instantly the generators stopped. Then Barnett felt a cold breeze on his face. He wiped his streaming eyes and looked up.

A lucky stab had closed the ceiling vents, cutting off the yellow gas. He had accidentally opened the locks, and the gas in the ship was being replaced by the cold night air of the planet. Soon the atmosphere was breathable.

Victor climbed shakily to his feet, but Agee didn't move. Barnett gave the old pilot artificial respiration, cursing softly as he did. Agee's eyelids finally fluttered and his chest began to rise and fall. A few minutes later, he sat up and shook his head.

'What *was* that stuff?' Victor asked.

'I'm afraid,' Barnett said, 'that our alien friend considered it a breathable atmosphere.'

Agee shook his head. 'Can't be, Captain. He was here on an oxygen world, walking around with no helmet –'

'Air requirements vary tremendously,' Barnett pointed out. 'Let's face it – our friend's physical makeup was quite different from ours.'

'That's not so good,' Agee said.

The three men looked at each other. In the silence that followed, they heard a faint, ominous sound.

'What was that?' Victor yelped, yanking out his blaster.

'Shut up!' Barnett shouted.

They listened. Barnett could feel the hairs lift on the back of his neck as he tried to identify the sound.

It came from a distance. It sounded like metal striking a hard non-metallic object.

The three men looked out the port. In the last glow of sunset, they could see the main port of *Endeavor I* was open. The sound was coming from the ship.

'It's impossible,' Agee said. 'The freeze-blasters —'

'Didn't kill him,' Barnett finished.

'That's bad,' Agee grunted. 'That's very bad.'

Victor was still holding his blaster. 'Captain, suppose I wander over that way —'

Barnett shook his head. 'He wouldn't let you within ten feet of the lock. No, let me think. Was there anything on board he could use? The piles?'

'I've got the links, Captain,' Victor said.

'Good. Then there's nothing that —'

'The acid,' Agee interrupted. 'It's powerful stuff. But I don't suppose he can do much with that stuff.'

'Not a thing,' Barnett said. 'We're in this ship and we're staying here. But get it off the ground now.'

Agee looked at the instrument panel. Half an hour ago, he had almost understood it. Now it was a cunningly rigged death trap – a booby trap, with invisible wires leading to destruction.

The trap was unintentional. But a spaceship was necessarily a machine for living as well as traveling. The controls would try to reproduce the alien's living conditions, supply his needs.

That might be fatal to them.

'I wish I knew what kind of planet he came from,' Agee said unhappily. If they knew the alien's environment, they could anticipate what his ship would do.

All they knew was that he breathed a poisonous yellow gas.

'We're doing all right,' Barnett said, without much confidence. 'Just dope out the drive mechanism and we'll leave everything else alone.'

Agee turned back to the controls.

Barnett wished he knew what the alien was up to. He stared at the bulk of his old ship in the twilight and listened to the incomprehensible sound of metal striking non-metal.

Kalen was surprised to find that he was still alive. But there was a saying among his people – 'Either a Mabogian is killed fast or he isn't killed at all.' It was not at all – so far.

Groggily, he sat up and leaned against a tree. The single red sun of the planet was low on the horizon and breezes of poisonous oxygen swirled around him. He tested at once and found that his lungs were still securely sealed. His life-giving yellow air, although vitiated from long use, was still sustaining him.

But he couldn't seem to get oriented. A few hundred yards away, his ship was resting peacefully. The fading red light glistened from its hull and, for a moment, Kalen was convinced that there were no aliens. He had imagined the whole thing and now he would return to his ship . . .

He saw one of the aliens loaded down with goods, enter his vessel. In a little while, the airlocks closed.

It was true, all of it. He wrenched his mind back to grim realities.

He needed food and air badly. His outer skin was dry and cracked, and in need of nutritional cleaning. But food, air and cleansers were on his lost ship. All he had was a single red kerla nut and the thetnite bomb in his body pouch.

If he could open and eat the nut, he could regain a little strength. But how could he open it?

It was shocking, how complete his dependence on machinery had been! Now he would have to find some way of doing the most simple, ordinary, everyday things – the sort of things his ship had done automatically, without the operator even thinking about them.

Kalen noticed that the aliens had apparently abandoned their own ship. Why? It didn't matter. Out on the plain, he would die before morning. His only chance for survival lay inside their ship.

He slid slowly through the grass, stopping only when a wave of dizziness swept over him. He tried to keep watch on his ship. If the aliens came after him now, all would be lost. But nothing happened. After an eternity of crawling, he reached the ship and slipped inside.

It was twilight. In the dimness, he could see that the vessel was old. The walls, too thin in the first place, had been patched and repatched. Everything spoke of long, hard use.

He could understand why they wanted his ship.

Another wave of dizziness swept over him. It was his body's way of demanding immediate attention.

Food seemed to be the first problem. He slipped the kerla nut out of his pouch. It was round, almost four inches in diameter, and its hide was two inches thick. Nuts of this sort were the main ingredient of a Mabogian spaceman's diet. They were energy-packed and would last almost forever, sealed.

He propped the nut against a wall, found a steel bar and smashed down on it. The bar, striking the nut, emitted a hollow, drum-like sound. The nut was undamaged.

Kalen wondered if the sound could be heard by the aliens. He would have to chance it. Setting himself firmly, he flailed away. In fifteen minutes, he was exhausted and the bar was bent almost in half.

The nut was undamaged.

He was unable to open the nut without a Cracker, a standard device on every Mabogian ship. No one ever thought of opening a nut in any other way.

It was terrifying evidence of his helplessness.

He lifted the bar for another whack and found that his limbs were stiffening. He dropped the bar and took stock.

His chilled outer hide was hampering his motions. The skin was hardening slowly into impervious horn. Once the hardening was completed, he would be immobilized. Frozen in position, he would sit or stand until he died of suffocation.

Kalen fought back a wave of despair and tried to think. He had to treat his skin without delay. That was more important than food. On board his own ship, he would wash and bathe it, soften it and eventually cure it. But it was doubtful whether the aliens carried the proper cleansers.

The only other course was to rip off his outer hide. The second layer would be tender for a few days, but at least he would be mobile.

He searched on stiffening limbs for a Changer. Then he realised that the aliens wouldn't have even this piece of basic apparatus. He was still on his own.

He took the steel bar, bent it into a hook and inserted the point under a fold of skin. He yanked upward with all his strength.

His skin refused to yield.

Next, he wedged himself between a generator and the wall and inserted the hook in a different way. But his arms weren't long enough to gain leverage, and the tough hide held stubbornly.

He tried a dozen different positions, unsuccessfully. Without mechanical assistance, he couldn't hold himself rigidly enough.

Wearily, he dropped the bar. He could do nothing, nothing

at all. Then he remembered the thetnite bomb in his pouch.

A primitive part of his mind which he had not previously known existed said that there was an easy way out of all this. He could slip the bomb under the hull of his ship, while the aliens weren't looking. The light charge would do no more than throw the ship twenty or thirty feet into the air, but would not really damage it.

The aliens, however, would undoubtedly be killed.

Kalen was horrified. How could he think such a thing? The Mabogian ethic, ingrained in the fiber of his being, forbade the taking of intelligent life for any reason whatsoever. *Any* reason.

'But wouldn't this be justified?' that primitive portion of his mind whispered. 'These aliens are diseased. You would be doing the Universe a favor by getting rid of them and only incidentally helping yourself. Don't think of it as murder. Consider it extermination.'

He took the bomb out of his pouch and looked at it, then hastily put it away. 'No!' he told himself, with less conviction.

He refused to think any more. On tired, almost rigid limbs, he began to search the alien ship, looking for something that would save his life.

Agee was crouched in the pilot's compartment, wearily marking switches with an indelible pencil. His lungs ached and he had been working all night. Now there was a bleak gray dawn outside and a chill wind was whipping around *Endeavour II*. The spaceship was lighted but cold, for Agee didn't want to touch the temperature controls.

Victor came into the crew room, staggering under the weight of a heavy packing case.

'Barnett?' Agee called out.

'He's coming,' Victor said.

The captain wanted all their equipment up front, where they could get at it quickly. But the crew room was small and he had used most of the available space.

Looking around for a spot to put the case, Victor noticed a door in one wall. He pressed its stud and the door slid smartly into the ceiling, revealing a room the size of a closet. Victor decided it would make an ideal storage space.

Ignoring the crushed red shells on the floor, he slid the case inside.

Immediately, the ceiling of the little room began to descend.

Victor let a yell that could be heard throughout the ship. He leaped up – and slammed his head against the ceiling. He fell on his face, stunned.

Agee rushed out of the pilot's compartment and Barnett sprinted into the room. Barnett grabbed Victor's legs and tried to drag him out, but Victor was heavy and the captain was unable to get a purchase on the smooth metal floor.

With rare presence of mind, Agee up-ended the packing case. The ceiling was momentarily stopped by it.

Together, Barnett and Agee tugged at Victor's legs. They managed to drag him out just in time. The heavy case splintered and, in another moment, was crushed like a piece of balsa wood.

The ceiling of the little room, descending on a greased shaft, compressed the packing case to a six-inch thickness. Then its gears clicked and it slid back into place without a sound.

Victor sat up and rubbed his head. 'Captain,' he said plaintively, 'Can't we get our own ship back?'

Agee was doubtful of the venture, too. He looked at the deadly little room, which again resembled a closet with crushed red shells on the floor.

'Sure seems like a jinx ship,' he said worriedly. 'Maybe Victor's right.'

'You want to give her up?' Barnett asked.

Agee squirmed uncomfortably and nodded. 'Trouble is,' he said, not looking at Barnett, 'we don't know what she'll do next. It's just too risky, Captain.'

'Do you realise what you'd be giving up?' Barnett challenged. 'Her hull alone is worth a fortune. Have you looked at her engines? There's nothing this side of Earth that could stop her. She could drill her way through a planet and come out the other side with all her paint on. And you want to give her up!'

'She won't be worth much if she kills us,' Agee objected.

Victor nodded emphatically. Barnett stared at them.

'Now listen to me carefully,' Barnett said. 'We are *not* going to give up this ship. She is *not* jinxed. She's alien and filled with alien apparatus. All we have to do is keep our hands off things until we reach drydock. Understand?'

Agee wanted to say something about closets that turned into hydraulic presses. It didn't seem to him a promising sign for the future. But, looking at Barnett's face, he decided against it.

'Have you marked all the operating controls?' Barnett asked.

'Just a few more to go,' Agee said.

'Right. Finish up and those are the only ones we'll touch. If we leave the rest of the ship alone, she'll leave us alone. There's no danger if we just keep *hands off*.'

Barnett wiped perspiration from his face, leaned against a wall and unbuttoned his coat.

Immediately, two metal bands slid out of openings on either side of him and circled his waist and stomach.

Barnett stared at them for a moment, then threw himself forward with all his strength. The bands didn't give. There was a peculiar clicking sound in the walls and a slender wire filament slid out. It touched Barnett's coat appraisingly, then retreated into the wall.

Agee and Victor stared helplessly.

'Turn it off,' Barnett said tensely.

Agee rushed into the control room. Victor continued staring. Out of the wall slid a metal limb, tipped with a glittering three-inch blade.

'*Stop it*!' Barnett screamed.

Victor unfroze. He ran up and tried to wrench the metal limb out of the wall. It twisted once and sent him reeling across the room.

With the precision of a surgeon, the knife slit Barnett's coat down the middle, not touching the shirt underneath. Then the limb slid out of sight.

Agee was punching controls now and the generators whined, the locks opened and closed, stabilizers twitched, lights flickered. The mechanism that held Barnett was unaffected.

The slender filament returned. It touched Barnett's shirt and paused an instant. The internal mechanism chittered alarmingly. The filament touched Barnett's shirt again, as if unsure of its function in this case.

Agee shouted from the control room, 'I can't turn it off! It must be fully automatic!'

The filament slid into the wall. It disappeared and the knife-tipped limb slid out.

By this time, Victor had located a heavy wrench. He rushed over, swung it above his head and smashed it against the limb, narrowly missing Barnett's head.

The limb was not even dented. Serenely, it cut Barnett's shirt from his back, leaving him naked to the waist.

Barnett was not hurt, but his eyes rolled wildly as the filament came out. Victor put his fist in his mouth and backed away. Agee shut his eyes.

The filament touched Barnett's warm living flesh, clucked approvingly and slid back into the wall. The bands opened. Barnett tumbled to his knees.

For a while, no one spoke. There was nothing to say. Barnett stared moodily into space. Victor started to crack his knuckles over and over again, until Agee nudged him.

The old pilot was trying to figure out why the mechanism had slit Barnett's clothing and then stopped when it reached living flesh. Was this the way the alien undressed himself? It didn't make sense. But then, the press-closet didn't make sense, either.

In a way, he was glad it had happened. It must have taught Barnett something. Now they would leave this jinxed monstrosity and figure out a way of regaining their own ship.

'Get me a shirt,' Barnett said. Victor hurriedly found one for him. Barnett slipped it on, staying clear of the walls. 'How soon can you get this ship moving?' he asked Agee, a bit unsteadily.

'*What*?'

'You heard me.'

'Haven't you had enough?' Agee gasped.

'No. How soon can we blast out?'

'About another hour,' Agee grumbled. What else could he say? The captain was just too much. Wearily, Agee returned to the control room.

Barnett put a sweater over the shirt and a coat over that. It was chilly in the room and he had begun to shiver violently.

Kalen lay motionless on the deck of the alien ship. Foolishly, he had wasted most of his remaining strength in trying to rip off his stiff outer hide. But the hide grew progressively tougher as he grew weaker. Now it seemed hardly worthwhile to move. Better to rest and feel his internal fires burn lower . . .

Soon he was dreaming of the ridged hills of Mabog and the great port of Canthanope, where the interstellar traders swung down with their strange cargoes. He was there in twilight, looking over the flat roofs at the two great setting suns. But why were they setting together in the south, the blue sun and the yellow? How could they set together in the south? A physical impossibility . . . Perhaps his father could explain it, for it was rapidly growing dark.

He shook himself out of the fantasy and stared at the grim light of morning. This was not the way for a Mabogian space-man to die. He would try again.

After half an hour of slow, painful searching, he found a sealed metal box in the rear of the ship. The aliens had evidently overlooked it. He wrenched off the top. Inside were several bottles, carefully fastened and padded against shock. Kalen lifted one and examined it.

It was marked with a large white symbol. There was no reason why he should know the symbol, but it seemed faintly familiar. He searched his memory, trying to recall where he had seen it.

Then, hazily, he remembered. It was a representation of a humanoid skull. There was one humanoid race in the Mabogian Union and he had seen replicas of their skulls in a museum.

But why would anyone put such a thing on a bottle?

To Kalen, a skull conveyed an emotion of reverence. This must be what the manufacturers had intended. He opened the bottle and sniffed.

The odor was interesting. It reminded him of —

Skin-cleansing solution!

Without further delay, he poured the entire bottle over him-self. Hardly daring to hope, he waited. If he could put his skin back into working order . . .

Yes, the liquid in the skull-marked bottle *was* a mild cleanser! It was pleasantly scented, too.

He poured another bottle over his armored hide and felt the nutritious fluid seep in. His body, starved for nourishment, called eagerly for more. He drained another bottle.

For a long time, Kalen just lay back and let the life-giving fluid soak in. His skin loosened and became pliable. He could feel a new surge of energy within him, a new will to live.

He *would* live!

After the bath, Kalen examined the spaceship's controls, hoping to pilot the old crate back to Mabog. There were im-mediate difficulties. For some reason, the piloting controls weren't sealed into a separate room. He wondered why not? Those strange creatures couldn't have turned their whole ship into a deceleration chamber. They couldn't! There wasn't enough tank space to hold the fluid.

It was perplexing, but everything about the aliens was perplexing. He could overcome that difficulty. But when Kalen inspected the engines, he saw that a vital link had been removed from the piles. They were useless.

That left only one alternative. He had to win back his own ship.

But how?

He paced the deck restlessly. The Mabogian ethic forbade killing intelligent life, and there were no ifs or buts about it. Under no circumstances – not even to save your own life – were you allowed to kill. It was a wise rule and had served Mabog well. By strict adherence to it, the Mabogians had avoided war for three thousand years and had trained their people to a high degree of civilization. Which would have been impossible had they allowed exceptions to creep in. Ifs and buts could erode the soundest of principles.

He could not be a backslider.

But was he going to die here passively?

Looking down, Kalen was surprised to see that a puddle of cleaning solution had eaten a hole in the deck. How flimsily these ships were made – even a mild cleaning solution could damage one! The aliens themselves must be very weak.

One thetnite bomb could do it.

He walked to the port. No one seemed to be on guard. He supposed they were too busy preparing for takeoff. It would be easy to slide through the grass, up to his ship . . .

And no one on Mabog would ever have to know about it.

Kalen found, to his surprise, that he had covered almost half the distance between ships without realizing it. Strange, how his body could do things without his mind being aware of it.

He took out the bomb and crawled another twenty feet.

Because after all – taking the long view – what difference would this killing make?

'Aren't you ready yet?' Barnett asked, at noon.

'I guess so,' Agee said. He looked over the marked panel. 'As ready as I'll ever be.'

Barnett nodded. 'Victor and I will strap down in the crew room. Take off under minimum acceleration.'

Barnett returned to the crew room. Agee fastened the straps he had rigged and rubbed his hands together nervously. As far as he knew, all the essential controls were marked. Everything should go all right. He hoped.

For there were that closet and the knife. It was anyone's guess what this insane ship would do next.

'Ready out here,' Barnett called from the crew room.

'All right. About ten seconds.' He closed and sealed the airlocks. His door closed automatically, cutting him off from the crew room. Feeling a slight touch of claustrophobia, Agee activated the piles. Everything was fine so far.

There was a thin slick of oil on the deck. Agee decided it was from a loose joint and ignored it. The control surfaces worked beautifully. He punched a course into the ship's tape and activated the flight controls.

Then he felt something lapping against his foot. Looking down, he was amazed to see that thick, evil-smelling oil was almost three inches deep on the deck. It was quite a leak. He couldn't understand how a ship as well built as this could have such a flaw. Unstrapping himself, he groped for the source.

He found it. There were four small vents in the deck and each of them was feeding a smooth, even flow of oil.

Agee punched the stud that opened his door and found that it remained sealed. Refusing to grow panicky, he examined the door with care.

It *should* open.

It didn't.

The oil was almost up to his knees.

He grinned foolishly. Stupid of him! The pilot room was sealed from the control board. He pressed the release and went back to the door.

It still refused to open.

Agee tugged at it with all his strength, but it wouldn't budge. He waded back to the control panel. There had been no oil when they found the ship. That meant there had to be a drain somewhere.

The oil was waist-deep before he found it. Quickly the oil disappeared. Once it was gone, the door opened easily.

'What's the matter?' Barnett asked.

Agee told him.

'So that's how he does it,' Barnett said quietly. 'Glad I found out.'

'Does what?' Agee asked, feeling that Barnett was taking the whole thing too lightly.

'How he stands the acceleration of takeoff. It bothered me. He hadn't anything on board that resembled a bed or cot. No chairs, nothing to strap into. So he floats in the oil bath, which turns on automatically when the ship is prepared for flight.'

'But why wouldn't the door open?' Agee asked.

'Isn't it obvious?' Barnett said, smiling patiently. 'He wouldn't want oil all over the ship. And he wouldn't want it to drain out accidentally.'

'We can't take off,' Agee insisted.

'Why not?'

'Because I can't breathe very well under oil. It turns on automatically with the power and there's no way of turning it off.'

'Use your head,' Barnett told him. 'Just tie down the drain switch. The oil will be carried away at fast as it comes in.'

'Yeah, I hadn't thought of that,' Agee admitted unhappily.

'Go ahead, then.'

'I want to change my clothes first.'

'No. Get this damned ship off the ground.'

'But, Captain –'

'Get her moving,' Barnett ordered. 'For all we know, that alien is planning something.'

Agee shrugged his shoulders, returned to the pilot room and strapped in.

'Ready?'

'Yes, get her moving.'

He tied down the drain circuit and the oil flowed safely in and out, not rising higher than the tops of his shoes. He activated all the controls without further incident.

'Here goes.' He set minimum acceleration and blew on his fingertips for luck.

Then he punched the blast-switch.

With profound regret, Kalen watched his ship depart. He was still holding the thetnite bomb in his hand.

He had reached his ship, had even stood under her for a few seconds. Then he had crept back to the alien vessel. He had been unable to set the bomb. Centuries of conditioning were too much to overcome in a few hours.

Conditioning – and something more.

Few individuals of any race murder for pleasure. There are

perfectly adequate reasons to kill, though, reasons which might satisfy any philosopher.

But, once accepted, there are more reasons, and more and more. And murder, once accepted, is hard to stop. It leads irresistibly to war and, from there, to annihilation.

Kalen felt that this murder somehow involved the destiny of his race. His abstinence had been almost a matter of race-survival.

But it didn't make him feel any better.

He watched his ship dwindle to a dot in the sky. The aliens were leaving at a ridiculously slow speed. He could think of no reason for this, unless they were doing it for his benefit.

Undoubtedly they were sadistic enough for that.

Kalen returned to the ship. His will to live was as strong as ever. He had no intention of giving up. He would hang onto life as long as he could, hoping for the one chance in a million that would bring another ship to this planet.

Looking around, he thought that he might concoct an air substitute out of the skull-marked cleanser. It would sustain him for a day or two. Then, if he could open the kerla nut . . .

He thought he heard a noise outside and rushed to look. The sky was empty. His ship had vanished, and he was alone.

He returned to the alien ship and set about the serious business of staying alive.

As Agee recovered consciousness, he found that he had managed to cut the acceleration in half, just before passing out. This was the only thing that had saved his life.

And the acceleration, hovering just above zero on the dial, was still unbearably heavy! Agee unsealed the door and crawled out.

Barnett and Victor had burst their straps on the takeoff. Victor was just returning to consciousness. Barnett picked himself out of a pile of smashed cases.

'Do you think you're flying in a circus?' he complained. 'I told you *minimum acceleration*.'

'I started *under* minimum acceleration,' Agee said. 'Go read the tape for yourself.'

Barnett marched to the control room. He came out quickly.

'That's bad. Our alien friend operates this ship at three times our acceleration.'

'That's the way it looks.'

'I hadn't thought of that,' Barnett said thoughtfully. 'He must come from a heavy planet – a place where you have to blast out at high speed, if you expect to get out at all.'

'What hit me?' Victor groaned, rubbing his head.

There was a clicking in the walls. The ship was fully awake now, and its servos turned on automatically.

'Getting warm, isn't it?' Victor asked.

'Yeah, and thick,' Agee said. 'Pressure buildup.' He went back to the control room. Barnett and Victor stood anxiously in the doorway, waiting.

'I can't turn it off,' Agee said, wiping perspiration from his streaming face. 'The temperature and pressure are automatic. They must go to 'normal' as soon as the ship is in flight.'

'You damn well better turn them off,' Barnett told him. 'We'll fry in here if you don't.'

'There's no way.'

'He must have some kind of heat regulation.'

'Sure   there!' Agee said, pointing. 'The control is already set at its lowest point.'

'What do you suppose his normal temperature is?' Barnett asked.

'I'd hate to find out,' Agee said. 'This ship is built of extremely high melting-point alloys. It's constructed to withstand ten times the pressure of an Earth ship. Put those together . . .'

'You must be able to turn it off somewhere!' Barnett said. He peeled off his jacket and sweater. The heat was mounting rapidly and the deck was becoming too hot to stand on.

'Turn it *off*!' Victor howled.

'Wait a minute,' Agee said. '*I* didn't build this ship, you know. How should I know –'

'*Off*!' Victor screamed, shaking Agee up and down like a rag doll. '*Off*!'

'Let go!' Agee half-drew his blaster. Then, in a burst of inspiration, he turned off the ship's engines.

The clicking in the walls stopped. The room began to cool.

'What happened?' Victor asked.

'The temperature and pressure fall when the power is off,' Agee said. 'We're safe – as long as we don't run the engines.'

'How long will it take us to coast to a port?' Barnett asked.

Agee figured it out. 'About three years,' he said. 'We're pretty far out.'

'Isn't there any way we can rip out those servos? Disconnect them?'

'They're built into the guts of the ship,' Agee said. 'We'd need a full machine shop and skilled help. Even then, it wouldn't be easy.'

Barnett was silent for a long time. Finally he said, 'All right.'

'All right what?'

'We're licked. We've got to go back to that planet and take our own ship.'

Agee heaved a sigh of relief and punched a new course on the ship's tape.

'You think the alien'll give it back?' Victor asked.

'Sure he will,' Barnett said, 'if he's not dead. He'll be pretty anxious to get his own ship back. And he has to leave our ship to get in his.'

'Sure. But once he gets back in this ship . . .'

'We'll gimmick the controls,' Barnett said. 'That'll slow him down.'

'For a little while,' Agee pointed out. 'But he'll get into the air sooner or later, with blood in his eye. We'll never outrun him.'

'We won't have to,' Barnett said. 'All we have to do is get into the air first. He's got a strong hull, but I don't think it'll take three atomic bombs.'

'I hadn't thought of that,' Agee said, smiling faintly.

'Only logical move,' Barnett said complacently. 'The alloys in the hull will still be worth something. Now, get us back without frying us, if you can.'

Agee turned the engines on. He swung the ship around in a tight curve, piling on all the Gs they could stand. The servos clicked on, and the temperature shot rapidly up. Once the curve was rounded, Agee pointed *Endeavour II* in the right direction and shut off the engines.

They coasted most of the way. But when they reached the planet, Agee had to leave the engines on, to bring them around the deceleration spiral and into the landing.

They were barely able to get out of the ship. Their skins were blistered and their shoes burned through. There was no time to gimmick the controls.

They retreated to the woods and waited.

'Perhaps he's dead,' Agee said hopefully.

They saw a small figure emerge from *Endeavour I*. The alien was moving slowly, but he was moving.

They watched. 'Suppose,' Victor said, 'he's made a weapon of some kind. Suppose he comes after us.'

'Suppose you shut up,' Barnett said.

The alien walked directly to his own ship. He went inside and shut the locks.

'All right,' Barnett said, standing up. 'We'd better blast off in a hurry. Agee, you take the controls. I'll connect the piles. Victor, you secure the locks. Let's go!'

They sprinted across the plain and, in a matter of seconds, had reached the open airlock of *Endeavour I*.

Even if he had wanted to hurry, Kalen didn't have the necessary strength to pilot his ship. But he knew that he was safe, once inside. No alien was going to walk through those sealed ports.

He found a spare air tank in the rear and opened it. His ship filled with rich, life-giving yellow air. For long minutes, Kalen just breathed it.

Then he lugged three of the biggest kerla nuts he could find to the galley and let the Cracker open them.

After eating, he felt much better. He let the Changer take off his outer hide. The second layer was dead, too, and the Changer cut that off him, but stopped at the third, living layer.

He was almost as good as new when he slipped into the pilot's room.

It was apparent to him now that the aliens had been temporarily insane. There was no other way to explain why they had come back and returned his ship.

Therefore, he would find their authorities and report the location of the planet. They could be found and cured, once and for all.

Kalen felt very happy. He had not deviated from the Mabogian ethic, and that was the important thing. He could so easily have left the thetnite bomb in their ship, all set and timed. He could have wrecked their engines. And there *had* been a temptation.

But he had not. He had done nothing at all.

All he had done was construct a few minimum essentials for the preservation of life.

Kalen activated his controls and found that everything was

in perfect working order. The acceleration fluid poured in as he turned on the piles.

Victor reached the airlock first and dashed in. Instantly, he was hurled back.

'What happened?' Barnett asked.

'Something hit me,' Victor said.

Cautiously, they looked inside.

It was a very neat death trap. Wires from the storage batteries had been hooked in series and rigged across the port. If Victor had been touching the side of the ship, he would have been electrocuted instantly.

They shorted out the system and entered the ship.

It was a mess. Everything movable had been ripped up and strewn around. There was a bent steel bar in a corner. Their high-potency acid had been spilled over the deck and had eaten through in several places. The *Endeavour's* old hull was holed.

'I never thought *he'd* gimmick *us*!' Agee said.

They explored further. Toward the rear was another booby trap. The cargo hold door had been cunningly rigged to the small starter motor. If anyone touched it, the door would be slammed against the wall. A man caught between would be crushed.

There were other hookups that gave no hint of their purpose.

'Can we fix it?' Barnett asked.

Agee shrugged his shoulders. 'Most of our tools are still on board *Endeavour II*. I suppose we can get her patched up inside of a year. But even then, I don't know if the hull will hold.'

They walked outside. The alien ship blasted off.

'What a monster!' Barnett said, looking at the acid-eaten hull of his ship.

'You can never tell what an alien will do,' Agee answered.

'The only good alien is a dead alien,' Victor said.

Endeavour I was now as incomprehensible and dangerous as *Endeavour II*.

And *Endeavour II* was gone.

The Wager

BY E. C. TUBB

from *Science Fantasy*, November 1955

It is easy to forget, with the boom in the United States, that by the mid 1950s Britain also had its handful of competent magazines, and without a doubt their most prolific contributor was E. C. Tubb.

Edwin Charles Tubb was born in London on Wednesday 15 October 1919, and sold his first story, 'No Short Cuts', to John Carnell in 1950; it was published in the Summer 1951 *New Worlds*. By then Tubb had begun a steady sale of novels to the flourishing paperback market, and you need only refer to the listing of his works in this book's appendices to see the sheer volume of his output. This is not to say it was of low, hack quality. In fact Tubb was one of the few authors who produced work of above average quality for the paperbacks. And his work for the sf magazines, with their far more discerning audience, was top quality indeed, as the following novelette will reveal.

In 1956 Tubb assumed editorship of *Authentic,* and managed to increase its popularity even more, but sadly its publishers decided to fold the magazine in order to concentrate on the paperback field with Panther Books. Tubb put months of work into the magazine for minimal financial gain, and it took him some time to return to regular writing. However by 1959 he was back in top form, and, what's more, writing novels. A notable example is his 1963 book, *Window on the Moon*. In 1966 Rupert Hart-Davis published a collection of his short stories, *Ten From Tomorrow*, but this is only a fraction of his work. More recently he has been concentrating on a series about the character Earl Dumarest and his search for Earth, which has proved highly popular. He has produced several books from the television *Space 1999* series, and is also currently working on a historical series set in the days of the Roman Empire.

Tubb is an inspired fiction machine and there is so very much of his writings at present lost to general readership, that I hope the inclusion of his lengthy 'The Wager' in this volume will prompt others to search out his earlier work.

It had been raining and the streets were still wet. The big car skidded a little as it swung around corners, the squeal of its tyres mingling with the wail of its siren. On the front of the vehicle a red spotlight flared with intermittent life while the two big headlamps signalled its coming from a mile away.

It slewed around a corner, tore down a tree-lined road, and skidded to a halt beside a huddled knot of men. Captain Tom Mason, Homicide, swung open the front door and stepped out of the faint smell of rubber and burnt petrol into the clean air of the rain-washed night.

'Stick around,' he said to the driver. 'If anything comes over the radio let me know.' He turned as a man walked towards him. 'Clancy?'

'Yes, sir.' The uniformed policeman touched the peak of his cap. 'You made good time, Captain.'

'Nine minutes.' Mason didn't look at his watch. 'The rest of the boys here?'

'Yes, sir. They got here about three minutes ago.'

'I was on the other side of town.' Mason hunched the collar of his shabby raincoat higher around his neck. 'Did you find the body?'

'Yes, sir. You want to see it?'

'Later. What's your story?'

'I must have missed the killer by not more than a few seconds.' Clancy sounded disgusted. 'I was on the regular beat, coming up Third and Vine and along Pine Avenue. I heard a yell and saw someone running. I grabbed him and he told me that he'd just seen a murder. I investigated and phoned in right away.'

'Pine Avenue? That's this street, isn't it?'

'That's right.'

'Where were you when you heard the yell?'

'Just coming out of Third and Vine. About a hundred yards down the avenue. I ran straight here.'

'And the witness?'

'I've got him. You want to see him?'

'Later. Did you see anything else? Hear anything?'

'No, sir. The night was quiet, we don't get much noise in this section, and the yell was all I heard.' Clancy shifted on his feet. 'It's pretty dark along here, the Avenue is only built up along one side, but I didn't see anything.'

'Not surprising.' Mason stared towards the huddle of men. Flashbulbs flickered like summer lightning and, from the distance, he heard the straining engine of a car. He looked at the officer.

'When the reporters get here keep them off my neck. Tell them I'll have a statement for them later. They can get it at Headquarters.' He smiled thinly at the officer's expression. 'Don't worry, Clancy, you'll get your picture in the papers.'

'That doesn't interest me, sir.'

'No? Then you're the first cop I've met it doesn't.' He looked around as the driver of his car came towards him.

'Reports from the road-blocks, sir. They're holding four suspects.'

'Good. Have them brought here to me. Tell the patrols to search this area. Stop and question everyone they see. Take names and addresses, identification, the usual thing. Hold everyone who cannot or will not account for himself.' He waited until the man had returned to the car and then stepped towards the huddled knot of men.

Prentice, his assistant, came towards him. 'Almost finished, Tom. Want the details?'

'Yes.'

'The deceased is a Roger Gorman. About forty-five. Well dressed and wearing a light gabardine raincoat. Gloves, stick, soft hat, ring on the little finger of his left hand, gold wrist watch, fat wallet. You get the picture?'

'Yes.'

'Cards in the wallet says that he was a member of the Prestonville Chamber of Commerce. A couple of photographs of what could be his wife and kid. Driving licence, Lodge membership cards, business cards, a hotel key, the Grand Union, some other stuff not important as yet. You can check it all later back at Headquarters.'

'Get on with it,' said Mason tiredly. 'What else?'

'Nothing much as yet. The killer was obviously a maniac and I've sent word to check any escapes from the mental homes. I . . .'

'What makes you think he was killed by a maniac?'

'You'll see. It wasn't robbery, the wallet is intact. He was from out of town and could hardly have had local enemies. He seemed to be a decent, normal business type out for a walk before turning in. The hotel is just a few blocks from here. I've sent a man to collect his luggage.'

'You've figured all this out in, how long?'

'About five minutes.' Prentice looked pleased with himself. 'Not bad, uh?'

'Not good either. You've been reading too much. Sherlock Holmes went out with gas lighting.' He looked around. 'Where's that witness Clancy told me he had?'

'Waiting in the car. You want to see him?'

'Not yet.' He sighed. 'I suppose I'd better look at the body now.'

He moved forward, Prentice at his side, and halted beside something covered with a rubber sheet. An officer stood by it and, as he saw Mason, he stopped and lifted the sheet from what lay underneath it. Mason stared down, his face impassive, and Prentice swung the beam from a flashlight he carried onto the corpse.

'See? I told you that it was the work of a maniac.'

'Or someone trying to give us that impression?' Mason didn't look at his assistant. Hardened as he was to crime and the inhumanity of man towards man, yet he had never grown to relish the sight of death. Privately he considered it to be the worse part of his job and, staring down at what lay revealed in the light of the flashlight, he found nothing to alter his opinion. It wasn't just that the man was dead, it was what had been done to the corpse.

It didn't have a head.

The witness was a human derelict stinking of cheap wine and redolent with dirt. He blinked up at Mason and ran the tip of his tongue between snags of teeth. His clothing was damp and he looked half-numbed as though things were happening too fast for him. He didn't look towards where the body lay.

'You saw the actual murder?' Mason shivered slightly in his

thin raincoat. He knew that all this questioning could have been done in the comfort of Headquarters but he had a theory that first impressions were valuable and he wanted to get all the facts before witness and suspects had time to forget or alter what they knew and had seen.

'Well,' the witness seemed doubtful, 'I didn't really see it. I was sitting down and heard something and when I looked up there was a man on the ground and another man was running away.'

'In which direction?'

'That way.' The witness pointed to the unlit side of the avenue. 'He was tall and ran like he was scared or something. I was still looking after him when the cop arrived.'

'Did you shout?'

'No.'

'Did you make any sound at all? Did you call to the man, for example?'

'Not me.'

'That sound you heard, what was it? A cry for help? A scream?'

'I don't know,' said the man. He belched. 'I was asleep and it must've woke me up. I saw the fellow though.'

'Which one?'

'The one running away, like I told you.'

'Would you know him again?'

'I don't know.' The man looked cunning. 'I reckon so. Witnesses get paid, don't they?'

'Not for lying,' said Mason curtly. 'Would you know him again if you saw him?'

'I reckon so. In this light anyway. I wouldn't know about in a room.'

'It won't be in a room.' Mason stared towards where Prentice was ushering four people towards him. 'Stay here. Watch those people. If you recognise anyone let me know. Don't speak and don't move. Understand?'

The witness nodded and Mason walked towards the four people.

The first suspect was quickly cleared. He was a small, balding, nervous man. He plucked at Mason's sleeve and whispered something. The Captain frowned.

'Speak up. You all know why you are here. A crime has been committed and all I want to know is who you are, where you were going, who can vouch for you. Once cleared you can go home.' He looked down at the little man. 'Well?'

'It's my wife, Captain. I didn't want her to know where I was. My name is Blake, Edward Blake, and I can prove where I was from nine o'clock until when the officer stopped me.'

'Where were you?'

'At Madame Cormay's.' The little man blushed. 'You know how it is, Captain.'

'I know,' said Mason. He heard of the notorious Madame Cormay. One day the vice squad was going to do the work they were paid to do and she would be put out of business. He gestured towards an officer. 'Take this man and check his story. Take him home and check where he lives. You know what to do.' He looked at the remaining three suspects. Two were men the third a woman. She clung to the hand of one of the men and Mason guessed that they were together.

They were and their story was simple. They were married, but not to each other, and for obvious reasons they didn't want any investigations made at their respective homes. Mason sent them off with two officers and left it to them to make up their own alibis. He stared at the remaining man.

'Your name?'

'Holden. Gort Holden.'

'Address?'

'Central Plaza.'

'All right, Mr. Holden. You heard what I said to the others. As you live in a hotel I'm afraid that I just can't send you home with an officer. That wouldn't prove anything. If you'll just let me know whom to contact to vouch for you I won't detain you any longer.' He paused, waiting, then as the man made no move held out his hand. 'Give.'

'Give you what?'

'Your papers. Your wallet, identity, social security card, any-thing and everything which will prove to me who and what you are.'

'I'm afraid that I can't do that.'

'Can't or won't?'

'Can't, sorry.' Gort smiled and made as though to walk away. Mason stopped him, his fingers hard on the other's arm.

'Not so fast. Maybe if you see why I'm so interested in you you'll change your mind.' Mason gestured to an officer. 'Take this man and show him. Bring him back afterwards to me.' He waited until the couple had moved off then looked towards the witness. The man grinned and nodded his head.

When Gort returned he looked pale and almost physically ill. He stood for a moment gulping at the rain-washed air and, in the light of the street lamps, his eyes looked haggard.

'You should have warned me,' he said. 'That man! It's horrible!'

'Sorry.' Mason didn't feel regret. 'That man was murdered a short while ago. The murderer was seen making his escape. We blocked all roads and are checking the vicinity and all people who fail to identify themselves. I take it that you have no serious objection to being identified?'

'By the person who saw the murderer? Of course not.'

'I didn't exactly mean that,' said Mason gently. 'There must be someone who would vouch for you. Your employer? Your family? Your associates?'

'Naturally.' Gort hesitated. 'But is that necessary? Surely if you have a witness to the crime he could clear me?'

'Perhaps.' In the dim light the Captain's face was enigmatic. 'You have no objection if we try?'

'Of course not.'

'I see.' Mason turned to the witness who had approached while they were talking. 'Well? Is this the man you saw?'

'Could be.' The man swayed closer and Gort recoiled from the sour odour of his breath. 'Yes, that's the man.'

'Are you positive?'

'Well . . .' The hesitation was obvious. 'The light was bad and my eyes ain't none too good, but I'd say he's the one. Same shaped head. Same height and the same colour clothing. He's your man all right.'

'Impossible!' Gort thrust himself towards the witness. 'You've never seen me before in your whole life. You are mistaken.' He appealed to Mason. 'You can't believe this man. He would say anything if he thought that it would please you.'

'Maybe.' Mason nodded towards an officer. 'But it's eye-witness testimony against your unsupported denial. I'm afraid that I shall have to hold you for further investigation.'

He turned back to the corpse as the officer led Gort away.

II

To Gort the whole thing seemed like a wild fantasy. He sat on a hard, narrow cot in a small, concrete room and stared at a tiny patch of blue sky high against one wall. The cell was cramped, primitive, and utterly bleak to a man used to the comforts of a galactic-wide civilisation. And the worst part of it all was that nothing he could do would save him. Intelligence, even that of a high order, couldn't combat iron bars and stone walls.

And he was beginning to doubt his own intelligence

Arrest had meant a bath, not that that mattered, his camouflage was proof against anything but the special solvents but, at the same time, that camouflage wasn't a permanent fixture and would need touching up from time to time. He had retained the clothing he had worn at the time of the arrest, and thinking of that clothing made him writhe with anger at his stupidity. To have worn it at all had been ridiculous. He should never have discarded his own special garments because, without them, he was helpless.

The thought of just how utter that helplessness was made him squirm.

He looked up as the door opened and Mason entered the cell. He waited until the door had been locked behind him then sat on the single chair and faced Gort.

'Well? Have you changed your mind yet?'

Gort didn't answer. He knew what the captain wanted, proof of his identity, but that very proof was the one thing he couldn't give. There wasn't a man or woman on the face of this planet who could vouch for him. There was absolutely no paper proof of his birth, education, employment, medical history, none of the thousand and one records normal to anyone living in this particular hemisphere.

'We've checked the Central Plaza and all they can tell us is that you booked in a week ago, two days before your arrest. We've searched your things without result. It isn't good enough.' He paused, waiting for Gort to speak.

'What else can I do?' Gort knew the answer and knew that he couldn't help.

'I've told you that more than once,' said Mason wearily. 'Who are you? Where do you normally live? Where do you work? Have you any friends of good standing who can vouch for you?' He made an expressive gesture of impatience. 'Don't think that I want to keep you here, I don't, but I can't release you until I know just who and what you are. Want to tell me?'

'I . . .' Gort swallowed and shook his head. The situation was impossible. The truth wouldn't be believed and, if it were, it would be the last thing he dared tell. For the first time he began to fully appreciate the warning he had been given.

'Never underestimate them,' Rhubens had said. 'They're ignorant, stupid, illogical but they have their own brand of native cunning. Once they get hold of an idea they never stop worrying at it until they find an answer. It needn't be the correct answer, but they want one just the same.' The commander had laughed with easy good humour. 'There's no need to warn you of the females but be careful of their law enforcement. They're fanatically security-conscious and they'll disregard ethics and everything else if they become the slightest bit suspicious.'

That had been eight days ago and he was only now beginning to realise what the commander had meant.

'The position,' said Mason grimly, 'is this. A man has been murdered in a particularly horrible way. Every other suspect in the area has been vouched for and is clear. You are the only possible suspect and, even more important, you have been identified by a witness. I hate to say this but, unless you decide to co-operate, you're heading straight for the electric chair. It's up to you to clear yourself if you want to avoid it.'

'Wait a moment.' Gort frowned as he tried to recall all he had learned. 'Isn't there something about a man being innocent until found guilty?'

'There is,' admitted the captain dryly. 'But I shouldn't count on it if I were you.'

'Then what about the evidence? I had no weapon. My clothes were clean and, above all, I wasn't carrying the . . .' Gort felt a recurrence of his sickness as he tried to say the word.

'The head?' Mason looked thoughtful. 'That's right you weren't, were you.'

'Then the evidence alone should clear me. You have no real justification for detaining me at all.'

'No?' Mason shrugged. 'I don't agree with you.' He stared curiously at the man on the bunk. 'Have you any Indian blood?'

'What?' Gort realised that he didn't know what the captain was driving at. 'No, I don't think so. Why?'

'You've been here five days now and the warder tells me that you haven't shaved once during that time. Pure Indians don't have to shave, they just don't grow whiskers.' Mason scrubbed at his own chin. 'Lucky devils. You're a vegetarian too, aren't you?'

'I don't eat flesh,' said Gort cautiously. 'Is that what you mean?'

'That's right.' Mason rose and stared down at his prisoner. 'But you're the first vegetarian I've ever met who refuses to eat meat, fish, eggs and any product of any animal. That must account for the way you felt when you saw the body. You should have warned me that you had a weak stomach.'

Gort snatched at the opportunity. 'I can't stand the sight of blood,' he said. 'Doesn't that prove my innocence?'

'Sorry, but no.' Mason banged on the door for the warder to come and let him out. 'If you want to do that you'd better start talking and you'd better do it fast. Public opinion has been aroused and, if you leave it too late, you may find yourself in the position of not being believed. Think it over.'

The door closed behind him and, alone once more, Gort stretched himself full-length on the bunk. The warning had been very plain. Clear yourself – or be used as a scapegoat. Desperately he racked his brains for some way out of this almost ludicrous situation. For a man who could repair an instantaneous warp-drive, who had an intelligence at least five times that of the brightest inhabitant of this world and who was a member of the Guardians, to be confined on a false accusation in a primitive jail was something he didn't like to think about.

He could hire a lawyer he supposed, they would allow him to use his money for that purpose, but a lawyer would want to know all about him and so he would be no better off. If he could get his clothing he stood a chance, Mason had said that they had been searched but the woven-in circuits and power source had been designed to avoid detection. But before he could get his clothes he would have to clear himself and . . .

Restlessly he sat up and stared at the window high above his head. With a smooth co-ordination of muscle he jumped and drew himself up so that his face was pressed against the bars. From his vantage point he could see the roof of a building opposite, a few fleecy clouds, and an expanse of clear blue sky. He stared at the sky for a long time and, somehow, the sight began to irritate him. Up there was all the help he needed or could possibly use.

But he wasn't up there.

III

Heltin wasn't satisfied with the ship but it was the best Jelkson would provide. He wasn't satisfied with his partner either, but it was a case of take it or leave it and Heltin, with expensive tastes and a liking for the dubious pleasures of the Rim worlds, had had no choice. Now he sat in the control chair and looked at the image on the screens.

'Is that it?' San Luchin leaned over the pilot's shoulder his cat-eyes blazing with anticipation. Heltin nodded.

'That's it. The quarry planet. Are your people ready?'

'Certainly. We have arranged a most ingenious wager. You will drop us at the same point as where I obtained the last trophy. You will give us three revolutions and then pick us up again. The one who has collected the greatest number of trophies will win twenty thousand milars.' He inhaled with a peculiar sibilance. 'It should be good sport.'

'Don't make it too good,' warned Heltin uneasily. 'You've been here before and you know that these things have a civilisation of sorts. It could be that you may find yourselves in serious trouble. It isn't just a question of landing and reaping a harvest, you know. The whole object is to pit your wits and skill against the inhabitants – and get away with it.' He hesitated. 'Are you certain that you wouldn't prefer a more isolated area?'

'No.' San Luchin was very positive. 'The entire attraction of the plan is that we shall be in some personal danger. We are taking only the essential protection-equipment and must use our full skill both to obtain the trophies and to escape detection. You have a hypno-tutor for the language?'

'Yes, the reels are ready in place. I couldn't get much local currency though, you'll have to make out the best you can.' Heltin adjusted the controls and the image on the screens suddenly jerked into close proximity. 'Hurry up with your preparations. I don't want to hang around here longer than I have to.'

'Why not? The Guardians can't spot your screens, can they?'

'I hope not,' said Heltin feelingly. 'That base on the moon looks awfully efficient to me.'

He slid the vessel closer to the planet as his passengers familiarised themselves with the language, and, judging the time to a nicety, he landed when the sun was on the other side of the planet. Cautiously, he opened the air lock and stared at the darkness outside.

A man, walking along the deserted street stared at the bulk of the ship then continued on his way. Heltin grinned, the invisibility screens were obviously doing their job and for a moment he was tempted to leave the vessel where it was rather than follow his original plan of waiting beneath the surface of one of the seas. He dismissed the notion. Even though the local inhabitants couldn't spot him, yet the Guardians might just be able to spot his radiation and, even with his altered screens, it would be wiser to shield himself with a mile of ocean. He turned as his passengers crowded towards the air lock.

San Luchin took the lead. He, like all the rest, wore something so near to the native clothing as to be unnoticeable. Each had camouflaged his personal characteristics and each carried a single offensive weapon, of a low order of efficiency and yet one ideally suited to the project in hand. Heltin watched as the five men dropped to the ground.

'Wait a minute,' he said sharply. 'You've forgotten something. What are you going to keep them in?'

'That is our affair,' San Luchin expressed his irritation with a peculiar gesture, a tensing and clawing of the right hand. 'We intend to enjoy the sport to the full and the harder we can make it the better it will be. Take off now and return for us in three revolutions.'

Heltin shrugged. 'It's your party. Good hunting.'

They nodded and moved away as the door slid shut. Before they had cleared the immediate area the ship had flickered from view and a moment later a rush of air told that it had left. San Luchin held a quick council.

'I suggest we separate to divergent areas,' he said in the newly acquired language. 'Aside from force jackets we shall be defenceless and, in order to prevent interference, we shall make no attempt at personal contact until we meet here at the appointed time. Agreed?'

They nodded and moved away, each taking a route as well away from the others as possible. San Luchin watched them go then, after a moment's thought, made his way towards the centre of town.

He hummed a little as he walked, a soft, almost feral purring of the breath and his eyes, as he stared at the surrounding crowds, glowed with mounting anticipation. He had been right to insist on a three-revolution stay. He had been right to make the hunt as severe as possible. For too long now there had been no real opportunity for good sport. Even the manufactured androids were but a poor substitute for the real thing. They were good, but they could only be as good as the builders made them and, once you had built a thing, you knew its exact capabilities. These things were different. Their capabilities were unknown and might prove to be delightfully dangerous.

He restrained the subconscious movement of his hand towards the weapon beneath his jacket. Not yet. The taking of trophies would be the easy part even though it was the ultimate thrill. He could afford to wait and enjoy the pleasure of antici-pation. First there were other things to attend to, the finding of a hide, the watching of the quarry, the obtaining of the cache. The humming grew louder as he stepped carefully through the crowds.

He hadn't enjoyed himself so much for years.

IV

Captain Mason sat in his office and stared at the litter of papers before him. It was night and a desk lamp threw a broad cone of light over the scattered sheets. Reports mostly, details of a search which, so far, had proven useless. He picked up a file and began to riffle the pages looking for the thousandth time for something, he didn't know what, to give him a clue to the most publicised murder for the past ten years.

He looked up as the assistant D.A. slammed into the room and helped himself to a chair.

'Still at it, Tom?'

'Still at it.' Mason sighed and accepted the cigarette the other man offered. 'Thanks. Going ahead with the trial, Bob?'

'What else can we do?' Bob Shaw thumbed a lighter and lit the cigarettes. 'The old man's out on a limb. The press is riding him hard and, unless he clears up this case he can kiss his chances in the coming election goodbye.'

'You think that you can get a conviction?'

'It's a certainty.' Bob stared at the lined face of the captain. 'What's the matter? Don't you believe that Holden did it?'

'I'm not certain he did,' admitted Mason slowly. 'Somehow it just doesn't add up.' He picked up the file. 'No motive. No weapon. No stains on his clothing. He could just have been walking down the road as he claims when we picked him up.'

'You're forgetting the witness,' reminded Shaw. 'He's willing to swear that Holden is the man he saw running from the scene of the crime.'

'That wino? Who'd believe him?'

'The jury will, and that's all that matters.' Shaw dragged at his cigarette. 'He broken down yet?'

'Not yet.'

'That won't help him either. Playing dumb isn't the right way to prove innocence. If you've got nothing to hide then why not speak up? Quit feeling sorry for him, Tom, if he's in trouble then it's his own fault.'

'Maybe.' Mason sighed as he put down the file. 'I'm still not happy about it though. You haven't really got a case against him at all. Any good lawyer could rip it apart and get it thrown out of court.'

'You think so?' Shaw blew smoke through his nose. 'I don't agree. Look, we can forget the motive angle. The dead man was a bit of a playboy and we can suggest that our friend was a little jealous or something. That part doesn't matter. The man's dead, that's all we've got to worry about, and Holden's a sitting duck to take the rap.'

'Even if he's innocent?'

'Tell that to the birds. He's as guilty as hell, that's why he clammed up, he knows that as soon as he starts talking we're going to check and trip him up.' Shaw stared at Mason. 'Listen. He threw the knife away, that's simple, there's a big piece of waste ground right next to where the killing took place and it's got a storm drain at the end of it. He dumped his cargo too, doubled back, and then tried to make out he was only taking a walk. It was his bad luck he was seen by a witness and that we managed to cordon the area so soon. Five more minutes and he would have got clean away.'

'And the blood?'

'Luck or . . .' Bob shrugged. 'We'll settle for luck.' He rose to his feet. 'Did you get anywhere with his prints?'

'No. They aren't on file anywhere.'

'Maybe he's a draft dodger too,' suggested Bob. 'Anyway, don't let it get you down, Tom. After all, what's it to you?' He left and the captain frowned down at the file again.

It was easy for Bob to talk, easier still for him to sit back and be cynical even if it sent an innocent man to the chair, but Mason couldn't forget that an officer's duty wasn't just to assume guilt, he should also help to prove innocence.

And something was wrong.

He knew it. He felt it every time he saw the prisoner. The man wasn't insane, and what sane man would decapitate another? He wasn't even a killer, though Mason knew that any man given the right conditions could become a killer. It was something intangible, something not quite fitting into the correct groove and, the more he thought about it, the more it began to worry him.

The fingerprints for example. Holden had been printed as a matter of routine and his prints sent to the agencies for checking. That they weren't on file wasn't too extraordinary, it merely meant that he had never worked in a defence plant, been previously arrested, served with the armed forces, worked for a big company, or applied for a passport. What was extraordinary was the prints themselves.

Mason stared at them, frowning at the strange, utterly unnatural pattern. He knew that all normal prints fell into defined categories depending on the arches and whorls but Holden's were in a class by themselves. No arches, no whorls, a series of herringbone patterns overlaid by a writhing mass of circular lines, the whole blurred and distorted to an almost unrecognisable extent. It was puzzling and mentally Mason began reviewing the case against Gort.

The knife? Shaw had explained that and, if the crime had been premeditated, that was just what the murderer would have done. Motive? Unessential, it wasn't his job to prove motive. The blood? Luck as Shaw had said, or . . . ?

The blood!

Hastily Mason thumbed through the file until he found what he was looking for, an eight by ten blow-up of the scene of the crime. He squinted at it, something nagging at his brain then, with quick impatience, flipped the switch on an intercom.

'Desk? Mason here. Get me Doc Wheelan.' He waited, fingers drumming on the edge of his desk. 'Doc? Mason here. How much blood does a body contain?' He frowned at the sounds coming from the speaker. 'No, I'm not joking, this could be serious.' He listened again. 'That much? If someone were to slash off a head would it spurt out? Most of it? Depends? Look, you know the case I'm working on, well, as far as I can tell from the photographs there was hardly any blood at all. How do you account for that?' He listened again. 'O.K. O.K., so I didn't notice it at the time. Hell, Doc, it was raining, the night was dark and I had other things on my mind. The report? No, I didn't read it, why should I have done? The man was dead, wasn't he, and even I could see the cause. Can you boil it down?' Mason's face hardened as he listened to the voice from the speaker. 'Are you certain? You are? O.K., Doc, keep your shirt on. I only wanted to know.'

Slowly he broke the connection, his face heavy with thought then, abruptly, he threw the switch again.

'Desk? Mason here. Bring down the prisoner Gort Holden. Bring him down right away.'

He waited staring down at the photograph, the crease between his eyes a living question mark.

The simplicity of it was such that Gort felt utterly ashamed of not having thought of it before. In order to escape he needed his special clothing so, as he was still not in prison garb and wouldn't be until after the trial, he deliberately destroyed the clothes he was wearing. The warder had shrugged when he saw the wreckage and, as the prisoner had more clothes of his own, what was simpler than to fetch them?

It was as easy as that.

Dressed once more in his protective clothing. Gort felt a new man. He sat on the edge of the bunk and wondered just what would be best for him to do. He could slice out the bars of the window and float out to freedom. He could cut the lock from the door and get out that way. He could generate the force-field which would protect him from all missile and most energy weapons and nothing these people could do would stop him. He could also trip the emergency signal and call to the base for help.

But to do any of these things would be both an admission of failure and betrayal of his trust.

First, he had aroused enough suspicion as it was without arousing more. Calling for help now was both unnecessary and unjustified and, if he did, he would have some awkward questions to answer when he got back to base. A Guardian, even a young one, was supposed to be able to use his own initiative. Sitting on the edge of the bunk he decided to do nothing for the time being. Being able to escape any time he wanted to made all the difference and, even though he didn't like to admit it, his recent experience had taught him a lot.

It had taught him that a man was only as good as his technology. Even with his high intelligence, his so-called superiority over these primitives, yet he had been helpless without his gadgets. In a way he'd been even worse than the natives because they didn't tend to rely on force-fields and all the other appurtenances common to his own civilisation. It was a sobering thought and he was still brooding over it when the warder came to take him to Mason.

The captain wasted no time.

'There's something funny about you Holden and I want to know what it is. There's another matter too . . .' His voice trailed off as he glanced at the photograph. 'But never mind that for now.' He dropped the glossy print and gestured to a chair. 'Sit down.'

Gort sat down. Strangely enough he didn't feel in the slightest bit upset. Maybe it was because he now knew himself to be invulnerable or it may have been that, for the first time since his arrest, he was beginning to enjoy himself.

'Do you still refuse to give me data about yourself?' Mason asked the question as though he didn't really expect an answer and, for a moment, Gort was tempted to tell him the truth. He resisted the insane impulse, this was no time for joking.

'I do.'

'Then let me tell you something about yourself.' Mason relaxed in his chair and stared at his prisoner. 'You may not have known it but you've been under constant surveillance since your arrest. For example we know that you have never once shaved. You have never eaten any product of any dead or living animal and, as far as we can determine, you have never slept.' He stared thoughtfully at Gort. 'Another thing, your fingerprints aren't normal. I have never seen a pattern like them before and I think that it's safe to say another such pattern does not exist.' He leaned forward his eyes suspicious.

"*What are you, Holden*?"

Not who, *what*! The significance of the word sent a chill up Gort's spine. Mason was suspicious, maybe it was only the vague glimmerings of an idea as yet but, remembering Rhubens' advice, Gort knew that he dared take no chances. He smiled.

'What? You mean who, don't you?'

'Perhaps.' Mason didn't elaborate. 'Are you going to talk?'

'I can tell you a few things,' said Gort. 'I don't know why I have no need to shave. I've never thought about it before, it's just one of those things, you know how it is.'

'Do I?'

'Well, you said yourself that Indians never had to shave so what's so peculiar about it?' Gort gestured with his hands. 'I'm a vegetarian, yes, I've never denied it but that's no crime. I just don't like eating dead tissue or the products of living organisms. I may be fanatical on the subject but my stomach's my own.'

'And the sleeplessness?'

'That's nonsense,' lied Gort. 'I sleep just the same as anyone else but I've trained myself to take my rest in snatches. I'll drop off for ten minutes or half an hour, wake up for a few minutes, then drop off again.' He smiled. 'I've got a theory about it.'

Mason didn't smile. 'You still haven't told me anything,' he reminded. 'Do you want to be tried for murder?'

'You won't convict me,' said Gort positively. 'I'm innocent.' He looked at the photograph. 'Is that the scene of the crime?'

'Yes,' Mason picked it up, hesitated, then handed it to Gort. 'You might be able to help me. When you saw the body did you notice any blood?'

'Blood?' Gort paused, the photograph in his hand. 'I can't remember, is it important?'

'It could be,' said Mason seriously. 'Something odd has come up and I want to be certain that I'm right. If you could remember it would help a lot.'

Gort nodded and threw his mind back to recall the incident. He concentrated and suddenly, he could smell the rain-wet night, hear the soft sounds made by the shoes of the men, see the huddled and headless figure sprawled on the grass. He controlled his revulsion and forced himself to scan the area.

'There was a little blood at the upper limit of the corpse,' he said carefully. 'Is that what you want to know?'

'How much blood?' Then, as Gort hesitated. 'A smear or two, a pint, a gallon? Was the grass covered with it or was it only in one small area?'

'There wasn't a lot. Just a heavy smear on the grass.'

'Yes,' said Mason heavily. 'That's what I thought.' He stared at Gort. 'I've just read the medical report and spoken to the doctor. It appears that the head was removed with an incredibly sharp instrument which apparently had the power to cauterise the wound as it cut. The single smear of blood apparently came from a minor wound caused after death. I use the word 'apparent' because, as far as we know, no such instrument exists.' He paused and stared at Gort. 'Just as fingerprints such as yours do not exist.'

'But they do,' said Gort and held up his hands. 'I have them.'

'Exactly.' Mason reached for his intercom. 'You needn't worry about being put on trial for murder. I am going to inform Security and you will be held for further questioning. I'm sorry, Holden, but you realise that I cannot chance the fact that you may be a spy.'

The phone jangled just as he was about to speak and, with an irritated expression, he lifted the receiver. 'Mason here. What is it?'

Watching him Gort could see his expression change from irritation to incredulity. 'What! Three of them? Where?' He listened, one hand making swift notations on the pad before him. 'All without heads? Wait! Any blood? You don't know? Check on it then, and hurry!'

His eyes met those of Gort and, as if the sight had reminded him of something, he reached again for the intercom. The squawking of the phone interrupted him for a second time.

'No blood? Are you positive? Good. Yes, I'll be right over. Yes, looks like the same man at work again. Cordon the area and proceed as usual.'

Mason slammed down the receiver, reached for the intercom, then slumped in sudden immobility.

Gort rose. He had about half a minute to make his escape, the paralysis wouldn't last longer than that for fear of causing death, but before he went he had something to do. Quickly he wiped the photograph, took the officer's wallet card from his pocket and, with easy strides, moved towards the door.

A second application of the paralysis vibration cleared his path and, before Mason could recover, he was in the street and on his way to freedom. Almost he felt sorry for the captain but what else could he have done? A more rigorous confinement would have necessitated the loss of his protective clothing and all hope of escape. As it was he had merely walked out leaving unanswered questions. Mason, no matter what his suspicions, couldn't now verify them.

Gort was free to continue his interrupted vacation.

V

San Luchin sat in his hotel room and trembled as he listened to the newscast. The fools! The unutterable fools to have gone trophy hunting so soon after arrival. And yet, fools though they were, their action had made the hunt even more exciting.

A large-scale map of the city was spread before him on the floor and he scanned it, marking the areas where the bodies had been found, his cat-eyes blazing with interest as he extrapolated the probable results of the mistimed hunting. Obviously they had underestimated the resources of this planet. According to the newscast the areas were now cordoned and every person discovered within them would be questioned and examined. Equally obvious they would have to discard their trophies and, at the same time, run a risk of discovery.

He bared his teeth as he thought about it, almost envying them their position, and yet, at the same time recognising their danger. Not of personal annihilation, of course, their protective force-fields would safeguard them from that, but of their being kept so busy that they would inevitably lose the wager. Also, and this was most important, they had to avoid all unnecessary suspicion. Not that the natives mattered, they didn't, but the watchful Guardians did and this was too fine a quarry planet for them to lose it so soon.

The foolish part had been in taking trophies where the bodies were certain to be almost immediately discovered.

Restlessly he began to pace the floor. His own plans were made, he had scanned the area, knew just where and when to strike, and even had his containers for his trophies ready and waiting. He paused beside the plastic suitcases – how strange that this race should know of plastics. Ideal for his purpose, they were light, strong, and of a size both designed for good capacity and lack of unessential bulk. He was still examining them when the knock came at the door.

'Yes?'

'Police, open up.'

'One moment.' Quickly he checked to make sure that his eyes were hidden by contact lenses, his camouflage perfect and his clothing adjusted. He opened the door before the uniformed officer had time to knock again.

'Can I help you?'

'You can answer some questions,' snapped the officer. He was big, broad, a holstered weapon hanging at his belt and his uniform cap pushed back on his bald skull. San Luchin stared fascinatedly at that skull, mentally imagining it mounted on the wall of his trophy room, and wondered again at the incredible variety of trophies it was possible to obtain on this Planet. He remembered to smile.

'Certainly. What would you like to know?'

'Where were you during the past two hours? Have you any identity? Is there anyone who can vouch for you?' The officer droned the questions and San Luchin guessed that he was merely conducting a routine investigation. He relaxed a little and reached inside his jacket for a wallet.

'Here, driver's licence, social security card, lodge membership cards and insurance policy. I'm a stranger in town, drove in on business, and I've kept pretty well to my room for the past few hours.' He smiled again. 'Got a touch of flu, I guess. The receptionist should be able to verify that.'

'I've already checked,' said the officer. He stared at the papers the wallet contained. 'Sorry to trouble you Mr Jones, but you know how it is on this job. With a maniac prowling the city we just can't be too careful.' He closed the wallet and handed it back. 'If you ask me this is a waste of time. Hell, anyone would know that the killer wouldn't hang around the scene of his operations. Anyway, what's the good of checking every resident just for suspicious characters?'

'It must be hard on you,' sympathised San Luchin. He knew better than to be dogmatic. 'Think you'll find them?'

'Them?' The officer raised his eyebrows. 'Who said anything about 'them'?'

It had been a mistake but he hadn't been able to resist the deliberate provocation. A good hunter learns the reactions of his quarry and San Luchin knew himself to be a good hunter. He forced himself to look away from that tempting trophy.

'Sorry, I guess that I was getting confused. Three bodies, you know . . .' He gestured with his hands. The officer nodded.

'That's right, but there can only be one killer nutty enough to do what he did.' He slid back his cap and scratched his naked scalp. 'Well, guess that I'd better be getting on with the job. Goodnight, Mr Jones.'

'Goodnight.' San Luchin leaned against the closed door and gulped at the thick, slightly arid air. Desperately he fought to control his reactions. Not yet! Not yet! Not yet! The thought hammered within his skull and gradually calmed the seething emotions within him. Almost he had yielded to temptation and he had a momentary glimpse of precognition. The trophy taken, then the inevitable flight, the hunt in which the hunter would be the hunted. The pitting of wits against wits, skill against skill, and all the time there would be the temptation to acquire more and more trophies. He closed his eyes and quivered in orgiastic mental pleasure.

When he opened them again he was ice calm.

The others had yielded to temptation and were now probably devoid of hides, trophies and caches. In effect they would have had to start again with the handicap of wasted time. As strangers in the city they would be suspect and . . .

He was also a stranger.

The wallet had been taken from a native he had met and killed for the single purpose of establishing his hide. The body he had hidden in thick undergrowth at the edge of the city trusting to luck that it would not be discovered and its identity established too soon. Now, because of the general suspicion, it was almost certain that very thing would happen.

The officer had been tired but these things were, in their way, remarkably efficient. He would remember the name, the foreign accent, the mistake of the word 'them.' The hotel receptionist too might begin to wonder about the strange guest who stayed close to his room. A part of his mind told him that he was worrying unnecessarily but another part, the cold, calculating hunter's part, warned him constantly of the danger of under-estimation. He was still undecided when the officer returned to his room.

This time he didn't knock, but walked straight in, and San Luchin cursed the carelessness which had made him forget to lock the door.

'What do you want?'

'Just one more question.' The officer's eyes slid around the room. 'You said that you drove into town on business?'

'That's right.'

'What sort of business?'

'Pedlar.' San Luchin saw at once that he had chosen the wrong word. 'I sell things.'

'A drummer.' The officer nodded. 'What's your line?'

'Cases, suitcases.' The cache gave its own answer. 'Satisfied?'

'Sure,' the officer fumbled at his notebook. 'Just one other thing.' He looked apologetic. 'You speak sort of funny, you know, as if you might be a foreigner or something. Are you?'

'No.' San Luchin searched his hypnotically acquired knowledge of the language for semantically soothing words. 'I've an impediment, it plays hell with my trade, but the regular man's sick just now and I didn't want to lose a contract.' Sickly he realised that he was making things worse.

'So you own the business?' The officer moved towards the telephone on the bedside table. 'Good, that makes things a lot easier. I'll just check with your home town and that'll finish it. Number?'

'I've got it here,' San Luchin fumbled inside his jacket and stepped closer. Now that he knew what he had to do he felt a terrible relief. Anyway, the trophy would be spectacular and, even more important, it would make the game so much more exciting.

He stepped towards the officer.

VI

Gort could feel the tension of the city. People clustered in little knots and groups, their eyes suspicious as they stared at every passer-by, and the wail of sirens echoed from the high buildings as carloads of police hurried from point to point. It was late, almost midnight, but every light was on and the main streets were brilliantly lit. Gort knew that, unless he took precautions, it would only be a matter of time before he was stopped, questioned, and held for arrest. Mason must have circulated his description and every officer would be on the look out for him. He needed time to plan his next move.

An all-night restaurant flashed gaudy neon at him from across the street and he swung towards it, not feeling really at ease until the doors had swung shut behind him. The place was almost empty, a few of the high stools being occupied by morose men and blowzy women, and, after a quick look round, Gort sat in one of the booths. A waiter, his pale face as tired as his apron, wiped automatically at the table and thrust forward a fly-blown menu.

'Coffee.' Gort stared at the almost empty restaurant. 'How's business?'

'You kidding?' The waiter scowled. 'Normally the place is jumping this time of night. Late diners on their way home from the movies, transients, drifters, early-shift workers, we get 'em all. Now look at it. Much more of this and we might as well shut up for good.' He moved away to fetch the order and Gort took advantage of the privacy to check the contents of the stolen wallet.

Money, not too much but enough for immediate emergencies. Some papers, an identification card, a badge, and the usual trivia most men carry about with them. The money would be useful, all that Gort had carried was probably still locked in the precinct safe together with his wrist watch, loose change, keys and other unessentials. He shrugged, he could afford to lose them, they were only local products, and he could return the wallet later. He looked up as the waiter brought his coffee.

'Thanks. What's all the fuss about?'

'Don't you know?' The waiter was too tired to think it strange and was glad of the opportunity to talk. 'It's this killer that's still running around. You meant you haven't heard?'

'I'm a night-worker,' explained Gort. 'My radio's broken and I didn't get a paper. What's the latest?'

'He killed a copper, sliced off his head in a hotel room.' The waiter shook his head. 'I don't get it. That's four dead so far and all the same way.' He licked his lips with morbid interest. 'Four so far, all at different points of the city and all without heads. What the hell would he be wanting with a lot of heads? The guy must be way off the beam.'

'In a hotel room?' Gort looked thoughtful. 'They must know who he is then.'

'Some lousy foreigner from what I can make out. He skipped and they're looking for him now.' The waiter sucked at his teeth. 'They got a description, he's an odd looking character, and if he's on the streets they'll find him.' He swabbed at the table. 'Something wrong with the coffee?'

'It's cold. Fetch me some more will you, without milk this time.'

Alone, Gort considered what he had just heard. He had thought it odd that his escape had caused so much excitement then, as he remembered Mason's telephone conversation he began to understand. A city-wide search for an insane killer, obviously the same killer who had caused the original trouble – and he had walked out right into the middle of it.

The waiter brought the milkless coffee and Gort concentrated on some deep thinking.

The trouble was that these people were so suspicious. He could understand it, of course, all they had to go on was paper-proof and interchangeable identity, but that meant a tremendous amount of work in checking that each person was who he was supposed to be. Even documents weren't enough, personal relationships counted for much more and, unless a man had someone who could vouch for him, he could easily get into serious trouble. Gort had paper-proof, as Captain Mason he should be safe from unauthorised detection unless the person checking him knew the captain personally. Or, no, every policeman would have been warned of the stolen papers so, in a way, he was no better off. For a moment Gort toyed with the idea of stealing someone else's papers then, almost at once, dismissed the notion. Self-preservation was one thing but deliberate, unnecessary crime was something else. And anyway, he had no money.

Like it or not it seemed that he would have to terminate his vacation.

He didn't want to, he had been enjoying himself and he didn't know when the opportunity would arise again for a holiday on this particular world. Educationally it had little to offer, in effect it served as an example of what a civilised world was not, and, even though he had quite a long life ahead of him, yet there were still many more worlds to see. Even Rhubens who had been stationed at the moon base for the past twenty periods had only been down once because, as he said, the stultifying effects were too grave to risk more often. Sitting at the table staring at the brown liquid before him, Gort could agree with the commander. He felt almost stupid, his brain working only with a tremendous effort, and it was quite possible that, if he stayed too long, he might seriously impare his faculties.

Which was one of the reasons why Earth was in such strict quarantine.

The waiter was hovering around again, perhaps waiting for a chance to engage in conversation or perhaps because he was suspicious. Gort rose, payed for the untouched coffee with one of the stolen bills, pocketed his change and stepped out into the street.

A man approached him as he neared a corner, a civilian fortunately, and Gort stopped.

'Going towards Edwards and Main, mister?'

'No.' Gort had memorised a map of the city. 'Eleventh and Spring. Why?'

'We're making up a party.' The man gestured towards a car almost filled with men and women. 'It's pretty dark that way and it could be that the killer's lurking down there. If you lived that way I'd take you home for a couple of dollars. Where did you say you were heading?'

'Eleventh and Spring.'

'Then Sam could run you there.' He turned and shouted towards another man. 'Hey, Sam! Can you take one more?'

'It doesn't matter,' said Gort hastily. 'I've got some business to attend to before then. Thanks anyway.'

He walked off before the man could stop him again, crossing the street and wishing he wasn't so conspicuously alone. He had better leave. He could catch a train or bus, stop off at some small, isolated place, and send out the recall signal for the ship to drop down and pick him up. Staying, while it could be exciting, could also embroil him to a dangerous extent and he didn't want to be reprimanded for immature behaviour.

It was while passing through some back streets that he first learned he was being followed.

At first it didn't register, he had become so used to the lack of contact from the people around him and, when it did, he could hardly believe it. Someone was following him but, that someone wasn't a native of this planet! He halted, keening his mind for maximum reception, and, despite the nullifying effect of the planetary field, he could catch the emissions of another mind. The man, whoever he was, had halted too and was watching Gort with an almost gloating eagerness. Obviously he didn't suspect that Gort was other than what he appeared and, very obviously, he wasn't a Guardian.

But whoever and whatever he was he shouldn't have been here at all.

Slowly Gort continued walking, part of his mind taking care of his progress while the other, greater part, attempted to solve the mystery. Behind him he could sense that the man was coming nearer and, as he approached, his mental pattern became clearer. Gort cursed the peculiarities of this planet which prevented him from using his talents, the mental impression was fogged and blurred to an incredible extent and all he could catch was a sense of hate, of fury, and an overriding, almost sickening sense of hunger.

Gort activated his force-field just as the sear-blade lashed towards the back of his neck.

For a moment there was a struggle as energy combated energy. Sparks showered from the edge of the blade then it grew hot and began to smoke. The man, apparently half-dazed from the transmitted shock, dropped the weapon as Gort swung towards him. He recoiled, his eyes reflecting his hate and, as Gort moved closer he snatched at one of the buttons on his jacket.

'Turn it off!' Gort radiated the command with the full strength of his mind and, at the same time, grabbed at the figure before him. For a moment the two fields strained in conflict then, as that of the Guardian, more powerful and with greater efficiency began to override that of the other, Gort repeated his command.

'Turn it off, you fool! Quick!'

The answer was a blast of hate followed by a quick surge of fear. Confused impressions radiated towards him then, as Gort released his hold and stepped back, smoke and fire seemed to burst from the figure. For a moment he stood, lined in flame, then, as the overloaded protective field collapsed, he slumped and dissolved in smoking ruin.

Slowly Gort stooped and picked up the useless sear-blade.

Even in the early hours the railway terminal was fairly busy and Gort felt quite safe as he sat in the waiting room and waited for the night to pass. He was glad of the security because he had a lot to think about and, the more he thought about it, the nastier it appeared.

Of course, in a way, it had been inevitable. Someone, sometime was sure to stumble on the planet, drop down for a quick look, then try to make something from what they had found. The important thing was that they had managed to do it without registering on the detector screens of the moon-based Guardians. That was serious but, even more serious, was the trail of suspicion which the visitors were leaving behind them.

Gort sighed as he tried to collate his thoughts. Normally it would have been easy. As a Guardian he was a telepath and as a telepath he was automatically a Guardian but things, on this world, weren't normal. Telepathy was non-existent here. Trying to read the minds of the natives was like trying to read the thoughts of a steel ball. It couldn't be done. Whether that was due to the unique planetary field, or whether the very barriers behind which the natives lived affected his faculties, Gort didn't know, but the fact remained that, unless a broadcaster was right next to him, his ability was useless.

And there was more than just the one.

He relaxed and closed his eyes in pretended sleep as a policeman, suspicion clear in his expression, walked down the rows of seats. Gort had taken the precaution of buying a ticket for a train leaving shortly after dawn and he had a good reason for being where he was. He felt the presence of the officer as he halted and stared at him then, apparently satisfied by the slip of pasteboard Gort had stuck in his hat-brim, moved on.

The mental impressions he had received from the dying man had betrayed the presence of others similar to himself. Four others to be exact. And there was something about a ship, a rendezvous, and a time. The whole had been coloured with an overwhelming rage and a bitter self-blame at the loss of a wager. Recalling it made Gort feel mentally unclean.

Visitors from Outside would naturally be equipped with protective force-fields similar to, but usually less powerful than, the one he himself was wearing. Such fields always radiated and that radiation could be picked up by the proper detectors. Unfortunately he didn't have a proper detector and neither did he have the facilities for making one. Even if he had it would have been almost impossible for him to locate, hunt down, and render helpless four separated wearers of protective force-field jackets. The city was too big for that and, without his telepathic ability, Gort was suffering under a tremendous handicap.

He was like a man who owned a car, he could travel faster than any horse – until he lost his car.

He opened his eyes as a man sat down beside him.

'Sorry.' The man was fat, middle-aged, and obviously frightened. 'I didn't mean to wake you.'

'You didn't.' Gort felt that conversation would allay suspicion. The policeman was still patrolling the waiting room. 'Waiting for a train?'

'Yeah, and it can't come too soon for me.' The fat man dabbed at his sweating face. 'I'm getting out of here while I'm safe. You heard the latest?'

'No?'

'That killer's been at work again. Five more people murdered and all found without heads.' He shuddered. 'That makes a total of eight, nine if you count the copper, and they still haven't got him. It just goes to show you how good the police are.'

'They'll catch him.' Gort didn't think so but it seemed the right thing to say. 'Any clues?'

'They've found some of the heads. A boy picked up a suitcase and the damn thing was filled with them. What sort of man would go round doing a thing like that?'

Gort could tell him but he didn't think that the information would help.

'The police are going crazy,' continued the fat man. 'They've shot two men by mistake already and the jails are full of suspects.' He twisted his mouth as though he wanted to spit. 'A hell of a lot of good that's doing. The killer just keeps collecting more heads. They say that they know who he is though.'

'They do?'

'Yeah. A man name of Jones. He killed the cop in his hotel room. They're supposed to have seen him and shot him, but either they're lying or they were using water pistols. You can't tell me that a man can keep on running with bullets inside of him.' He lapsed into silence and glowered at the approaching figure of the policeman.

Gort waited until he had passed then rose to his feet. The pattern was getting clearer and he cursed himself for not having seen it before. Mason had given him the clue, and, aside from that, he should have suspected the use of a sear-blade when he had looked at the original corpse. But it had been so abrupt, so savage, that he had lost control of his reactions. He knew that it could never happen again, death, no matter how ugly, had lost its power to affect him, but he would have preferred to obtain his education the normal way. What had confused him was the fact that, to him, a sear-blade was a normal weapon. He had forgotten that here they were unknown.

Somehow he had to stop the interlopers.

VII

San Luchin was enjoying himself. He crouched in the dark angle of the building and watched the bobbing lights of his pursuers as they hesitantly came towards him. The sight almost made him betray himself just to see whether or not they would repeat their useless attempts to kill him but, as his foot struck the suitcase by his side, he resisted the temptation.

The main thing now was to secure the safety of his trophies.

He had collected with the eye of a connoisseur rather than for sheer quantity. He had been clever too, far cleverer than those other fools who had taken trophies without regard as to time or circumstance. Aside from his latest acquisition, a female with a peculiar shade of red in its long, shoulder-length hair, he had been most circumspect. Now, as he stared towards the lightening sky, he knew that it was time for him to retreat to his hiding place.

He had found one, a dingy, smelly, dirty lodging down in the poorer quarters of the city. A place where, as he suspected, his stolen money would grant him the few hours grace he needed until it was time to leave for the rendezvous. He waited until the bobbing lights were almost upon him then, his protective screen fully activated, he darted with deceptive speed from where he crouched.

A man shouted behind him. Guns roared in the confined space between the buildings and lead whined as it ricocheted from his force-field. Twenty seconds and he was around a selected corner. A door stood before him, it was locked but it opened as he fused the primitive mechanism. Through the building, his cat-eyes equally at home in the dark as the light, down a stair and up another, a second door and back onto the streets again with the entire block between him and his pursuers.

Again he repeated the manoeuvre, smiling with self-satisfaction at having planned the escape routes so well. To be hunted by things which, though they couldn't hurt him, yet betrayed the glimmerings of intelligence, was, to San Luchin, almost as good as the actual taking of a trophy itself. Mentally he decided to give Heltin a bonus for his services in finding this planet. He would return, of course, the next time armed with greater knowledge of local conditions. The mistake this time had lain

in lack of preparation. They should have a base camp, somewhere the hunters could rest and plan their sport, a central
location from which the hunters could strike out in distant
areas and so be able to operate alone. Working with other
hunters was never the same as lone sport. They tended to be
too eager, too unthinking of the full consequences of their
haste. Rivalry seemed to upset their judgement.

They became greedy.

It was after dawn when San Luchin reached his hiding place.
The blowzy woman who let him in betrayed no surprise at the
sight of his suitcase. To her he was a top-story man working the
city under cover of darkness and, naturally, the suitcase was to
contain his loot. All that mattered to her was that he paid well
and caused no trouble. The pay she had taken in advance, the
trouble she hoped would never come but, if it did, she wasn't
totally helpless.

She locked the door after him and jerked her thumb towards
the back room.

'Want anything to eat?'

'No thank you.' San Luchin was only eager to inspect his
trophies but he couldn't tell her that. Instead he stared at her
lined face, mentally visualising it on the wall of his trophy-
room. It would do and, even if he chose to discard it, it would
count for purposes of the wager.

The woman snuffled and wiped her nose.

'See anything of the killer?' If it was a joke it didn't sound
like one. 'I've been listening to the radio, seems to me the city's
all upset.' She stared shrewdly at her lodger. 'It's a wonder you
didn't get stopped.'

'I did.' The smile was awkward but he managed it. 'Twice.
But that was before . . .' He closed one eye and hefted the suitcase.

'A good haul, eh?' Interest lightened her features. 'Let's have
a look.' She misunderstood his hesitation. 'You can trust me,
hell, I'm square, you can ask any of the boys. Maybe I can
steer you onto a good fence if the stuff's right.' She reached
towards the suitcase. 'Let's have a look.'

He let her touch the handle, enjoying the mental image of
what she would do if she saw the contents then, as she fumbled
with the catch, he reluctantly moved it from her reach.

'Sorry, but this is private.' He looked towards the back room from where had come the sounds of muttered conversation. 'Anyone in there?'

'A couple of the boys.' If she felt anger at what had just happened she didn't show it. 'Playing cards and killing a bottle. You want in?'

San Luchin shook his head and climbed the rickety stairs to his filthy room. He felt soiled when he looked at it but that couldn't be helped. Personal discomfort was one of the pleasures of the hunt. Not that it mattered, he was impatient to check his trophies for possible damage and, more important, eager to see that he had a representative collection. The time of rendezvous was getting close and he would have little time for other than a hasty hunt for the purpose of winning the wager. That he would win it he had no doubt, he knew his own capabilities.

Locking the door he set the suitcase on the bed and, opening it, lost himself in the pleasure of what it contained.

Time passed and it began to grow warm. It grew more than warm, it grew hot and, as he loosened his jacket, he felt the first impact of danger.

Too late!

Energy writhed around him, the trapped energy of his protective force-field, normally controlled and safe but now breaking loose. Desperately he tore at his smouldering garments then, as the safety margin was reached and passed, he turned into a literal living flame.

It lasted a split second then, with a gush of released energy, he disrupted, the burning components of his clothing setting fires springing from the rotten woodwork and soiled bedclothes.

Within minutes the room was a raging inferno in which nothing living, or recognisable, could exist.

Gort thought that he had been rather clever. He looked around at the littered components on the bench and listened, not without guilt, to the muffled sounds coming from a deep cupboard. The sounds were caused by the owner and sole employee of the radio repair shop now bound and helpless after admitting his first customer. Gort had paralysed him, put him out of the way, locked the shop and set to work.

Now, several hours, later, he smiled with quiet pride at what he had made.

It was something which would have caused nothing but

derision from the base techs but it was the best he had been able to do. Knowledge, no matter how advanced, is useless without tools and technology. Gort had the knowledge but he had had to build from hopelessly inefficient materials. That he had succeeded at all was something near to a miracle.

On a thick base he had assembled a mass of tubes, wires, altered resistances, adapted transistors, unrecognisable condensers, and a circuit which would have appalled the most knowledgeable mechanic in the business. It was a broadcasting unit of a very special kind designed to do one job and one job only. It would radiate energy which would set up hysterisis in a force-field and amplify it beyond normal tolerance.

He hoped.

Taking off his jacket he picked at a seam and, with exaggerated care, removed a thin, lustrous wire. He set it carefully aside on an insulated table and took a second and a third wire from the jacket. Then, having robbed his own force-field of its power-source, he stripped and, carefully folding the clothes, put them into a metal box. From the outside of the box he ran wires to the ground, then, finally satisfied, he returned to his wires.

Delicately he attached them to his hook-up, taking care that one should not touch the other, fastening them with insulated tools and working with a slow, careful sureness unknown to any but an expert. When he had finished he was trembling with reaction from strain. He waited a moment, checked the hook-up and, turning his back to the bench, closed a switch.

Light blazed from behind him as the power flowed from the wires into the circuit, was transmited on a special frequency, and surged over the city. Opposite him, the ground-wires on the metal box containing his clothes glowed red, white, began to slump, then faded to black again. The light died and, when he turned, the semi-molten mess on the bench defied recognition.

Dressed again Gort considered his next move. The unit he had built had worked and he knew that every force-field in the city other than his own had dissolved into fuming energy. The visitors, whoever they were, would logically have been wearing those fields so, again logically, they had ceased to exist.

All that remained now was the ship.

The rendezvous, Gort knew, was set for tonight. The location was somewhere near or in the city, but just where he didn't know. Normally that wouldn't have mattered. His own detectors, though weak, would have been able to pick up the colossal radiation from any ship. But, if the ship was screened to avoid Guardian detection then it was certain to be able to avoid his own.

Frowning, he sat on the edge of the bench to consider. The dying mind of the visitor had visualised a stretch of ground bounded at one end by a poorly lit road, and Gort felt that it should be familiar. Within his skull the efficient mechanism of his mind began to correlate data and, when he finally slid off the bench, he was smiling.

He reached for the telephone on the counter and, after looking in the directory, dialed a number.

'Police? I want to speak to Captain Mason. That's right, Mason. Who's speaking? Holden. Gort Holden. That's right.'

He waited while the wires hummed.

'Mason? Holden here. I want you to tell me something.' Gort smiled at the noises coming from the instrument. 'Never mind where I am. I'm sorry about your wallet but I'll send it back to you. You can replace the money from that which you took off me. Now listen. That witness of yours, did he say that he'd seen me running towards some waste ground?' Gort frowned at the instrument. 'Please don't waste time. I know that you can probably trace this call but that doesn't matter. Did he? He did? Thanks, that's all I want to know. See you there tonight.' Gort went to hang up then let the receiver hang from its cord. They would be tracing his call and he didn't want to stop them. Someone had to free the irate owner of the shop.

VIII

He spent the afternoon and evening in a cinema, enjoying the sheer primitiveness of the reproduction medium and marvelling again at the inventive genius of these terribly handicapped people. It was dark when he stepped out onto the street and already people, scared of the mysterious 'killer' were hurrying home. An alley gave him all the concealment he needed and, beneath his touch, his force-field shielded gravity and sent him rising like a balloon. To steer himself towards the scene of the first crime was simple and, as he hovered in the shielding darkness, he grinned down at the shapes of lurking figures below.

Mason had the place surrounded.

After that there was nothing to do but wait. He didn't know the exact time of the rendezvous, only that it was for tonight, but he guessed that it would be around midnight or a little later. Actually it was two hours past midnight and he almost missed the ship altogether.

A rush of air warned him, that and a slight occlusion of his marker-points. Gently he lowered himself towards the invisible bulk until, as he penetrated the outer screens, he saw the scarred hull of the ship itself.

He was standing outside when Heltin opened the air lock.

'San Luchin?' The explorer stared outside. 'Where are you?'

Gort moved a step closer.

'San Luchin? Hurry up, will you, I want to get away from here.' He cursed monotonously as Gort didn't move. 'What's the matter? You hurt or something?' Impulsively he jumped from the air lock. 'I . . .'

Gort caught him as he fell, paralysed and helpless. Quickly he carried him back into the ship and, when Heltin recovered consciousness, he stared up into the disguised features of the Guardian.

'What goes on? Who are you?' Heltin climbed to his feet. 'Where are the people I brought here?'

'How many did you bring?' Gort used mental communication and the fact that he did so seemed to shock Heltin into an awareness of his position. He sagged and almost fell and when he had finally straightened his features were a peculiar greenish colour.

'The Guardians!'

'That's right. Well?'

'I'm just a pilot,' babbled the hapless man. 'I'm working on charter. All I know is that I dropped San Luchin with four of his friends here three revolutions ago.' He swallowed. 'You know about them?'

'What did you bring them here to do?'

'I don't know.' It was useless and Heltin knew it. To lie to the Guardians, or to any telepath was a waste of time. He turned to the attack. 'Well, what of it? So I've broken a few Regs, no great crime in that, is there?'

'Enough to earn you quite a period of immiolation.' Gort was deliberately casual. 'You knew that San Luchin and his friends were hunters. You knew that they came here to collect trophies. You knew just what that meant to the inhabitants of this planet. You've not only broken quarantine but you've broken the Prime Ethic. I'd guess that you've earned permanent immiolation.'

'No I haven't!' Heltin seemed about to collapse. 'These things aren't human. You know they're not. How could I have broken the Prime Ethic when I haven't killed or caused the death of a human being.' He looked triumphantly at Gort. 'You know that I speak the truth, you damn mind-leeches should be able to know that, and you know that all I've done is to bust quarantine.'

He was right. Technically the inhabitants of this planet weren't human and so Heltin hadn't been guilty of breaking the Prime Ethic. That was reserved for races who obeyed the one great requirement of the galactic federation. No member of any one race must ever kill a member of that race. It was the dividing line between human and non-human, men and monsters and, unfortunately, the inhabitants of Earth were still in the monster stage.

'You can't touch me,' sneered Heltin. 'So I get a few periods immiolation, so what? Get on with it, Guardian, let's get it over with.'

Gort nodded, his mind busy with strange concepts. Heltin was guilty but, because of a technicality, he was going to get away with it. Unless . . .

Gort stepped forward and felt the slight body before him. No protective clothing. He jerked his hand towards the air lock.

'Outside.'

'What? Say, what are you up to. You can't do this to me.'

'Get outside or I'll throw you out at two diameters. Quick now!' He used the power of his mind and Heltin obeyed as he had to obey. Gort stood at the open air lock and threw Mason's wallet towards the shivering man. 'Right. Now walk to that road, drop that wallet, and come back here on the run.'

It was murder and yet, in a way, it wasn't. The Guardians had strong powers and were permitted to use their discretion. If Heltin returned he would be taken to the moon base to stand his trial. If he didn't . . .

The watching policemen had waited hours and must have been getting tired but they woke up at the sight of a strange figure coming from nowhere. Heltin ignored the first challenge, he took fright at the second, he began to run at the third. The roar of many weapons blasted his body to a shapeless pulp.

Later, when well on his way to the moon base, Gort had time to assess his vacation. He had got out of a difficult situation without revealing his extra-terrestrial origin. He had stopped and punished the menace of an unauthorised visitation to a quarantined planet. He had provided a suitable suspect for the mysterious 'killer' and so had made Mason happy. He had taken charge of the ship which had slipped past the detector screens and so would make Rhubens happy too. Promotion would be inevitable and Gort smiled as he thought about it.

Not such a bad vacation after all.

Appendices

I hope this volume has whetted your appetite for the science fiction of the period, and to that end I am supplying the following appendices.

They comprise the four following sections:

(A) *Checklist of Author's Works:* This details the sf/fantasy and associated works published during the period April 1946 to March 1945 for the ten authors included in this anthology plus ten others representative of the period.

(B) *Summary of Magazine Issues:* A guide to the frequency and number of the issues of the sf/weird magazines covered in this book.

(C) *Glossary of Magazine Editors:* A Who's Who of sf/fantasy editors of the period, with a guide to the number of issues for which they were responsible.

(D) *Note on Cover Artists:* A guide to the cover artists of the period and the magazines they illustrated.

Notes on Layout

Appendix A
Following the name of the author and his birth/death dates are six columns, which read from left to right as follows:

1 Story number.
2 Story Title.
3 Story length, i.e.:
    s = short story (up to 10,000 words).
    nt = novelettes (10–20,000 words).
    na = novella (20–30,000 words).
    sn = short novel (30–50,000 words).
    n = novel (over 50,000 words). If serialised then n3,
        say = three episodes. (The date that follows is
        that of the first episode.)
4 Publication in which story appeared. (List of abbreviations follows the checklist.)
5 and 6 Date of publication, month and year.
If the story title is followed by a symbol it means the story was published under a pseudonym. Details are given after each author. A collaboration with another author (unless disguised under a single pen-name) is noted after the title as follows:
w. F. N. Waldrop, means collaboration with F. N. Waldrop.
A letter in brackets after the story title indicates the story is part of a connected series, and details are again given after each author's listing.
Because of the profusion of reprint magazines in this period I have exercised some restrictions. Stories are listed if they are reprinted in an sf magazine after an original appearance in a mainstream publication or another country's sf magazine. Also if the previous publication was outside the period covered.

Appendix B
In each case the year runs from April to March following on from the first appearance of *Amazing Stories* in April 1926. Thus the one issue of *10 Story Fantasy* appeared sometime between April 1950 and March 1951. (Full details are given in this volume's introduction.) Foreign reprint editions are in most cases omitted.

Appendix C
Only editors directly responsible for the magazines are listed, and where relevant their immediate assistants or supervisors. The number in brackets following the magazine issue dates is the number of issues for which the editor was responsible.

Appendix D

For convenience the artists are linked with the magazine publishers. Following the artist's name is the number of covers he illustrated (where known or estimated), together with a percentage of the total issues as a guide to his output.

These appendices do not profess to be definitive, but every endeavour has been made to be as complete as possible. I would appreciate anyone pointing out errors and omissions.

(A) CHECKLIST OF AUTHORS' WORKS: April 1946— March 1956

1 POUL ANDERSON (born 1926)

1	Tomorrow's Children (w. F. N. Waldrop)	nt	ASF	Mar 47
2	Logic	nt	ASF	Jul 47
3	Genius	nt	ASF	Dec 48
4	Prophecy	s	ASF	May 49
5	Entity (w. J. Gergen)	s	ASF	Jun 49
6	The Double-Dyed Villains ... (A) ...	nt	ASF	Sep 49
7	Time Heals	s	ASF	Oct 49
8	Gypsy	s	ASF	Jan 50
9	The Perfect Weapon	s	ASF	Feb 50
10	Trespass (w. G. R. Dickson)	s	FSQ	Spr 50
11	The Helping Hand	nt	ASF	May 50
12	The Long Return...	nt	FcS	Sep 50
13	Star Ship	s	PS	Fal 50
14	The Star Beast	nt	SSS	Sep 50
15	Quixote and the Windmill...	s	ASF	Nov 50
16	Flight to Forever...	nt	SSS	Nov 50
17	Tiger By the Tail... (B)	nt	PS	Jan 51
18	Witch of the Demon Seas*	na	PS	Jan 51
19	World of the Mad	s	IMG	Feb 51
20	The Acolytes	s	WB	Feb 51
21	Incomplete Superman	nt	FcS	Mar 51
22	Duel on Syrtis	s	PS	Mar 51
23	Interloper	s	F&SF	Apr 51
24	Inside Earth	nt	GSF	Apr 51
25	Honourable Enemies ... (B)	s	FcS	May 51
26	Heroes Are Made (w. G. R. Dickson) (C)	s	OW	May 51
27	Earthman, Beware!	s	SSS	Jun 51
28	The Missionaries	s	OW	Jul 51
29	The Virgin of Valkarion	nt	PS	Jul 51
30	Terminal Quest	s	SSS	Aug 51
31	Lord of a Thousand Suns	nt	PS	Sep 51
32	Swordsman of Lost Terra	nt	PS	Nov 51
33	Son of the Sword...	s	ADV	Jan 52
34	Sargasso of Lost Starships...	nt	PS	Jan 52
35	Captive of the Centaurianess	nt	PS	Mar 52
36	Garden in the Void	nt	GSF	May 52
37	War-Maid of Mars	nt	PS	May 52
38	The Star Plunderer	s	PS	Sep 52
39	*Vault of the Ages*	n		*book,* 52

40	Un-Man ... (D)	sn	ASF	Jan	53
41	The Green Thumb	s	SFQ	Feb	53
42	Security	nt	SSF	Feb	53
43	Ashtaru The Terrible	s	FM	Mar	53
44	Three Wishes	s	FAN	Mar	53
45	Courier of Chaos	s	FSF	Mar	53
46	Horse Trader	nt	GSF	Mar	53
47	When Half-Gods Go	s	F&SF	May	53
48	Rachaela	s	FF	Jun	53
49	In Hoka Signo Vinces (w. G. R. Dickson) ... (C)	s	OW	Jun	53
50	Enough Rope (A)	nt	ASF	Jul	53
51	The Temple of Earth	nt	RS	Jul	53
52	The Nest	s	SFA	Jul	53
53	Sam Hall	nt	ASF	Aug	53
54	The Disintegrating Sky	s	FU	Aug	53
55	Sentiment, Inc	nt	SFS	♯ 1,	53
56	The Troublemakers	nt	CSF	Sep	53
57	Three Hearts and Three Lions	sn2	F&SF	Sep	53
58	The Escape	n2	SSF	Sep	53

Two-part serial, only one part published. Appeared later in bookform as *Brain Wave*.

59	Silent Victory	sn	2SA	Win	53
60	The Adventure of the Misplaced Hound (w. G. R. Dickson) ... (C)	s	USF	Dec	53
61	The Chapter Ends	s	DSF	Jan	54
62	The Sensitive Man	na	FU	Jan	54
63	The Immortal Game	s	F&SF	Feb	54
64	Butch	nt	*TtC*	bk,	54
65	Ghetto	nt	F&SF	May	54
66	Question and Answer	sn2	ASF	Jun	54
67	The Ambassadors of Flesh ... (B)	s	PS	Sum	54
68	Teucan	s	CSF	Jul	54
69	*Brain Wave* (full version of no 58)	n		book,	54
70	Contact Point (w. T. R. Cogswell) ...	s	IF	Aug	54
71	The Big Rain ... (D)	na	ASF	Oct	54
72	*The Broken Sword*	n		book,	54
73	The Stranger Was Himself	s	FU	Dec	54
74	Elliptic Orbit	s	IF	Dec	54
75	The Snows of Ganymede	na	SS	Win	55
76	Yo Ho Hoka! (w. G. R. Dickson) (C)	nt	F&SF	Mar	55
77	The Long Way Home	n4	ASF	Apr	55
78	Time Patrol ... (E)	nt	F&SF	May	55
79	Snowball	nt	IF	May	55
80	Out of the Iron Womb	nt	PS	Sum	55
81	Soldier from the Stars	nt	FU	Jun	55

82	Butch (reprinting of no 64)	nt	NW	Jul	55
83	Inside Straight	s	F&SF	Aug	55
84	The Tiddleywink Warriors (w. G. R. Dickson ... (C)	s	F&SF	Aug	55
85	Joy in Mudville (w. G. R. Dickson (C)	nt	F&SF	Nov	55
86	Delenda Est ... (E)	nt	F&SF	Dec	55
87	The Corkscrew of Space	s	GSF	Feb	56
88	Catalysis	s	IF	Feb	56
89	Superstition	s	F&SF	Mar	56

Pseudonyms: *A. A. Craig (no 18).
Series: A   Galactic Patrol (nos 6, 50).
        B   Dominic Flandry (nos 17, 25, 67).
        C   Hoka (nos 26, 49, 60, 76, 84, 85).
        D   Un-Man (nos 40, 71).
        E   Time Patrol (nos 78, 86).
    Note: Many of Anderson's stories fit within the framework of his *Future History* series. See SS Win 55 for chart.

2 RAY BRADBURY (born 1920)

1	The Miracles of Jamie	s	CHM	Apr	46
2	Rocket Skin	s	TW	Spr	46
3	One Timeless Spring	s	CLR	Apr	46
4	The Smiling People	s	WT	May	46
5	Her Eyes, Her Lips, Her Limbs* ...	s	CFN	Jun	46
6	The Million Year Picnic ... (A) ...	s	PS	Sum	46
7	Lorelei of the Red Mist (w. L. Brackett)	na	PS	Sum	46
8	Chrysalis	s	AS	Jul	46
9	The Night	s	WT	Jul	46
10	Electrocution*	s	CFN	Aug	46
11	The Creatures That Time Forgot ...	nt	PS	Fal	46
12	Homecoming	s	MMS	Oct	46
13	Let's Play 'Poison'	s	WT	Nov	46
14	The Small Assassin	s	DM	Nov	46
15	A Careful Man Dies	s	ND	Nov	46
16	The Handler	s	WT	Jan	47
17	The Man Upstairs	s	HPR	Mar	47
18	Rocket Summer	s	PS	Spr	47
19	Tomorrow and Tomorrow	s	FA	May	47
20	The Cistern	s	MMS	May	47
21	The Emissary				
22	Uncle Einar				
23	The Next in Line	s	DC	bk,	47
24	The Maiden				
25	The Night Sets				
26	Jack-in-the-Box				

152	A Sound of Thunder (reprinting of no 124)	s	PS	Jan	54
153	The Dwarf	s	FAN	Jan	54
154	The Marriage Mender	s	CLR	Jan	54
155	Dinner at Dawn	s	EW	Feb	54
156	The Watchful Poker Chip	s	BEY	Mar	54
157	Interval in Sunlight	s	ESQ	Mar	54
158	All Summer in a Day	s	F&SF	Mar	54
159	Shopping for Death	s	McL	Jun	54
160	At Midnight, in the Month of June...	s	EQ	Jun	54
161	They Knew What They Wanted ...	s	SEP	Jun	54
162	The Wonderful Death of Dudley Stone	s	CHM	Jul	54
163	Promotion to Satellite (reprinted from TW Fal 43)	s	FSM	Sum	54
164	The Swan	s	CSP	Sep	54
165	The Strawberry Window	s	*STA*	#3	54
166	The Piper (reprinted from TW Feb 43)	s	FSM	Spr	55
167	The Last, the Very Last	s	RPT	Jun	55
168	The Trolley	s	GH	Jul	55
169	The Dragon	s	ESQ	Aug	55
170	The Mice	s	ESC	Oct	55
171	*Switch on the Night*	n		*book,*	55
172	Summer in the Air	s	SEP	Feb	56
173	The Dragon (reprinting of no 169) ...	s	F&SF	Mar	56

Pseudonyms: *William Elliott (nos 5, 10).
　　　　　　　　**Brett Sterling (no 50).
　　　　　　　　　†Leonard Spaulding (no 84).
　　　　　　　　　‡Leonard Douglas (no 122).

Series: All stories marked (A) form part of *The Martian Chronicles* series (nos 6, 42-4, 46, 54-5, 60, 71, 73, 81-2, 88, 96-7, 102, 119).

Note: I am indebted to the checklist compiled by William F. Nolan for the May 1963 *Magazine of Fantasy and Science Fiction* for much of the above information.)

3 ARTHUR C. CLARKE (born 1917)

1	Loophole	s	ASF	Apr	46
2	Rescue Party	s	ASF	Mar	46
3	Technical Error	s	FTy	Dec	46
4	Castaway*	s	FTy	Apr	47
5	The Fires Within**	s	FTy	Aug	47
6	Inheritance*	s	NW	#3	47
7	Inheritance (reprinting of no 6) ...	s	ASF	Sep	48

50	No Morning After	... ...	s	*TtC*	book	54
51	The Deep Range	nt	ARGb	Apr	54
52	The Sentinel (reprinting of no 29) ...	s	NW	Apr	54
53	The Secret Weapon	s	ADV	Jun	54
54	Patent Pending	s			54
55	The Deep Range (first US printing of no 51)	nt	*STA*	# 3	54
56	? (see note)	s	F&SF	Jul	55
57	The Star	s	INF	Nov	55
58	What Goes Up	s	F&SF	Jan	56

Pseudonyms: *Charles Willis (nos 4, 6, 24).
**E. G. O'Brien (no 5).

Note: Clarke titled the story 'This Earth of Majesty', but Boucher ran it as '?' asking readers to title it. It was subsequently titled 'Refugee' and 'Royal Prerogative'.

4 DAMON KNIGHT (born 1922)

1	The Third Little Green Man	s	PS	Sum	48
2	Tiger Ride (w. J. Blish)	s	ASF	Oct	48
3	No Winter, No Summer*	s	TW	Oct	48
4	The Weakness of Rvog (w. J. Blish)	s	TW	Feb	49
5	The Star Beast	s	PS	Spr	49
6	Gravity Trap	s	SSS	Jul	49
7	Not with a Bang	s	F&SF	Win	50
8	To Serve Man	s	GSF	Nov	50
9	The Secret People (w. J. Blish) ...	s	FcS	Nov	50
10	The Mighty Fallen	s	FSQ	Spr	51
11	Ask Me Anything	s	GSF	May	51
12	Don't Live in the Past	nt	GSF	Jun	51
13	Cabin Boy	s	GSF	Sep	51
14	World without Children	nt	GSF	Dec	51
15	The Analogues	s	ASF	Jan	52
16	Catch That Martian	s	GSF	Feb	52
17	Ticket to Anywhere	s	GSF	Apr	52
18	It Kud Habben Tu Yu!	s	IMG	Sep	52
19	The Beachcomber	s	IMG	Dec	52
20	In the Beginning	s	FSF	Jan	53
21	Double Meaning	na	SS	Jan	53
22	Four in One	nt	GSF	Feb	53
23	Definition	s	SS	Feb	53
24	The Worshippers	s	SSF	Mar	53
25	Turncoat	na	TW	Apr	53
26	Babel II	s	BEY	Jul	53
27	Natural State	na	GSF	Jan	54

28	Anachron	s	IF	Jan	54
29	Special Delivery	s	GSF	Apr	54
30	Rule Golden	na	SFA	May	54
31	The Earth Quarter	nt	IF	Jan	55
32	Dulcie & Decorum	s	GSF	Mar	55
33	You're Another	nt	F&SF	Jun	55
34	The Country of the Kind	s	F&SF	Feb	56
35	A Likely Story	s	INF	Feb	56

Pseudonyms: *Donald Laverty (w. J. Blish: no 3).

5 HENRY KUTTNER (1914-58)

1	The Cure**	s	ASF	May	46
2	The Dark World	n	SS	Sum	46
3	Rain Check**	s	ASF	Jul	46
4	The Little Things	s	TW	Fal	46
5	Call Him Demon*	s	TW	Fal	46
6	Absalom	s	SS	Fal	46
7	I Am Eden	nt	TW	Dec	46
8	Time Enough**	s	ASF	Dec	46
9	Tomorrow and Tomorrow**	n2	ASF	Jan	47
10	Trouble on Titan...	s	TW	Feb	47
11	Juke-Box†	s	TW	Feb	47
12	Way of the Gods	nt	TW	Apr	47
13	Project**	s	ASF	Apr	47
14	Lands of the Earthquake	n	SS	May	47
15	Jesting Pilot**	s	ASF	May	47
16	Fury‡	n3	ASF	May	47
17	The Big Night°	s	TW	Jun	47
18	Dream's End	s	SS	Jul	47
19	Atomic!	s	TW	Aug	47
20	Dark Dawn*	s	TW	Aug	47
21	Noon°	s	TW	Aug	47
22	Lord of the Storm*	n	SS	Sep	47
23	Exit the Professor ... (A)	s	TW	Oct	47
24	Margin for Error**	nt	ASF	Nov	47
25	The Power and the Glory	nt	TW	Dec	47
26	Don't Look Now	s	SS	Mar	48
27	Pile of Trouble ... (A)	s	TW	Apr	48
28	Ex Machina** ... (B)	nt	ASF	Apr	48
29	The Mask of Circe	n	SS	May	48
30	When The Earth Lived (reprinted from TW Oct 37)	s	SS	Jul	48
31	Happy Ending	s	TW	Aug	48
32	The Time Axis	n	SS	Jan	49

33	The Black Sun Rises (first US appearance; reprinted from Canadian SSS Jun 44)	s	SSS	Jan 49
34	Private Eye**	nt	ASF	Jan 49
35	The Prisoner in the Skull**	nt	ASF	Feb 49
36	See You Later ... (A)	s	TW	Jun 49
37	Hollywood on the Moon (reprinted from TW Apr 38)	nt	SS	Jul 49
38	The Portal in the Picture	n	SS	Sep 49
39	Cold War (w. C. L. Moore) ... (A)	s	TW	Oct 49
40	Roman Holidayˣ (reprinted from TW Aug 39)	s	SS	Jan 50
41	The Voice of the Lobster	nt	TW	Feb 50
42	Earth's Last Citadel (w. C. L. Moore) (reprinted from ARG Apr 43) ...	n	FN	Jul 50
43	As You Were	nt	TW	Aug 50
44	The Sky is Falling=	s	PS	Fal 50
45	The Energy Eaters (w. A. K. Barnes) (reprinted from TW Oct 39)... ...	s	SS	Sep 50
46	Carry Me Home=	nt	PS	Nov 50
47	The Odyssey of Yiggar Throlg= ...	s	SS	Jan 51
48	Golden Apple=	s	FFM	Mar 51
49	Android=	nt	F&SF	Jun 51
50	World's Pharaohˣ (reprinted from TW Dec 39)	s	FSM	Sum 51
51	We Shall Come Back=	nt	SFQ	Nov 51
52	The Well of the Worlds	sn	SS	Mar 52
53	The Ego Machine	nt	SSF	May 52
54	A Million Years to Conquer (reprinted from SS Nov 40)	sn	FSM	Sep 52
55	Satan Sends Flowers	s	FAN	Jan 53
56	Baby Face (reprinted from TW Spr 45)	s	FSM	Mar 53
57	Science is Goldenˣ (reprinted from TW Apr 40)	s	FSM	May 53
58	The Visitors=	s	SFQ	May 53
59	Home is the Hunter (w. C. L. Moore)	s	GSF	Jul 53
60	Or Else	s	AS	Aug 53
61	Humpty Dumpty** ... (C)	nt	ASF	Sep 53
62	A Wild Surmise (w. C. L. Moore) ...	s	*STA*	#1, 53
63	Where The World is Quiet=	s	FU	May 54
64	A God Named Kroo (reprinted from TW Win 44)	nt	FSM	Sum 54
65	Dames in Poisonˣ (reprinted from TW Jun 42)	s	FSM	Fal 54

66	Swing Your Lady^x (reprinted from TW Win 44)	s	FSM	Win 55
67	Two-Handed Engine (w. C. L. Moore)	s	F&SF	Aug 55

Pseudonyms: *Keith Hammond (w. C. L. Moore: nos 5, 20, 22).
**Lewis Padgett (w. C. L. Moore: nos 1, 3, 8-9, 13, 15, 24, 28, 34-5, 61).
†Woodrow Wilson Smith (no 11).
‡Lawrence O'Donnell (w. C. L. Moore: no 16).
°Hudson Hastings (w. C. L. Moore: nos 17, 21).
xKelvin Kent (w. A. K. Barnes: nos 40, 57; solo: 50, 65-6).
=C. H. Liddell (w. C. L. Moore: nos 44, 46-9, 51, 58, 63).

Series: A Lancelot Hogben (nos 23, 27, 36, 39).
B Gallegher (no 28).
C Baldy (no 61).

6 RICHARD MATHESON (born 1926)

1	Born of Man and Woman	s	F&SF	Sum	50
2	Third from the Sun	s	GSF	Oct	50
3	The Waker Dreams	s	GSF	Dec	50
4	Clothes Make the Man	s	WB	Feb	51
5	Through Channels	s	F&SF	Apr	51
6	'Drink My Red Blood'	s	IMG	Apr	51
7	The Thing	s	MSS	May	51
8	Witch War	s	SS	Jul	51
9	Dress of White Silk	s	F&SF	Oct	51
10	Return	s	TW	Oct	51
11	Mountains of the Mind	nt	MSF	Nov	51
12	Letter to the Editor	s	IMG	Jan	52
13	SRL Ad	s	F&SF	Apr	52
14	The Foodlegger	s	TW	Apr	52
15	Lover When You're Near Me	s	GSF	May	52
16	Shipshape Home	s	GSF	Jul	52
17	To Fit the Crime	s	FAN	Nov	52
18	Brother to the Machine	s	IF	Nov	52
19	Mad House	s	FAN	Jan	53
20	The Disinheritors	s	FSM	Jan	53
21	Wet Straw	s	WT	Jan	53
22	Death Ship	s	FSM	Mar	53
23	Disappearing Act...	s	F&SF	Mar	53
24	The Last Day	s	AS	Apr	53
25	The Wedding	s	BEY	Jul	53
26	Lazarus II	s	FSM	Jul	53
27	Slaughter House	s	WT	Jul	53

7 ROSS ROCKLYNNE (born 1915)

25	Winner Take All ...	...	...	...	...	s	*TtC* bk, 54

Pseudonyms: *H. F. Cente (no 20).

8 ROBERT SHECKLEY (born 1928)

1	Final Examination	s	IMG	May 52
2	Fear in the Night	s	TDW	52
3	Proof of the Pudding	s	GSF	Aug 52
4	We Are Alone	s	FSF	Nov 52
5	Warrior Race	s	GSF	Nov 52
6	The Impacted Man	s	ASF	Dec 52
7	Cost of Living	s	GSF	Dec 52
8	The Leech*	s	GSF	Dec 52
9	Writing Class	s	IMG	Dec 52
10	The Demons	s	FF	Feb 53
11	Feeding Time**	s	FF	Feb 53
12	Watchbird	s	GSF	Feb 53
13	The Last Weapon	s	STA	# 1, 53
14	Fool's Mate	s	ASF	Mar 53
15	The Monsters	s	F&SF	Mar 53
16	Seventh Victim	s	GSF	May 53
17	Operating Instructions	s	ASF	May 53
18	Specialist	s	GSF	May 53
19	What Goes Up	s	SFA	May 53
20	Restricted Area	s	AS	Jun 53
21	Warm	s	GSF	Jun 53
22	The Altar	s	FAN	Jul 53
23	The King's Wishes	s	F&SF	Jul 53
24	Diplomatic Immunity	s	GSF	Aug 53
25	Ask a Foolish Question	s	SFS	# 1, 53
26	Fishing Season	s	TW	Aug 53
27	Wild Talents, Inc.	s	FAN	Sep 53
28	Closed Circuit	s	SFA	Sep 53
29	The Hour of Battle	s	SSF	Sep 53
30	Beside Still Waters	s	AS	Oct 53
31	The Special Exhibit	s	ESQ	Oct 53
32	Potential	s	ASF	Nov 53
33	What a Man Believes	s	FAN	Nov 53
34	Ultimatum!	s	FSF	Nov 53
35	Keep Your Shape	s	GSF	Nov 53
36	The Perfect Woman	s	AS	Dec 53
37	One Man's Poison	s	GSF	Dec 53
38	The Odour of Thought	s	STA	# 2, 53
39	Time Check for Control	s	SFD	# 1, 54
40	Hands Off	s	GSF	Apr 54
41	Carrier	nt	IF	Apr 54

42	Paradise II	s	*TtC*	bk, 54
43	Off-Limits Planet	s	IMG	May 54
44	Man of the Hour	s	SFD	# 2, 54
45	Spacemen in the Dark	s	SFD	# 2, 54
46	The Hungry	s	FAN	Jun 54
47	Something for Nothing	s	GSF	Jun 54
48	The Ogre Test	s	PS	Sum 54
49	The Accountant	s	F&SF	Jul 54
50	A Thief in Time	s	GSF	Jul 54
51	The Odour of Thought (reprinting of no 38)	s	NW	Jul 54
52	Subsistence Level**	s	GSF	Aug 54
53	The Academy	s	IF	Aug 54
54	The Last Weapon (reprinting of no 13)	s	NW	Aug 54
55	Milk Run	s	GSF	Sep 54
56	The Battle	s	IF	Sep 54
57	Hex on Hax	s	PS	Fal 54
58	The Slow Season	s	F&SF	Oct 54
59	Conquerors' Planet	s	FU	Oct 54
60	Ghost V	s	GSF	Oct 54
61	Minority Group	s	FU	Nov 54
62	The Laxian Key	s	GSF	Nov 54
63	Skulking Permit	s	GSF	Dec 54
64	Uncle Tom's Planet**	s	GSF	Dec 54
65	Squirrel Cage	s	GSF	Jan 55
66	The Fortunate Person	s	FU	Feb 55
67	The Lifeboat Mutiny	s	GSF	Apr 55
68	The Deep Hole to China	s	FU	Jun 55
69	The Necessary Thing	s	GSF	Jun 55
70	Earth, Air, Fire and Water	s	ASF	Jul 55
71	Deadhead	s	GSF	Jul 55
72	Paradise II (reprinting of no 42)	s	NW	Jul 55
73	Hunting Problem	s	GSF	Sep 55
74	Disposal Service	s	BB	55
75	A Ticket to Tranai	nt	GSF	Oct 55
76	Warrior's Return	s	GSF	Nov 55
77	The Body	s	GSF	Jan 56
78	Trap**	s	GSF	Feb 56
79	The Skag Castle	nt	FU	Mar 56

Pseudonyms: *Phillips Barbee (no 8).
**Finn O'Donnevan (nos 11, 52, 64, 78).

9 THEODORE STURGEON (born 1918)

1	Memorial	s	ASF	Apr 46
2	The Chromium Helmet	nt	ASF	Jun 46

3	Mewhu's Jet	nt	ASF	Nov	46
4	Cellmate	s	WT	Jan	47
5	Blabbermouth	s	AS	Feb	47
6	Maturity	nt	ASF	Feb	47
7	Fluffy	s	WT	Mar	47
8	Bianca's Hands	s	ARGb	May	47
9	Tiny and the Monster	nt	ASF	May	47
10	The Sky Was Full of Ships	s	TW	Jun	47
11	Largo	s	FA	Jul	47
12	Unite and Conquer	s	ASF	Oct	47
13	Thunder and Roses	nt	ASF	Nov	47
14	The Deadly Ratio	s	WT	Jan	48
15	There is no Defense	nt	ASF	Feb	48
16	The Professor's Teddy Bear	s	WT	Mar	48
17	Abreaction	s	WT	Jul	48
18	Memory	s	TW	Aug	48
19	The Purple Light	s	SrS	Sep	48
20	That Low	s	FFM	Oct	48
21	The Love of Heaven	s	ASF	Nov	48
22	The Perfect Host	s	WT	Nov	48
23	Messenger	s	TW	Feb	49
24	The Martian and the Moron	s	WT	Mar	49
25	Prodigy	s	ASF	Apr	49
26	Die, Maestro, Die	s	DD	May	49
27	Farewell to Eden	s	*IfM*	May	49
28	Minority Report	s	ASF	Jun	49
29	One Foot and the Grave	nt	WT	Sep	49
30	The Hurkle is a Happy Beast	s	MoF	Fal	49
31	What Dead Men Tell	nt	ASF	Nov	49
32	The Dreaming Jewels	n	FA	Feb	50
33	The Stars Are the Styx	nt	GSF	Oct	50
34	Rule of Three	nt	GSF	Jan	51
35	'Shadow, Shadow, on the Wall . . .'	s	IMG	Feb	51
36	Last Laugh	s	OW	Mar	51
37	Ghost of a Chance (reprinting of 'The Green-Eyed Monster', UW Jun 43)	s	SUS	Spr	51
38	Make Room for Me!	s	FA	May	51
39	The Travelling Crag	nt	FA	Jul	51
40	Excalibur and the Atom	na	FA	Aug	51
41	The Incubi of Parallel X	nt	PS	Sep	51
42	Never Underestimate	s	IF	Mar	52
43	The Sex Opposite	nt	FAN	Fal	52
44	Baby Is Three	na	GSF	Oct	52
45	Killdozer! (reprinting from ASF Nov 44)	na	FFM	Dec	52
46	Saucer of Loneliness	s	GSF	Feb	53

47	The Fabulous Idiot	nt	*MTH*,	bk	53
48	Morality	nt	*MTH*,	bk	53
49	The Way Home	s	AS	Apr	53
50	The World Well Lost	s	USF	Jun	53
51	. . . And My Fear Is Great	na	BEY	Jul	53
52	The Dark Room	nt	FAN	Jul	53
53	The Wages of Synergy	nt	SS	Aug	53
54	Talent	s	BEY	Sep	53
55	The Touch of Your Hand	nt	GSF	Sep	53
56	A Way of Thinking	nt	AS	Oct	53
57	The Silken-Swift	s	F&SF	Nov	53
58	Mr Costello, Hero	s	GSF	Dec	53
59	The Clinic	s	*STA*	# 2,	53
60	The Music	s	*EPU*,	bk	53
61	The Education of Drusilla Strange	nt	GSF	Mar	54
62	Beware the Fury	s	FAN	Apr	54
63	Granny Won't Knit	na	GSF	May	54
64	The Golden Helix	na	TW	Sum	54
65	To Here and Easel	na	*SSN*,	bk	54
66	When You're Smiling	s	GSF	Jan	55
67	Who?	nt	GSF	Mar	55
68	Hurricane Trio	nt	GSF	Apr	55
69	The Heart	s	OW	May	55
70	The Riddle of Ragnarok (w. D. Ward)	s	FU	Jun	55
71	Twink	s	GSF	Aug	55
72	So Near the Darkness...	nt	FU	Nov	55
73	The (Widget), The (Wadgett), and Boff	sn2	F&SF	Nov	55
74	Bright Segment	nt	*CVR*,	bk	55
75	Won't You Walk—	nt	ASF	Jan	56
76	Half-Way Tree Murder	s	SMM	Mar	56

Note: I am indebted to the checklist compiled by Sam Moskowitz for the September 1962 *Magazine of Fantasy & Science Fiction* for much of the above information.

10 E. C. TUBB (born 1919)

1	No Short Cuts	s	NW	Sum	51
2	Greek Gift	s	NW	Aut	51
3	*Saturn Patrol*[1]	sn		book	51
4	*Planetfall*[2]	sn		book	51
5	Entrance Exam	s	NW	Win	51
6	Grounded	s	SFy	Win	51
7	Without Bugles ... (A)	s	NW	Jan	52
8	*Argentis*[3]	sn		book	52
9	Third Party	s	NW	Mar	52

56	*The Metal Easter*[11]	n		book	54
57	*Journey to Mars*	n		book	54
58	*Menace from the Past*[9]	n		book	54
59	Episode	s	NEB	Apr	54
60	Unwanted Heritage (reprinting of no 15)	s	SPW	Apr	54
61	*City of No Return*	n		book	54
62	Death Deferred	s	AUT	May	54
63	Tomorrow	nt	SFy	May	54
64	Homecoming	s	USF	May	54
65	Forbidden Fruit	nt3	VSB	May	54
66	Illusion[12]	s	VSB	May	54
67	*The Stellar Legion*	n		book	54
68	*The Hell Planet*	n		book	54
69	*The Resurrected Man*...	n		book	54
70	Occupational Hazard	s	SFy	Jul	54
71	*The Hand of Havoc*[5]	sn		book	54
72	Project One	na	NEB	Aug	54
73	Logic	s	AUT	Sep	54
74	Homeward Bound[12]	s	BSF	Sep	54
75	Emergency Exit[13]	s	BSF	Sep	54
76	Bitter Sweet	s	SFy	Sep	54
77	Hidden Treasure of Kalin	s	AUT	Oct	54
78	Closing Time	s	NEB	Oct	54
79	Homecoming (UK reprinting of no 64)	s	NW	Oct	54
80	*Enterprise 2115*[5]	n		book	54
81	Into Thy Hands	s	NW	Nov	54
82	Star Haven	na	AUT	Dec	54
83	Operation Mars ... (A)	nt	NEB	Dec.	54
84	Skin Deep[13]	s	BSF	Dec	54
85	The Robbers	s	NW	Dec	54
86	The Enemy Within Us	s	SFy	Dec	54
87	Short Circuit[14]	s	NW	Jan	55
88	Nonentity	s	AUT	Feb	55
89	Death-Wish[15]	s	AUT	Feb	55
90	School for Beginners	s	NW	Feb	55
91	The Last Day of Summer	s	SFy	Feb	55
92	*Murder* Most Innocent	s	AUT	Mar	55
93	Lover, Where Art Thou?[16]	s	AUT	Mar	55
94	Oversight[13]	s	BSF	Mar	55
95	Logical Deduction[14]	s	NW	Mar	55
96	The Veterans[17]	s	NW	Mar	55
97	Brutus[13]	s	AUT	Apr	55
98	Poor Henry	s	SFy	Apr	55
99	Star Ship	n3	NW	Apr	55

Pseudonyms:
[1] King Lang (no 3).
[2] Gill Hunt (no 4).
[3] Brian Shaw (no 8).
[4] Charles Gray (nos 12 (53), 15).
[5] Charles Grey (nos 14, 17-18, 29, 31, 34-5, 38, 41, 50, 71, 80).
[6] Volsted Gridban (nos 16, 20, 23-5).
[7] Gordon Kent (no 22).
[8] Eric Storm (nos 37, 51).
[9] Carl Maddox (nos 47, 58).
[10] Morley Carpenter (no 48).
[11] Roy Sheldon (no 56).
[12] Anthony Armstrong (nos 66, 74).
[13] George Holt (nos 75, 84, 94, 97, 110, 128, 133).
[14] Gavin Neal (nos 87, 95, 105).
[15] Eric Wilding (nos 89, 121).
[16] Alice Beecham (no 93).
[17] Norman Dale (no 96).
[18] R. H. Godfrey (no 100).
[19] Phillip Martyn (no 101).
[20] Julian Carey (nos 102, 118).
[21] Alan Guthrie (nos 103, 108, 116, 131, 144).
[22] Douglas West (no 115).
[23] Duncan Lamont (nos 124, 132, 145).
[24] Frank Weight (no 127).
[25] Anthony Blake (nos 135, 139).
[26] Ken Wainwright (no 136).
[27] Frank Winnard (no 137).
[28] Alan Innes (no 140).
[29] Carl Moulton (no 141).
[30] John Seabright (no 143).

Series: A *Alien Dust* (nos 7, 12 (53), 13, 21, 33, 83; revised and connected as a novel, published in 1955).

With each successive volume it has become increasingly harder to choose an additional ten authors as representative of the period. Not because they are hard to find, but because there are so many who are so good, and all could equally well fit into my criteria. However, ten is my limit and ten I have chosen. They are:

James Blish	Alan E. Nourse
Leigh Brackett	Frederik Pohl
John Christopher	Eric Frank Russell
Lester Del Rey	Richard S. Shaver
Robert Heinlein	John Wyndham

They include three Britons and seven Americans, one of whom is a woman, hitherto sadly absent from this series.

11 JAMES BLISH (1921-75)

1	Chaos, Co-ordinated*	nt	ASF	Oct	46
2	Mistake Inside	s	SS	Mar	48
3	Tiger Ride (w. D. Knight)	s	ASF	Oct	48
4	No Winter, No Summer**	s	TW	Oct	48
5	Against the Stone Beasts	s	PS	Fal	48
6	The Bounding Crown (reprinted from Canadian SS&FS Dec 44)	s	SSS	Jan	49
7	The Weakness of Rvog (w. D. Knight)	s	TW	Feb	49
8	The Box	s	TW	Apr	49
9	The Homesteader	s	TW	Jun	49
10	Let the Finder Beware	sn	TW	Dec	49
11	Okie ... (A)	nt	ASF	Apr	50
12	There Shall Be No Darkness	nt	TW	Apr	50
13	Battle of the Unborn	s	FcS	May	50
14	The Bore	s	FSQ	Sum	50
15	The Secret People (w. D. Knight) ...	s	FcS	Nov	50
16	Sunken Universe† (reprinted from SSS May 42) ... (B)	s	SSS	Nov	50
17	Bindlestiff ... (A)	nt	ASF	Dec	50
18	The Void is my Coffin	s	IMG	Jun	51
19	Blackout in Cygni	s	PS	Jul	51
20	Sword of Xota	sn	2SA	Sum	51
21	Elixir	s	FcS	Sep	51
22	Bridge ... (A)	nt	ASF	Feb	52
23	Surface Tension ... (B)	nt	GSF	Aug	52
24	Testament of Andros	s	FSF	Jan	53
25	Beanstalk	na	FT	bk	53
26	Sargasso of Lost Cities ... (A) ...	sn	2SA	Spr	53
27	Turn of a Century	s	DSF	Mar	53
28	First Strike	s	F&SF	Jun	53
29	Common Time	s	SFQ	Aug	53
30	The Duplicated Man (w. Robert A. W. Lowndes)	n	DSF	Aug	53
31	A Case of Conscience	na	IF	Sep	53
32	Earthman, Come Home ... (A) ...	nt	ASF	Nov	53
33	FYI	s	STA	# 2,	53
34	Beep	nt	GSF	Feb	54
35	At Death's End ... (A)	nt	ASF	May	54
36	The Thing in the Attic ... (B) ...	nt	IF	Jul	54
37	The Book of Your Life	s	F&SF	Mar	55
38	Translation	s	FU	Mar	55
39	With Malice to Come	s	F&SF	May	55
40	Watershed ... (B)	s	IF	May	55
41	One-Shot ... (C)	s	ASF	Aug	55
42	King of the Hill ... (C)	s	INF	Nov	55

43	Giants in the Earth (revision of no 25)	sn	SFS	Jan	56
44	A Time to Survive ... (B)	na	F&SF	Feb	56
45	To Pay the Piper	s	IF	Feb	56

Pseudonyms: *John MacDougal (w. R. Lowndes: no 1).
            **Donald Laverty (w. D. Knight: no 4).
            †Arthur Merlyn (no 16).

Series: A   *Okie* (Flying Cities) (nos 11, 17, 22, 26, 32, 35).
        B   *Pantropy* (nos 16, 23, 36, 40, 44).
        C   *CIG* (nos 41, 42).

12   LEIGH BRACKETT (born 1915)

1	Lorelei of the Red Mist (w. R. Bradbury)	na	PS	Sum	46
2	The Moon That Vanished...	nt	TW	Oct	48
3	The Beast-Jewel of Mars	nt	PS	Win	48
4	Quest of the Starhope...	s	TW	Apr	49
5	Queen of the Martian Catacombs (A)	na	PS	Sum	49
6	Sea Kings of Mars	n	TW	Jun	49
7	Enchantress of Venus	na	PS	Fal	49
8	The Lake of Gone Forever	nt	TW	Oct	49
9	The Dancing Girls of Ganymede ...	n	TW	Feb	50
10	The Truants	s	SS	Jul	50
11	The Citadel of Lost Ages	nt	TW	Dec	50
12	Black Amazone of Mars ... (A) ...	na	PS	Mar	51
13	The Starmen of Llyrdis	sn	SS	Mar	51
14	Child of the Green Light (reprinted from SSS Feb 42)	s	SSS	Apr	51
15	The Woman from Altair	nt	SS	Jul	51
16	The Shadows	s	SS	Feb	52
17	The Last Days of Shandakor	nt	SS	Apr	52
18	The Veil of Astellar (reprinted from TW Spr 44)	nt	FSM	Sum	52
19	Shannach — The Last...	nt	PS	Nov	52
20	The Big Jump	sn	SpS	Feb	53
21	Citadel of Lost Ships (reprinted from PS Mar 43)	nt	TOP	Spr	53
22	Shadow over Mars (reprinted from SS Fal 44)	sn	FSM	Mar	53
23	The Ark of Mars...	nt	PS	Sep	53
24	Mars Minus Bisha	s	PS	Jan	54
25	Runaway	nt	SS	Spr	54
26	Teleportress of Alpha C	nt	PS	Win	55
27	The Tweener	s	F&SF	Feb	55
28	Last Call from Sector 9G	na	PS	Sum	55

Series: A   Eric John Stark (nos 5, 12).

13   JOHN CHRISTOPHER (Christopher
     Samuel Youd, born 1922)

1	Christmas Tree*	s	ASF	Feb	49
2	Colonial*	nt	ASF	Apr	49
3	Monster*	s	SFy	Sum	50
4	Tree of Wrath	s	WB	Jan	51
5	Socrates	s	GSF	Mar	51
6	Balance	s	NW	Mar	51
7	Man of Destiny	s	GSF	May	51
8	In the Balance* (reprinting of no 6)	s	FcS	Jul	51
9	The Tree (reprinting of no 4)	s	NW	Aut	51
10	Resurrection	na	SFy	Spr	52
11	Breaking Point	s	NW	May	52
12	Mr Kowtshook	s	AS&F	Jan	53
13	Aristotle	s	SFQ	Feb	53
14	Relativity	s	SSF	Feb	53
15	The Drop	s	GST	Mar	53
16	The Prophet	s	NW	Mar	53
17	Mr Kowtshook (reprinting of no 12)	s	SFy	Spr	53
18	Breaking Point (reprinting of no 11)...	s	AS&F	Apr	53
19	The Rather Improbable History of				
	Hillary Kiffer**	s	AS&F	Apr	53
20	Death Sentence**...	s	IMG	Jun	53
21	The Prophet (reprinting of no 16) ...	s	TW	Jun	53
22	Explosion Delayed**	s	SSF	Jul	53
23	Planet of Change	s	AUT	Aug	53
24	Blemish	s	AUT	Nov	53
25	Museum Piece	s	ORB	Win	54
26	Rocket to Freedom	s	IMG	Feb	54
27	Aristotle (reprinting of no 13)	s	AUT	Feb	54
28	Death Sentence (reprinting of no 20)	s	SFy	Spr	54
29	Museum Piece	s	NW	Apr	54
30	Escape Route	s	NW	Jun	54
31	The New Wine**...	s	FSM	Sum	54
32	Rich and Strange...	s	CRR		
33	Begin Again	s	ESQ		
34	Weapon	s	22C	bk	54
35	A Time of Peace...	s	22C	bk	54
36	The $64 Question	s	22C	bk	54
37	The Name of This City	s	IF	Oct	54
38	Vacation	s	IF	Nov	54
39	Talent for the Future	s	FU	Dec	54
40	Talent (reprinting of no 39)	s	NEB	Dec	54
41	Conspiracy	s	AUT	Jan	55
42	Manna	s	NW	Mar	55
43	Decoy	s	SFS	Jul	55

44 Manna (reprinting of no 42) ... ...   s   IT   Nov 55

Pseudonyms: *C. S. Youd (real name) (nos 1-3,8).
                **William Vine (nos 19, 20, 22, 31).

14 LESTER DEL REY (born 1915)

1	Over the Top	s	ASF	Nov 49
2	Imitation of Death	s	FcS	May 50
3	Omega and the Wolf-Girl	s	OTWA	Jul 50
4	Shadows of Empire	s	F&ST	Sum 50
5	No Head for My Bier	s	FA	Sep 50
6	When the World Tottered	sn	FA	Dec 50
7	. . . And It Comes Out Here	s	GSF	Feb 51
8	The Last Spaceman	s	MSS	Feb 51
9	The Deadliest Female	s	WB	Feb 51
10	The Last Lunacy...	s	FcS	Mar 51
11	The Wind Between the Worlds ...	nt	GSF	Mar 51
12	Uneasy Lies the Head...	s	TSF	Spr 51
13	Absolutely No Paradox	s	SFQ	May 51
14	'If Ye Have Faith . . .'	nt	OW	May 51
15	And There Was Light	s	FcS	Jul 51
16	Operation Distress	s	GSF	Aug 51
17	'The Years Draw Nigh'	s	ASF	Oct 51
18	Fool's Errand	s	SFQ	Nov 51
19	Instinct	s	ASF	Jan 52
20	*Marooned on Mars*	n		book 52
21	*Rocket Jockey**	n		book 52
22	Forgive Us Our Debts	s	FSF	May 52
23	Pursuit	nt	SSF	May 52
24	Unreasonable Facsimile	s	FST	Jul 52
25	No Place Like Home	s	ASF	Aug 52
26	Moon Blind**	nt	SSF	Sep 52
27	Stacked Deck	s	AS	Nov 52
28	I Am Tomorrow	nt	DSF	Nov 52
29	Unto Him That Hath*	nt	SSF	Nov 52
30	Idealist	s	*STA*	♯ 1, 53
31	*Attack from Atlantis*	n		book 53
32	Police Your Planet**	n4	SFA	Mar 53
33	Stability	s	VOR	♯ 1, 53
34	Let 'Em Breathe Space!	nt	SSF	Jul 53
35	*Battle on Mercury**	n		book 53
36	A Pound of Cure	s	*STA*	♯ 2, 53
37	*Step to the Stars*	n		book 54
38	*Rockets to Nowhere**	n		book 54
39	No Strings Attached	s	IF	Jun 54

40	Idealist (reprinting of no 30)	s	NW	Jun	54
41	Battleground	s	FU	Jul	54
42	No More Stars†	nt	BEY	Jul	54
43	Superstition	nt	ASF	Aug	54
44	A Pound of Cure (reprinting of no 36)	s	NW	Sep	54
45	The Life Watch	nt	FU	Sep	54
46	For I Am a Jealous People!	nt	*SSN*	bk	54
47	Alien	s	*STA*	# 3,	54
48	In The Still Waters	s	FU	Jun	55
49	Preferred Risk‡	n4	GSF	Jun	55
50	Victory	nt	ASF	Aug	55
51	Alien (reprinting of no 47)	s	NW	Aug	55
52	Keepers of the House...	s	FU	Jan	56
53	The Dwindling Years	s	GSF	Jan	56

Pseudonyms: *Philip St. John (nos 21, 29, 38).
           **Erik van Lhin (nos 26, 32, 35).
           †Charles Satterfield (w. F. Pohl: no 42).
           ‡Edson McCann (w. F. Pohl: no 49).

15 ROBERT A. HEINLEIN (born 1907)

1	The Green Hills of Earth	s	SEP	Feb	47
2	Space Jockey	s	SEP	Apr	47
3	Columbus Was a Dope	s	SS	May	47
4	It's Great to be Back	s	SEP	Jul	47
5	Jerry Is a Man	s	TW	Oct	47
6	Water Is for Washing...	s	ARG	Nov	47
7	*Rocket-Ship Galileo*	n		book	47
8	The Black Pits of Luna	s	SEP	Jan	48
9	Nothing Ever Happens on the Moon	nt2	BL	Apr	48
10	Gentlemen, Be Seated!	s	ARG	May	48
11	Ordeal in Space	s	T&C	May	48
12	*Space Cadet*	n		book	48
13	Our Fair City	s	WT	Jan	49
14	*The Red Planet*	n		book	49
15	Gulf	n2	ASF	Nov	49
16	The Long Watch	s	ALM	Dec	49
17	Delilah and the Space-Rigger	s	BB	Dec	49
18	The Man Who Sold the Moon ...	nt	*MSM*	bk	50
19	Satellite Scout	n4	BL	Aug	50
20	Destination Moon	nt	ShS	Sep	50
21	Planets in Combat	n2	BB	Sep	51
22	The Puppet Masters	n3	GSF	Sep	51

23	'—And He Built a Crooked House—' (reprinted from ASF Feb 41) ...	s	FFM	Dec	51
24	The Year of the Jackpot	nt	GSF	Mar	52
25	Gentlemen, Be Seated! (reprinting of no 10)	s	FFM	Jun	52
26	Tramp Space Ship	n4	BL	Sep	52
27	Beyond This Horizon* (reprinting from ASF Apr-May 42)...	n	2SA	Win	25
28	Project Nightmare	s	AS	Apr	53
29	*Starman Jones*	n		book	53
30	Skylift	s	IMG	Nov	53
31	Star Lummox	n3	F&SF	May	54
32	Ordeal in Space (reprinting of no 11)	s	NEB	Aug	54
33	Rebellion on the Moon (reprinting of no 16)	s	NEB	Apr	55
34	*Tunnel in the Sky*	n		book	55
35	The Green Hills of Earth (reprinting of no 1)	s	NEB	Jan	56
36	Double Star	n3	ASF	Feb	56

Pseudonyms: *Anson MacDonald (no 27).

16 ALAN E. NOURSE (born 1928)

1	High Threshold	s	ASF	Mar	51
2	The Universe Between	nt	ASF	Sep	51
3	Tiger by the Tail...	s	GSF	Nov	51
4	Love Thy Vimp	s	F&SF	Apr	52
5	Counterfeit	nt	TW	Aug	52
6	Final Barrier	s	FSF	Sep	52
7	Marley's Chain	s	IF	Sep	52
8	Wanderlust	s	IMG	Oct	52
9	In Sheep's Clothing	s	FSM	Nov	52
10	Q-B-B	nt	OW	Dec	52
11	Nightmare Brother	s	ASF	Feb	53
12	Peacemaker	s	SFA	Feb	53
13	Family Resemblance	s	ASF	Apr	53
14	Derelict	s	IF	May	53
15	Infinite Intruder	s	SSF	Jul	53
16	Heir Apparent	s	IMG	Oct	53
17	The Dark Door	s	GSF	Dec	53
18	Consignment	s	SFA	Dec	53
19	Letter of the Law	s	IF	Jan	54
20	The Fifty-Fourth of July	s	IMG	Mar	54
21	Journey for the Brave	s	IMG	Apr	54
22	Sixty-Year Extension	nt	PS	May	54

23	The Link　...	s	IF	Jun	54
24	My Friend Bobby　...	s	ORB	Jul	54
25	The Image of the Gods　...	s	ORB	Sep	54
26	Symptomaticus Medicus　...	s	USF	Sep	54
27	The Brain Sinner	nt	PS	Spr	55
28	The Canvas Bag	s	F&SF	Apr	55
29	Grand Rounds　...	s	FU	Aug	55
30	Meeting of the Board...	s	IF	Oct	55
31	The Expert Touch　...	s	F&SF	Nov	55
32	An Ounce of Cure　...	s	IT	Nov	55
33	Brightside Crossing　...	s	GSF	Jan	56

17　FREDERIK POHL (born 1919)

1	A Hitch in Time*　...	s	TW	Jun	47
2	Donovan Had a Dream*　...	nt	TW	Oct	47
3	Star of the Undead**	s	FB	♯ 2, 48	
4	Darkside Destiny* (reprinted from Canadian SSS Jun 44)	s	SSS	Apr	49
5	Let the Ants Try*　...	s	PS	Win	49
6	The Little Man on the Subway* (w. I. Asimov)	s	FB	♯ 6, 50	
7	When Time Went Mad (w. D. Wyle and F. A. Kummer)　...	nt	TW	Feb	50
8	Legal Rites* (w. I. Asimov)　... ...	s	WT	Sep	50
9	The Genius Beasts*　...	nt	FcS	Jan	51
10	Danger Moon*　...	na	SFQ	Aug	51
11	Gravy Planet (w. C. M. Kornbluth)	n3	GSF	Jun	52
12	A Big Man with the Girls* (w. J. Merril)	s	FSF	Mar	53
13	The Ghost Maker　...	s	BEY	Jan	54
14	The Midas Plague　...	nt	GSF	Apr	54
15	Gladiator-at-Law (w. C. M. Kornbluth)　...	n3	GSF	Jun	54
16	No More Stars‡	nt	BEY	Jul	54
17	The Tunnel under the World	nt	GSF	Jan	55
18	Pythias　...	s	GSF	Feb	55
19	The Candle Lighter	s	GSF	Mar	55
20	Target One	s	GSF	Apr	55
21	The Middle of Nowhere	s	GSF	May	55
22	Grandy Devil　...	s	GSF	Jun	55
23	Preferred Risk†	n4	GSF	Jun	55
24	The Mapmakers	nt	GSF	Jul	55
25	Rafferty's Reasons	s	FU	Oct	55
26	With Redfern on Capella XII‡　...	s	GSF	Nov	55
27	The Head Hunters (w. Morrison) ...	s	FU	Jan	56
28	The Census Takers　...	s	F&SF	Feb	56

29	Everybody's Happy But Me!	s	IMG	Feb	56
30	The Engineer (w. C. M. Kornbluth)	s	INF	Feb	56
31	Slave Ship	sn3	GSF	Mar	56

Pseudonyms: *James MacCreagh (nos 1, 2, 4-6, 8-10, 12).
           **Paul Dennis Lavond (w. D. Wylie: no 3).
           †Edson McCann (w. L. del Rey: no 22).
           ‡Charles Satterfield (no 25; w. L. del Rey, no 16).
      (also story no 7 was attributed only to Dirk Wylie).

18 ERIC FRANK RUSSELL (born 1905)

1	Metamorphosite	na	ASF	Dec	46
2	The Timid Tiger	s	ASF	Feb	47
3	Venturer of the Martian Mimics (reprinted from *Tales of Wonder*, Aut 40)	nt	WT	Mar	47
4	Relic	nt	FTy	Apr	47
5	'Hobbyist'	nt	ASF	Sep	47
6	Dreadful Sanctuary	n3	ASF	Jun	48
7	Displaced Person	s	WT	Sep	48
8	Muten*	s	ASF	Oct	48
9	The Ponderer	s	WT	Nov	48
10	Late Night Final	nt	ASF	Dec	48
11	The Big Shot	s	WT	Jan	49
12	A Present from Joe	s	ASF	Feb	49
13	The Glass Eye	s	ASF	Mar	49
14	The Undecided	nt	ASF	Apr	49
15	U-Turn*	s	ASF	Apr	50
16	Dear Devil	nt	OW	May	50
17	Exposure	s	ASF	Jul	50
18	The Rhythm of the Rats	s	WT	Jul	50
19	First Person Singular	nt	TW	Oct	50
20	Follower	s	ASF	Nov	50
21	MacHinery	s	TW	Dec	50
22	Invisible (reprinted from FTy # 1, 1938)	s	FSQ	Win	51
23	Test Piece	s	OW	Mar	51
24	Afternoon of a Fahn	s	IMG	Apr	51
25	. . . And Then There Were None ...	na	ASF	Jun	51
26	The Witness	s	OW	Sep	51
27	Ultima Thule	s	ASF	Oct	51
28	The Illusionaries	s	PS	Nov	51
29	The Star Watchers	n	SS	Nov	51
30	I'm a Stranger Here Myself	s	OW	Mar	52
31	Fast Falls the Eventide	s	ASF	May	52

32	Take a Seat	...	...	...	...	...	...	s	SS	May	52
33	I Am Nothing	...	...	...	...	...	s	ASF	Jul	52
34	Hell's Bells*	...	...	...	...	...	s	WT	Jul	52
35	The Sin of Hyacinth Peuch	...	...	s	FAN	Fal	52
36	A Little Oil	...	...	...	...	...	s	GSF	Oct	52
37	Last Blast	...	...	...	...	...	nt	ASF	Nov	52
38	The Timeless Ones	...	...	...	...	s	SFQ	Nov	52
39	Somewhere a Voice	...	...	...	...	nt	OW	Jan	53
40	Design for Great-Day	...	...	...	...	na	PS	Jan	53
41	It's in the Blood	...	...	...	...	...	s	FU	Jun	53
42	A Great Deal of Power	...	...	...	s	FU	Aug	53
43	This One's on Me	...	...	...	...	s	NEB	Aut	53
44	Postscript	...	...	...	...	...	...	s	SFP	Oct	53
45	Sustained Pressure	...	...	...	...	nt	NEB	Dec	53
46	Bitter End	...	...	...	...	...	s	SFP	Dec	53
47	Appointment at Noon	...	...	...	s	AS	Mar	54
48	The Door	...	...	...	...	...	...	s	USF	Mar	54
49	Fly Away Peter	...	...	...	...	nt	NEB	Apr	54
50	Weak Spot	...	...	...	...	...	s	ASF	May	54
51	Boomerang	...	...	...	...	...	s	NEB	Dec	54
52	I Hear You Calling	...	...	...	...	s	SFy	Dec	54
53	Nothing New	...	...	...	...	...	s	ASF	Jan	55
54	Diabologic	...	...	...	...	...	s	ASF	Mar	55
55	Allamagoosa	...	...	...	...	...	s	ASF	May	55
56	The Waitabits	...	...	...	...	nt	ASF	Jul	55
57	Tieline*	...	...	...	...	...	...	s	ASF	Jul	55
58	Proof	...	...	...	...	...	...	s	FU	Jul	55
59	Saraband in C Sharp Minor	...	...	s	SFS	Jul	55
60	Call Him Dead	...	...	...	...	...	n3	ASF	Aug	55
61	Down, Rover, Down	...	...	...	...	s	NEB	Nov	55
62	Minor Ingredient	...	...	...	...	s	ASF	Mar	56

Pseudonyms: *Duncan H. Munro (nos 8, 15, 34, 57).

19   RICHARD S. SHAVER 1907-75)

(Whilst this index starts strictly from Apr 46, for continuity's sake I am including Shaver's five stories before that date.)

1	'I Remember Lemuria'	...	...	...	sn	AS	Mar	45
2	Thought Records of Lemuria	...	...	nt	AS	Jun	45
3	Cave City of Hel	...	...	...	...	...	nt	AS	Sep	45
4	Quest of Brail	...	...	...	...	...	sn	AS	Dec	45
5	Invasion of the Micro-Men	...	...	nt	AS	Feb	46
6	The Masked World	...	...	...	...	n	AS	May	46
7	An Adam from the Sixth	...	...	...	s	FA	May	46
8	Luder Valley	...	...	...	...	...	nt	AS	Jun	46

51	The World of the Lost[xx]	n	FA	Mar	50
52	Palace of Darkness ¶	nt	OW	Sep	50
53	Green Man's Grief	s	FcS	Jan	51
54	Glass Woman of Venus§	nt	OW	Jan	51
55	Lightning over Saturn (w. C. S. Geier)	nt	OW	Oct	51
56	Journey to Nowhere	s	OW	Oct	51
57	Yelisen	nt	OW	Dec	51
58	Of Stegner's Folly	s	IF	Mar	52
59	The Sun-Smiths	n3	OW	Jul	52
60	Beyond the Barrier	n4	OW	Nov	52
61	The Dark Goddess	s	IMG	Feb	53
62	Paradise Planet	s	IMG	Apr	53
63	The Heart of the Game***	s	ORB	♯ 1,	53
64	She Was Sitting in the Dark♯	s	ScS	Dec	53
65	Why Skeets Malloy Has Two Heads	s	ORB	Jul	54

Pseudonyms: *D. Richard Sharpe (no 25).
 **Alexander Blade (no 30).
 §G. H. Irwin (nos 32, 43, 54).
 †Frank Patton (no 38).
 ‡Stan Raycraft (no 45).
 ††Wes Amherst (no 47).
 xEdwin Benson (real name used mistakenly on no 49).
 ¶Peter Dexter (nos 50, 52).
 xxPaul Lohrman (no 51).
 ***Richard English (no 63).
 ♯Richard Doret (no 64).

Series: Many of the above fit into his Lemuria framework, notably nos 1-6, 8, 11-15, 20, 22, 29, 35, 38, 42.

20 JOHN (WYNDHAM) BEYNON HARRIS
(1903-69)

1	The Living Lies*	s	NW	Oct	46
2	Time to Rest**	s	AkS	Win	49
3	Jizzle*	s	CLR	Jan	49
4	Technical Slip*	s	AkS	Spr	49
5	Adaptation*	s	ASF	Jul	49
6	Time to Rest* (reprinting of no 2) ...	s	NW	Sep	49
7	The Secret People* (reprinted from *Passing Show*, 1935)	n	FFM	Apr	50
8	The Moon Devils** (reprinted from WS Apr 34)	s	WSA	Sum	50
9	The Man from Beyond** (reprinted from WS Sep 34)	s	FSQ	Sum	50

10	The Eternal Eve	nt	AS	Sep	50
11	The Living Lies* (reprinting of no 1)	s	OW	Nov	50
12	Technical Slip* (reprinting of no 4)	s	IMG	Dec	50
13	The Revolt of the Triffids	n5	CLR	Jan	51
14	The Red Stuff*	nt	MSS	Feb	51
15	Tyrant And Slave-Girl on Venus* ...	nt	TSF	Spr	51
16	No Place Like Earth* (reprinting of no 15)	nt	NW	Spr	51
17	. . . And the Walls Came Tumbling Down	s	SS	May	51
18	Bargain from Brunswick	s	F&SF	Jun	51
19	Operation Peep	s	SUS	Sum	51
20	Pawley's Peepholes (reprinting of no 19)	s	SFy	Win	51
21	Pillar to Post	s	GSF	Dec	51
22	The Wheel	s	SS	Jan	52
23	Survival	s	TW	Feb	52
24	Jizzle	s	F&SF	Feb	52
25	Dumb Martian	s	GSF	Jul	52
26	*The Kraken Wakes*	n		book	52
27	Time Stops Today	s	FSF	Jan	53
28	Perfect Creature (reprinted from *Tales of Wonder,* 1937)	s	F&SF	Jan	53
29	Close behind Him	s	FAN	Feb	53
30	Reservation Deferred	s	FAN	Jun	53
31	More Spinned Against	s	FF	Jun	53
32	Confidence Trick	s	FAN	Aug	53
33	A Stray from Cathay	s	FF	Aug	53
34	How Do I Do?	s	BEY	Sep	53
35	Never on Mars	s	FU	Jan	54
36	Perforce to Dream	s	BEY	Jan	54
37	Opposite Numbers	s	NW	Apr	54
38	Chronoclasm	s	SFy	Sep	54
39	Compassion Circuit	s	FU	Dec	54
40	*The Chrysalids*	n		book	55
41	Compassion Circuit (reprinting of no 39)	s	NW	May	55
42	Wild Flower	s	FU	Nov	55

Pseudonyms: *John Beynon (nos 1, 3-7, 11, 12, 14-16).
               **John Beynon Harris (real name, nos 8, 9).

Publications have been abbreviated as follows:

Note: Magazines in roman type; books in italics.

   ADV = Adventure
   AFR = Avon Fantasy Reader

AkS = Arkham Sampler
ALM = American Legion Magazine
ARG = Argosy
ARGb = Argosy (British edition)
AS = Amazing Stories
AS&F = Avon Science Fiction & Fantasy Reader
ASF = Astounding SF
AUT = Authentic SF
BB = Blue Book
BEY = Beyond Fantasy Fiction
BL = Boy's Life
BSF = British Science Fiction Magazine (see BSP, VSB, VSM)
BSP = British Space Fiction Magazine (see BSF, VSB, VSM)
CAV = Cavalier
CFN = The Californian
CHM = Charm
CLR = Collier's
COPY = Copy
CQ = California Quarterly
CRR = Courier
CSF = Cosmos SF & Fantasy
CSP = Cosmopolitan
DBM = Detective Book Magazine
DD = Dime Detective
DM = Dime Mystery Magazine
DSF = Dynamic SF
EB = Everybody's
EP = Epoch
EQ = Ellery Queen's Mystery Magazine
ESC = Escapade
ESQ = Esquire
EW = Everywoman's
FA = Fantastic Adventures
FAN = Fantastic
F&SF = Magazine of Fantasy & Science Fiction (see MoF)
FB = Fantasy Book
FcS = Future combined with Science Fiction Stories (see FSF)
FF = Fantasy Fiction (see FM)
FFM = Famous Fantastic Mysteries
FM = Fantasy Magazine (see FF)
FN = Fantastic Novels
FSF = Future SF (see FcS)
FSM = Fantastic Story Magazine (see FSQ)
FSQ = Fantastic Story Quarterly (see FSM)
FSS = Futuristic Science Stories
FTy = Fantasy

FU = Fantastic Universe
GH = Good Housekeeping
GM = Gourmet
GSF = Galaxy SF
GSFN = Galaxy SF Novels
HPR = Harper's
HR = Heiress
IF = If, Worlds of SF
IMG = Imagination
INF = Infinity SF
IT = Imaginative Tales
LLP = Lilliput
McC = McCall's
McL = MacLean's
MH = Manhunt
MMS = Mademoiselle
MoF = Magazine of Fantasy (see F&SF)
MSF = Marvel Science Fiction (see MSS)
MSS = Marvel Science Stories (see MSF)
MTM = Mysterious Traveller Magazine
NAT = The Nation
NB = Nation's Business
ND = New Detective
NEB = Nebula
NS = New Story
NW = New Worlds
NY = New Yorker
ORB = Orbit SF
OTWA = Out of This World Adventures
OW = Other Worlds Science Stories (see ScS)
PS = Planet Stories
RPT = The Reporter
RS = Rocket Stories
SCR = Script
ScS = Science Stories (see OW)
SDM = The Saint Detective Magazine (see SMM)
SEP = Saturday Evening Post
7T = Seventeen
SFA = Science Fiction Adventures
SFD = Science Fiction Digest
SFP = Science Fiction Plus
SFQ = Science Fiction Quarterly
SFS = Science Fiction Stories
SFy = Science Fantasy
SHD = Shenandoah
ShS = Short Stories

SMM = The Saint Mystery Magazine (see SDM)
SpS = Space Stories
SPW = Spaceway
SrS = Senior Scholastic
SS = Startling Stories
SS&FS = Super Science & Fantastic Stories (Canadian)
SSF = Space SF
SSS = Super Science Stories
SUS = Suspense
T&C = Town & Country
TDW = Today's Woman
TDY = Today
TOP = Tops in SF
ToT = Tales of Tomorrow
TS = Touchstone
TSF = Ten Story Fantasy
TT = Torquasian Times
TW = Thrilling Wonder Stories
2SA = Two Complete Science Adventure Books
USF = Universe SF
UW = Unknown Worlds
VOR = Vortex SF
VSB = Vargo Stratten British SF Magazine (see BSF, BSP, VSM)
VSM = Vargo Stratten SF Magazine (see BSF, BSP, VSB)
WB = Worlds Beyond
WoF = Worlds of Fantasy
WoS = Wonders of the Spaceways
WT = Weird Tales

BOOKS

BMW = *Born of Man and Woman* by Richard Matheson
CVR = *Caviar* by Theodore Sturgeon
DC = *Dark Carnival* by Ray Bradbury
EPU = *E Pluribus Unicorn* by Theodore Sturgeon
FT = *Future Tense edited* by Kendall Foster Crossen
GAS = *Golden Apples of the Sun* by Ray Bradbury
IfM = *Invasion From Mars* edited by Orson Welles
IM = *The Illustrated Man* by Ray Bradbury
MC = *The Martian Chronicles* by Ray Bradbury
MSM = *The Man Who Sold the Moon* by Robert A. Heinlein
MTH = *More Than Human* by Theodore Sturgeon
NTS = *New Tales of Space and Time*
                edited by Raymond J. Healy
SSN = *Star Short Novels* edited by Frederik Pohl

STA = *Star Science Fiction Stories* (series)
edited by Frederik Pohl
TtC = *Time to Come* edited by August Derleth
22C = *The 22nd Century* by John Christopher
Other abbreviations used are:
bk, book; w, with (collaboration).

(B) SUMMARY OF MAGAZINE ISSUES, 1946 - 55

Magazine	Up to 1945/6	46/7	47/8	48/9	49/50	50/1	51/2	52/3	53/4	54/5	55/6	Total
I SF — North American												
A. MERRITT'S FANTASY	—	—	—	—	2	3	—	—	—	—	—	5
AMAZING STORIES	201	11	12	12	12	12	12	12	6	6	8	304
ARKHAM SAMPLER	—	—	1	4	3	—	—	—	—	—	—	8
ASTOUNDING SF	184	12	12	12	12	12	12	12	12	12	12	304
Avon FANTASY READER	—	1	4	4	3	3	3	—	—	—	—	18
Avon SCIENCE FICTION READER	—	—	—	—	—	3	—	—	—	—	—	3
Avon SF & FANTASY READER	—	—	—	—	—	—	—	1	1	—	—	2
CAPTAIN ZERO	—	—	—	—	3	—	—	—	—	—	—	3
COSMOS SF & FANTASY	—	—	—	—	—	—	—	—	3	1	—	4
DYNAMIC SF	—	—	—	—	—	—	—	2	4	—	—	6
FAMOUS FANTASTIC MYSTERIES	38	6	6	6	6	6	5	6	2	—	—	81
FANTASTIC	—	—	—	—	—	—	—	5	5	6	6	22
FANTASTIC ADVENTURES	54	6	9	12	12	12	12	12	—	—	—	129
FANTASTIC NOVELS	5	—	1	6	6	5	2	—	—	—	—	25
FANTASTIC SCIENCE FICTION	—	—	—	—	—	—	—	2	—	—	—	2
FANTASTIC STORY MAGAZINE	—	—	—	—	—	4	4	6	4	4	1	23
FANTASTIC UNIVERSE	—	—	—	—	—	—	—	—	5	9	12	26
FANTASY BOOK	—	—	2	2	2	2	—	—	—	—	—	8
FUTURE SF	17	—	—	—	—	6	6	6	6	3	1	45
GALAXY SF	—	—	—	—	—	6	12	12	12	12	11	65
GALAXY SCIENCE FICTION NOVEL	—	—	—	—	—	4	5	5	6	3	4	27

Magazine	Up to 1945/6	46/7	47/8	48/9	49/50	50/1	51/2	52/3	53/4	54/5	55/6	Total
						Number of Issues						
IF	—	—	—	—	—	—	1	6	6	12	7	32
IMAGINATION	—	—	—	—	—	3	6	7	12	12	7	47
IMAGINATIVE TALES	—	—	—	—	—	—	—	—	—	4	6	10
INFINITY	—	—	—	—	—	—	—	—	—	—	2	2
LES ADVENTURES FUTURISTES ...	—	—	—	2	8	—	—	—	—	—	—	10
Magazine of FANTASY & SCIENCE FICTION	—	—	—	—	2	4	6	10	12	12	12	58
MARVEL SCIENCE STORIES/ FICTION	9	—	—	—	—	4	2	—	—	—	—	15
ORBIT SF	—	—	—	—	—	—	—	—	2	3	—	5
OTHER WORLDS (SCIENCE STORIES)	—	—	—	—	3	7	7	10	4	—*	5	36
OUT OF THIS WORLD ADVENTURES	—	—	—	—	—	2	—	—	—	—	—	2
PLANET STORIES	26	4	4	4	4	5	6	6	6	4	2	71
ROCKET STORIES	—	—	—	—	—	—	—	—	3	—	—	3
SCIENCE FICTION ADVENTURES ...	—	—	—	—	—	—	—	3	5	1	—	9
SCIENCE FICTION DIGEST	—	—	—	—	—	—	—	—	1	1	—	2
SCIENCE FICTION PLUS	—	—	—	—	—	—	—	1	6	—	—	7
SCIENCE FICTION QUARTERLY ...	10	—	—	—	—	—	4	4	4	4	4	30
SCIENCE FICTION STORIES	12	—	—	—	—	—	—	—	1	3	6	22
SCIENCE STORIES	—	—	—	—	—	—	—	—	3	1*	—	4
SPACE SF	—	—	—	—	—	—	—	5	3	—	—	8
SPACE STORIES	—	—	—	—	—	—	—	3	2	—	—	5

SPACEWAY	—	—	—	—	—	—	—	—	2	4	2	8
STARTLING STORIES	38	5	6	6	6	6	7	12	7	3	3	99
SUPER SCIENCE STORIES	16	—	—	1	6	5	3	—	—	—	—	31
10 STORY FANTASY	—	—	—	—	—	1	—	—	—	—	—	1
THRILLING WONDER STORIES	139	5	6	6	6	6	6	6	5	4	—	189
TOPS IN SCIENCE FICTION	—	—	—	—	—	—	—	1	1	—	—	2
TWO COMPLETE SCIENCE ADVENTURE BOOKS	—	—	—	—	—	2	3	3	3	—	—	11
UNIVERSE SF	—	—	—	—	—	—	—	—	4	6	—	10
VORTEX SF	—	—	—	—	—	—	—	—	2	—	—	2
WONDER STORIES ANNUAL	—	—	—	—	—	1	2	1	—	—	—	4
WORLDS BEYOND	—	—	—	—	—	3	—	—	—	—	—	3
	749	50	63	77	96	124	129	159	160	130	111	1848

Note: * *Other Worlds* name changed to *Science Stories* for four issues.

SF — *United Kingdom*

AMAZING ADVENTURES	—	1	—	—	—	—	—	—	—	—	—	1
AMAZING SCIENCE STORIES	—	—	—	—	—	1	1	—	—	—	—	2
COSMIC SCIENCE STORIES	—	—	—	—	—	1	—	—	—	—	—	1
FANTASY	—	1	2	—	—	—	—	—	—	—	—	3
FUTURISTIC SCIENCE STORIES	—	—	—	—	—	4	1	4	5	2	—	16
FUTURISTIC STORIES	—	2	—	—	—	—	—	—	—	—	—	2

Magazine	Up to 1945/6	46/7	47/8	48/9	49/50	50/1	51/2	52/3	53/4	54/5	55/6	Total
NEBULA	—	—	—	—	—	—	—	2	5	4	5	16
NEW WORLDS	—	2	1	—	3	3	5	6	1	12	12	45
OUTLANDS	—	1	—	—	—	—	—	—	—	—	—	1
SCIENCE FANTASY	—	—	—	—	—	2	1	2	2	6	4	17
SCIENCE FICTION FORTNIGHTLY/(MONTHLY)/AUTHENTIC	—	—	—	—	—	6	13	12	12	12	12	67
SPACE FACT AND FICTION	—	1	—	—	—	—	—	—	1	7	—	8
STRANGE ADVENTURES	—	1	—	—	—	—	—	—	—	—	—	1
TALES OF TOMORROW	—	—	—	—	—	3	—	3	3	2	—	11
VARGO STATTEN SF MAGAZINE/BRITISH SF (SPACE) MAGAZINE	—	—	—	—	—	—	—	—	2	9	8	19
WONDERS OF THE SPACEWAYS	—	—	—	—	—	1	—	4	4	1	—	10
WORLDS OF FANTASY	—	—	—	—	—	4	—	4	4	2	—	14
WORLDS OF THE UNIVERSE	—	—	—	—	—	—	—	—	1	—	—	1
	—	8	3	—	3	25	21	37	40	57	41	235

SF — Australia

Magazine	Up to 1945/6	46/7	47/8	48/9	49/50	50/1	51/2	52/3	53/4	54/5	55/6	Total
AMERICAN SF SERIES	—	—	—	—	—	—	—	10	12	12	6	40
FUTURE SF	—	—	—	—	—	—	—	—	3	3	—	6
POPULAR SF	—	—	—	—	—	—	—	—	2	4	—	6
SCIENCE FICTION MONTHLY	—	—	—	—	—	—	—	—	—	—	8	8
SELECTED SCIENCE FICTION	—	—	—	—	—	—	—	—	—	—	5	5

THRILLS, INC … … … …	—	—	—	—	—	10	10	3	—	—	—	23
	—	—	—	—	—	10	10	13	17	19	19	88
SF — Europe												
FANTASIE EN WETENSCHAP (Holland) … …	—	—	4	—	—	—	—	—	—	—	—	4
FICTION (France) … … …	—	—	—	—	—	—	—	—	4	12	12	28
HAPNA! (Sweden) … … …	—	—	—	—	—	—	—	—	1	11	6	18
I ROMANZI DI URANIA (Italy) … …	—	—	—	—	—	—	—	12	24	24	24	84
JULES VERNE MAGASINET (Sweden)	287	44	—	—	—	—	—	—	—	—	—	331
PLANEET (Holland) … …	—	—	—	—	—	—	—	1	—	—	—	1
SCIENZA FANTASTICA (Italy) … …	—	—	—	—	—	—	—	7	—	—	—	7
SCIENCE FICTION MAGAZINE (France) … … …	—	—	—	—	—	—	—	—	4	—	—	4
URANIA (Italy) … … …	—	—	—	—	—	—	—	5	12	12	12	41
UTOPIA–GROSSBANDE (Germany) …	—	—	—	—	—	—	—	—	12	12	12	36
UTOPIA–KLEINBANDE (Germany) …	—	—	—	—	—	—	—	—	12	12	12	36
UTOPIA–KRIMINAL (Germany) …	—	—	—	—	—	—	—	—	—	—	2	2
UTOPIA (SONDERBANDE) (Germany)	—	—	—	—	—	—	—	—	—	—	1	1
V (France) … … … …	—	1	—	—	—	—	—	—	—	—	—	1
	287	45	4	—	—	—	—	25	69	83	81	594

Magazine	Up to 1945/6	46/7	47/8	48/9	49/50	50/1	51/2	52/3	53/4	54/5	55/6	Total
SF — Asia												
SEIUN (Japan)	—	—	—	—	—	—	—	—	—	1	—	1
SF — Central and South America												
ENIGMAS (Mexico)	—	—	—	—	—	—	—	—	—	—	8	8
HOMBRES DEL FUTURO (Argentina)	—	—	—	—	—	—	3	—	—	—	—	3
LOS CUENTOS FANTASTICOS (Mexico)	—	—	—	13	11	7	6	5	2	—	—	44
MAS ALLA (Argentina)	—	—	—	—	—	—	—	—	10	12	12	34
NARRACIONES TERRORIFICAS (Arg)	58	6	3	2	3	—	—	—	—	—	—	72
URANIA (Argentina)	—	—	—	—	—	—	—	—	2	—	—	2
	58	6	3	14	14	7	9	5	14	12	20	163
II Weird — North American												
BEYOND	—	—	—	—	—	—	—	—	5	5	—	10
BRIEF FANTASTIC TALES	—	—	—	—	—	1	—	—	—	—	—	1
DOC SAVAGE	157	12	6	5	1	—	—	—	—	—	—	181

	1	2	3	4	5	6	7	8	9	10	11	Total
FANTASY FICTION/STORIES	—	—	—	—	—	2	—	—	—	—	—	2
FANTASY MAGAZINE/FICTION	—	—	—	—	—	—	—	1	3	—	—	4
The MYSTERIOUS TRAVELER	—	—	—	—	—	—	3	2	—	—	—	5
MYSTIC	—	—	—	—	—	—	—	—	3	5	6	14
SUSPENSE	—	—	—	—	—	—	4	—	—	—	—	4
The VORTEX	—	—	1	—	—	—	—	—	—	—	—	1
WEIRD TALES	228	6	6	6	6	6	6	6	6	3	—	279
	385	18	13	11	7	9	13	9	17	13	6	501

Weird–United Kingdom

	1	2	3	4	5	6	7	8	9	10	11	Total
OUT OF THIS WORLD	—	—	—	—	—	—	—	—	—	2	—	2
STRANGE TALES (reprint)	2	—	—	—	—	—	—	—	—	—	—	2
SUPERNATURAL STORIES	—	—	—	—	—	—	—	—	—	5	3	8
UNKNOWN WORLDS (reprint)	30	3	3	3	2	—	—	—	—	—	—	41
WEIRD WORLD	—	—	—	—	—	—	—	—	—	—	2	2
	32	3	3	3	2	—	—	—	—	7	5	55

(C) GLOSSARY OF MAGAZINE EDITORS

ABBAS, Ben   Publisher/Editor *Fantasie en Wetenschap*, Dec 48-Mar 49 (4)

ARTHUR, Robert   Managing Editor *The Mysterious Traveler*, Nov 51-Sep 52 (5)

BELL, George   Editor *Universe SF*, June-Sep 53 (2)

BOUCHER, Anthony   Co-Editor *F & SF*, Fal 49-Aug 54 (39)

Editor *F & SF*, Sep 54-Aug 58 (48)

BROWNE, Howard   Assistant / Managing Editor *Amazing Stories*, Jan 43-Oct 47 (38)

Editor *Amazing Stories*, Jan 50-Aug 56 (64)

Assistant/Managing Editor *Fantastic Adventures*, Dec 42-Oct 47 (31)

Editor *Fantastic Adventures*, Jan 50-Mar 53 (39)

Editor *Fantastic*, Sum 52-Aug 56 (25)

Editor *Amazing Annual*, 1950 (1)

BUCHANAN, Lamont   Associate Editor *Weird Tales*, Nov 42-Sep 49 (42)

BUDWIG, Marge Sanders   Associate Editor *Other Worlds*, May 50-Jun 51 (9)

CAMPBELL, Herbert J.   Editor *Authentic*, Dec 52-Jan 56 (38)

CAMPBELL, John W.   Editor *Astounding SF* (*Analog*), Oct 37-Dec 71 (411)

CARNELL, Edward John   Editor *New Worlds*, Oct 46-Apr 64 (141)

Editor *Science Fantasy*, Win 51-Apr 64 (62)

COHEN, Sol Editor *Avon SF & Fantasy Reader*, Jan-Apr 53 (2)

COLE, L.B. Editor *Cosmos SF & Fantasy*, Sep 53-Jul 54 (4)

CRAWFORD, William L. Editor *Spaceway*, Dec 53-Jun 55 (8)

  as FORD, Garret Editor *Fantasy Book*, Sum 47-Win 51 (8)

DAFFRON, Katharine Editor *2 Complete Science Adventure Books*, Win 53-Spr 54 (2)

DEL REY, Lester Editor *Space SF*, May 52-Sep 53 (8)

Editor *Fantasy Fiction*, Feb-Aug 53 (3)

  as ST JOHN, Philip Editor *Science Fiction Adventures*, Nov 52-Sep 53 (6)

  as KAMPFAERT, Wade Editor *Rocket Stories*, Apr-Jul 53 (2)

  as HALL, Cameron Co-Editor *Fantasy Fiction*, Nov 53 (1)

DERLETH, August Editor *Arkham Sampler*, Win 48-Aut 49 (8)

ECHEVERRIA, Julio A. Editor *Urania*, Oct-Dec 53 (2)

EKSTROM, Kjel Editor *Häpna!*, Mar 54-Feb 65

ELLSWORTH, Fanny Managing Editor *Fantastic Story Magazine*, Sep 52-Jul 53 (6)

Executive Editor *Fantastic Story Magazine*, Sep 53-Win 54 (2)

Managing Editor *Startling Stories*, Sep 52-Aug 53 (11)

Executive Editor *Startling Stories*, Oct 53 (1)

Managing Editor *Thrilling Wonder Stories*, Oct 52-Aug 53 (6)

Executive Editor *Thrilling Wonder Stories*, Nov 53 (1)

Managing Editor *Space Stories*, Oct 52-Jun 53 (5)

ERISMAN, Robert O.   Editor *Marvel Science Stories/ SF*, Nov 50-May 52 (6)

ERNSTING, Walter   Editor *Utopia-Grossbande*, 53-   57
Editor   *Utopia - Kleinbande / Zukunftsromane*,   53-   57
Editor *Utopia-Kriminal*, Feb 56-Apr 58 (27)
Editor   *Utopia (Sonderbande)*, Dec 55-Dec 57 (12)

FAIRMAN, Paul W.   Editor *If*, Mar-Sep 52 (4)
Associate   Editor   *Amazing Stories*, Aug 52-Mar 53 (8)
Managing   Editor   *Amazing Stories*, Apr 53-Nov 54 (10)
Associate   Editor   *Fantastic Adventures*, Aug 52-Mar 53 (8)
Associate Editor *Fantastic*, Fal 52-Mar 53 (4)
Managing Editor *Fantastic*, May 53-Oct 54 (9)

FARREN, Phyllis   Associate Editor *Cosmos SF & Fantasy*, Sep 53-Jul 54 (4)

FEARN, John Russell as Vargo STATTEN   Editor *British SF/Space Fiction Magazine*, Sep 54-Feb 56 (14)

FORD, Garret   see William CRAWFORD

GERNSBACK, Hugo   Editor/Publisher Annuals: *Quip* (1949), *Newspeek* (1950), *Forecast* (1951) (3)
Editor/Publisher *Science Fiction Plus*, Mar-Dec 53 (7)

GERNSBACK, M. Harvey   Executive Editor *Science Fiction Plus*, Mar-Dec 53 (7)

GIBSON, Walter B.   Editor *Fantastic SF*, Aug-Dec 52 (2)

GILLINGS, Walter   Editor *Fantasy*, Dec 46-Aug 47 (3)

Editor *Strange Tales*, Feb-Mar 46 (2)

Editor *Science Fantasy*, Sum-Win 50 (2)

GNAEDINGER, Mary   Editor *Famous Fantastic Mysteries*, Sep 39-Jun 53 (81)

Editor *Fantastic Novels*, Mar 48-Jun 51 (20)

Editor *A. Merritt's Fantasy*, Dec 49-Oct 50 (5)

GOLD, Horace L.   Editor *Galaxy SF*, Oct 50-Oct 61 (115)

Editor *Beyond*, Jul 53-Jan 55 (10)

HAMILTON, Peter   Editor/Publisher *Nebula*, Aut 52-Jun 59 (41)

HAMLING, Frances   Managing Editor *Imagination*, Jan 53-Oct 58 (49)

HAMLING, William L.   Associate Editor *Amazing Stories*, Aug 46-Dec 47 (17)

Managing Editor *Amazing Stories*, Jan 48-Feb 51 (38)

Associate Editor *Fantastic Adventures*, Sep 46-Oct 47 (8)

Managing Editor *Fantastic Adventures*, Nov 47-Feb 51 (40)

Editor *Imagination*, Feb 51-Oct 58 (61)

Editor *Imaginative Tales/Space Travel*, Sep 54-Nov 58 (26)

HARRISON, Harry   Editor *Science Fiction Adventures*, Dec 53-May 54 (3)

as KAEMPFERT, Wade   Editor *Rocket Stories*, Sep 53 (1)

as HALL, Cameron   Co-Editor *Fantasy Fiction*, Nov 53 (1)

IRWIN, Theodore   Editor *Suspense*, Spr 51-Win 52 (4)

JAKOBSSEN, Ejler   Editor *Super Science Stories*, Jan 49-Aug 51 (15)

JOHNSON, Leslie J.   Editor *Outlands*, Win 46 (1)

JONES, Beatrice   Editor *Fantastic Universe*, Jan-Mar 54 (2)

JONES, Pat   Assistant Editor *Startling Stories*, Jan-Spr 54 (2)
Assistant Editor *Thrilling Wonder Stories*, Win-Spr 54 (2)
Assistant Editor *Fantastic Story Magazine*, Spr 54 (1)

KAEMPFERT, Wade   see Harry HARRISON

KAGAN, Michael   Assistant Editor *Amazing Stories*, Apr-Oct 53 (4)
Assistant Editor *Fantastic*, May-Nov 53 (4)

KEYES, Daniel   Editorial Associate *Marvel Science Stories*, Feb-Nov 51 (4)

KNIGHT, Damon   Editor *Worlds Beyond*, Dec 50-Feb 51 (3)
Assistant Editor *Super Science Stories*, Jan-Aug 51 (4)

LANDSBOROUGH, Gordon as HOLMES, L. G.   Editor *Authentic*, Feb-Aug 51 (10)

LANE, Arthur   Editorial Associate *Marvel Science Stories*, Nov 50-Feb 51 (2)
Editorial Associate *Marvel Science Stories*, May 51-May 52 (4)

LEVITAS, Gloria   Assistant Editor *F & SF*, Mar 54-May 56 (27)

LOWNDES, Robert A. W. Editor *Future SF*, May 50-Apr 60 (48)

Editor *Science Fiction Quarterly*, May 51-Feb 58 (28)

Editor *Dynamic SF*, Dec 52-Jan 54 (6)

Editor *Science Fiction Stories*, Win 53-May 60 (38)

McCOMAS, J. Francis Co-Editor *F & SF*, Fal 49-Aug 54 (39)

McILWRAITH, Dorothy Editor *Weird Tales*, May 40-Sep 54 (87)

MAHAFFEY, Beatrice Managing Editor *Other Worlds*, Mar 50-Oct 52 (20)

Editor *Other Worlds*, Nov 52-Jul 53 (9)

Editor *Science Stories*, Oct 53-Apr 54 (4)

Editor *Universe SF*, Dec 53-Mar 55 (8)

Editor (Creator) *Other Worlds*, May-Nov 55 (4)

Editor *Mystic*, Nov 53-Oct 55 (12)

MANNING, John S. (Possible house name. For Michael Nahum and Sol De Sale) Editor *Futuristic Science Stories*, Sum 50-Sum 54 (16)

Editor *Tales of Tomorrow*, Aut 50-Sum 54 (11)

Editor *Worlds of Fantasy*, Sum 50-Sum 54 (14)

Editor *Wonders of the Spaceways*, Win 50-Spr 54 (10)

Editor *Supernatural Stories*, May 54-Win 66 (106)

Editor *Out of This World*, Win 54-Spr 55 (2)

MARGULIES, Leo Editor/Publisher *Fantastic Universe*, Jun 53-Aug 56 (31)

MERWIN, Sam
Editor *Startling Stories*, Fal 44-Sep 51 (39)
Editor *Thrilling Wonder Stories*, Win 45-Oct 51 (38)
Editor *Fantastic Story Magazine*, Spr 50-Fal 51 (7)
Editor *Wonder Story Annual*, 1950-51 (2)
Editor *Fantastic Universe*, Jun-Oct 53 (3)
Associate Editor *Galaxy SF*, Dec 53-Sep 54 (10)
Associate Editor *Beyond*, Jan-Sep 54 (5)

MILLS, Robert P.
Managing Editor *F & SF*, Fal 49-Aug 58 (87)

MINES, Samuel
Editor *Startling Stories*, Nov 51-Fal 54 (25)
Editor *Thrilling Wonder Stories*, Dec 51-Sum 54 (15)
Editor *Fantastic Story Magazine*, Win 52-Fal 54 (13)
Editor *Space Stories*, Oct 52-Jun 53 (5)
Editor *Wonder Stories Annual*, 1952-53 (2)

MITCHELL, Curtis
Editor *Fantasy Fiction/Stories*, May-Nov 50 (2)

MOLESWORTH, Vol
Editor of various Australian reprint magazines

MONICELLI, Giorgio
Editor *I Romanzi di Urania*, Oct 52

MOSKOWITZ, Sam
Managing Editor *Science Fiction Plus*, Mar-Dec 53 (7)

NORTON, Alden H.
Editor-in-Chief at Popular: see editors GNAEDINGER and JAKOBSSEN

O'SULLIVAN, Jack

Editor *Planet Stories*, Mar 52-Sum 55 (19)
Editor *Tops in SF*, Spr 53 (1)

OSTERBAAN, N.

Editor *Planeet*, Jan 53 (1)

PAIGE, Evelyn

Assistant Editor *Galaxy SF*, Oct 51-Nov 53 (26)
Managing Editor *Galaxy SF*, Dec 53-Sep 56 (33)
Assistant Editor *Beyond*, Jul-Nov 53 (3)
Managing Editor *Beyond*, Jan 54-Jan 55 (7)

PALMER, Raymond A.

Editor *Amazing Stories*, Jun 38-Dec 49 (117)
Editor *Fantastic Adventures*, May 39-Dec 49 (90)
Editor *Imagination*, Oct-Nov 50 (2)
Editor *Other Worlds*, Nov 49-Oct 57 (46)
Editor *Science Stories*, Oct 53-Apr 54 (4)
Editor *Universe SF*, Dec 53-Mar 55 (8)
Editor *Mystic*, Nov 52-Jul 56 (16)

PARK, Marie A.

Associate Editor *Future SF*, Jun 54-Sep 56 (6)
Associate Editor *Science Fiction Stories*, Jan 55-May 60 (36)
Associate Editor *Science Fiction Quarterly*, Feb 55-Nov 56 (8)

PATERSON, Alistair

Editor *Vargo Statten SF Magazine*, Jan-Jul 54 (5)

PAYNE, Paul L.

Editor *Planet Stories*, Fal 46-Spr 50 (15)

PRATT, Dennis H.

Editor *Amazing (Strange) Adventures*, Sep 46-Feb 47 (2)
Editor *Futuristic Stories*, Oct-Dec 46 (2)

QUINN, James L.   Editor/Publisher *If*, Mar 52-Feb
                               59 (50)

RAINES, Theron   Editor *Startling Stories*, Win-Fal
                               55 (4)

REISS, Malcolm   General Manager/Editor *Planet
                               Stories*, Win 39-Sum 55 (71)
                               General Manager *2 Complete
                               Science Adventure Books*, Win
                               50-Spr 54 (11)
                               (Managing) Editor *Tops in SF*,
                               Spr-Fal 53 (2)

RENAULT, Maurice   Editor *Fiction*, Oct 53-Dec 65
                               (144)

ROWLES, Derrick   Editor *Authentic*, Feb-Jun 52 (5)

ST JOHN, Philip   See Lester DEL REY

SALTMAN, Jules   Editor *Orbit*, Sum 53-Nov 54 (5)

SEADOR, Dorothy B.   Associate Editor *Science Fiction
                               Stories*, Jan 55-May 60 (36)
                               Associate Editor *Science Fiction
                               Quarterly*, Feb 55-Nov 56 (8)
                               Associate Editor *Future SF*, Win
                               55-Apr 60 (21)

SHAFFER, Lila E.   Associate   Editor   *Amazing
                               Stories*, Oct 48-Feb 51 (29)
                               Managing   Editor   *Amazing
                               Stories*, Mar 51-Mar 53 (25)
                               Associate   Editor   *Fantastic
                               Adventures*, Oct 48-Feb 51 (29)
                               Managing   Editor   *Fantastic
                               Adventures*, Mar 51-Mar 53
                               (25)
                               Managing Editor *Fantastic*, Sum
                               52-Mar 53 (5)

SHAW, Larry T.   Associate Editor *If*, May 53-Mar
                               54 (6)
                               Editor *Infinity*, Nov 55-Nov 58
                               (20)

STATTEN, Vargo — See John Russell FEARN

STONE, Graham — Editor or Advisory Editor on many Australian reprint magazines (see also Vol MOLESWORTH)

SWAN, Gerald G. — Editor(?)/Publisher of many British reprint titles plus: *Space Fact & Fiction,* Mar-Oct 54 (8)

TARRANT, Catherine (Kay) — Assistant Editor *Astounding SF (Analog),* Mar 49-Feb 72 (276)

WHITEHORNE, Chester — Editor *Planet Stories,* Win 45-Sum 46 (3)
Editor *Vortex SF,* Sum-Fal 53 (2)
Editor *Science Fiction Digest,* Spr-Fal 54 (2)

WOLLHEIM, Donald A. — Editor *Avon Fantasy Reader,* Feb 47-Jan 52 (18)
Editor *Out of This World Adventures,* Jul-Dec 50 (2)
Editor *Avon SF Reader,* Spr 51-Win 52 (3)
Editor *10 Story Fantasy,* Spr 51 (1)

WULFF, Eve P. — Assistant Editor *If,* May 54-Apr 58 (31)

Note: Even though this volume deals solely with the period 1946-55, I have given the full dates where they overlap to avoid confusion.

(D) NOTE ON KEY COVER ARTISTS

The magazine's cover artist is all important because it is his work that first catches the public's eye. Yet unforgivably the artist is often, particularly in foreign reprint editions, not credited. The following list relates purely to English language magazines. A figure in italics is an estimate where I have endeavoured to identify the artist behind many of the uncredited covers. Since this is open to discussion I apologise for any errors in advance. The list is grouped under publishers.

CLARK PUBLISHING CO inc BELL PUBLICATIONS & PALMER PUBLICATIONS (*Other Worlds, Science Stories, Universe SF, Imagination* (2), *Mystic*)	Malcolm Smith	20	(38%)
	Robert Gibson Jones	10	(19%)
	Hannes Bok	6	(12%)
	Harold McCauley	6	(12%)
	Virgil Finlay	3	(6%)
	James B. Settles	2	
	Albert Nuetzell, J. Allen St John	1 each	
	Mel Hunter, Arnold Kohn	½ each	
	Unknown	2	
COLUMBIA PUBLICATIONS (*Dynamic SF, Future SF, SF Quarterly, Science Fiction*)	Milton Luros	22	(37%)
	Ed Emshwiller	9	(14%)
	Kelly Freas	9	(14%)
	Alex Schomburg	7	(11%)
	A. Leslie Ross	6	(9%)
	Leo Morey	3	
	Earle Bergey, P. Poulton,	2 each	
	R. Belarski, J. Coggins, V. Finlay	1 each	
	Unknown	1	
CROWNPOINT PUBLICATIONS (*Nebula*)	Robert Clothier	6	(37%)
	Ken McIntyre	3	(19%)
	James Rattigan	3	(19%)
	Alan Hunter	2	
	G. H. Irwin and James Stark	1 each	

FANTASY PUBLISHING CO INC *(Fantasy Book, Spaceway)*	Paul Blaisdell	5	(31%)
	Mel Hunter	3	(19%)
	Crozetti	2	
	Milo, N. Austen, J. Gaughan	1	each
	Unknown	1	
	No cover art	2	

FICTION HOUSE *(Planet Stories, Tops in SF, 2 Complete Science Adventure Books)*	Allen Anderson	38	(65%)
	Kelly Freas	16	(28%)
	Martin	3	
	Herman Vestal	1	

GALAXY PUBLISHING CORP *(Galaxy, Beyond)*	Ed Emshwiller	29	(39%)
	Mel Hunter	10	(13%)
	D. Sibley, R. Vider, R. M. Powers, J. Coggins	4	each
	J. Bunch, C. Bonestell, R. Arbib, F. Kirberger, R. Conrad, A. Krusz	2	each
	D. Stone, D. Hunter, A. Schomburg, S. Templar	1	each
	J. & B. Strimban, S. Willig	$\frac{2}{3}$	each
	Unknown	2	

| GERNSBACK PUBLICATIONS *(Science Fiction Plus)* | Frank R. Paul | 4 | (57%) |
| | Alex Schomburg | 3 | (43%) |

GREENLEAF PUBLISHING CO *(Imagination (from Feb '51), Imaginative Tales)*	Harold McCauley	23	(42%)
	Malcolm Smith	13	(24%)
	William E. Terry	13	(24%)
	Lloyd N. Rognan	3	
	R. Loehle	1	each
	H. Bok, W Hinton,		

HAMILTON & CO *(Authentic)*	John Richards† D.L.W. (?) Gordon C. Davies John Stewart D. A. Stowe, K. Woodward J. Kirby, Slater, Vann, J. Mortimer (†includes work possibly by Richards under the name Davis)	31 16 9 3 2 each 1 each	(46%) (24%) (13%)
HILLMAN PERIODICALS *(Worlds Beyond)*	H. R. van Dongen Paul Calle	2 1	(67%) (33%)
KING-SIZE PUBLICATIONS *(Fantastic Universe)*	Alex Schomburg Mel Hunter Kelly Freas Clarence Doore J. Richards, B. Lief, Emsh	10 6 5 2 1 each	(39%) (23%) (19%)
MERCURY PRESS/ FANTASY HOUSE *(F & SF)*	Chesley Bonestell Ed Emshwiller George Salter Nick Solovioff J. Coggins, F. Kirberger Mel Hunter, G. Gibbons B. Stone, A. Schomburg, S. Meltzoff, K. Freas Unknown	14 10 8 6 4 each 3 each 1 each 2	(24%) (17%) (14%) (10%)
NOVA & PENDULUM PUBLICATIONS *(New Worlds, Science Fantasy)*	Gerard Quinn Robert Clothier M. Bradshaw Reina W. Bull R. A. Wilkin, V. Caesari, Slack, Dennis, J. Kinnear, T. Maloney, Powell, Turner, N. Partridge	34 10 5 4 1 each	(56%) (16%) (8%)

POPULAR PUBLICATIONS *(A. Merritt's Fantasy, Famous Fantastic Mysteries, Super Science Stories, Fantastic Novels)*	Lawrence Stevens	51	(61%)
	Norman Saunders	12	(14%)
	Virgil Finlay	10	(12%)
	R. de Soto, H. van Dongen	3 each	
	Leo Morey	1	
	Unknown	3	

QUINN PUBLISHING CO *(If)*	Kenneth Fagg	12	(37%)
	A. Kurka, R. Joiner	3 each	
	B. Watkins, E. Valigursky, Mel Hunter, K. Freas,	2 each	
	M. Key, H. Jones, M. Reach, R. Swanson, C. Casler, H. Rossi	1 each	

| ROYAL PUBLICATIONS *(Infinity)* | R. Engle, Ed Emshwiller | 1 each | |

| SCION DISTRIBUTORS LTD/DRAGON PUBLICATIONS LTD *(Vargo Statten SF Magazine)* | John Richards | 19 | (100%) |

SPACE & FUTURE PUBLICATIONS *(Space SF, SF Adventures, Fantasy Fiction, Rocket Stories)*	Hannes Bok	5	(21%)
	H. R. van Dongen	4	(17%)
	A. Schomburg, E. K. Bergey	3 each	
	Ed Emshwiller, Civiletti, D. A. Ebel	2 each	
	Mel Hunter, C. Doore, P. Orban	1 each	

| SPECIFIC FICTION CORPORATION *(Vortex, SF Digest)* | Chester Martin | 3 | (75%) |
| | film strip | 1 | |

JOHN SPENCER & CO (*Futuristic Science Stories, Tales of Tomorrow, Worlds of Fantasy, Wonders of the Spaceways, Supernatural, Out of This World*)	G. Facey	23	(38%)
	Norman Light	14	(23%)
	Ray Theobald	12	(20%)
	Roland Turner	9	(15%)
	Unknown (? Gordon Davies)	3	

STADIUM PUBLISHING CORP (*Marvel Science Stories*)	Norman Saunders	3	(50%)
	Hannes Bok	2	(33%)
	Lee J. Ames	1	

STANDARD/BETTER PUBLICATIONS (*Startling Stories, Thrilling Wonder, Fantastic Story Mag, Space Stories, Wonder Story Annual*)	Earle K. Bergey	81	(58%)
	Alex Schomburg	19	(13%)
	Ed Emshwiller	17	(12%)
	Walter Popp	13	(9%)
	Jack Coggins	9	(6%)
	R. Belarski, A. Ebel, Ed Valigursky	1 each	

STREET & SMITH PUBLICATIONS (*Astounding SF*)	Hubert Rogers	25	(21%)
	H. R. van Dongen	17	(14%)
	Kelly Freas	17	(14%)
	William Timmins	13	(11%)
	Alejandro Canedo	10	(8%)
	Chesley Bonestell	8	(7%)
	Walt Miller	6	(5%)
	P. Orban, G. Pawelka	4 each	
	C. Schneeman, E. Emshwiller	2 each	
	S. Andre, G. Welker, Sniffen, Santry, Zboyan, E. Cartier, Brush, Pattee, G. Stine, A. R. Baer	1 each	
	Photographs	2	

WEIRD TALES INC (*Weird Tales*)	Matt Fox	10	(20%)
	Lee Brown Coye	7	(14%)
	Boris Dolgiv	5	(10%)
	Virgil Finlay	4 (1 reprint)	
	K. Freas, J. Arfstrom, W. H. Silvey	3 each	
	J. Eberle, J. Giunta,		

C. A. Kennedy,
B. Wayne   2 each
R. Clyne, A. Di Giannurio,
P. Kuhlhoff, M. Labonski,
E. Singer, A. Tilburne   1 each
M. Brundage, H. Delay
                                    1 reprint each

ZIFF-DAVIS		
(*Amazing, Fantastic,* *Fantastic Adventures*)		

Robert Gibson Jones	72	(36%)
Arnold Kohn	21	(11%)
Ed Valigursky	18½	(9%)
Walter Popp	10	(5%)
Harold McCauley	9	
Leo Ramon Summers	7	
Barye Phillips	5½	
Ed Swiatek	4½	
James B. Settles	4	
M. Smith, R. Naylor, Lawrence	3 each	
Julian S. Krupa	2½ each	
J. A. St John, J. Tillotson, M. Hunter, C. Doore, R. Castenir, V. Kramer, F. Novarro	2 each	
W. Parke, B. Hilbreth, J. Teason, R. Loehle, W. H. Jones, E. Blumenfeld, N. Saunders, R. Frank, H. Levey, G. Welker, Sussman, R. Frankenberg, R. M. Powers, W. T. Mars, R. Conrad, A. Marin, E. Schroeder, E. Barth, H. Sharp, W. Hinton, W. Slade	1 each	
Unknown	2	

Some collection! To save those of you who are wondering, from any unnecessary calculations, the following are the most prolific artists:

1	Earle K. Bergey	87
2	Robert Gibson Jones	82
3	Ed Emshwiller	71
4	Lawrence Stevens	54
5	Frank Kelly Freas	53
6	John Richards	50
7	Alex Schomburg	44
8	Harold McCauley	38
9	Allen Anderson	38
10	Malcolm Smith	36

Bibliography

Every effort has been made to consult original magazines and documents in the course of compiling this book, as well as standard reference works such as *Who's Who* and *Contemporary Authors*. The following have proved a valuable source of reference, and I hereby acknowledge their use and also recommend them for those readers interested in researching further:

BOOKS

Aldiss, Brian W. *Billion Year Spree* (Weidenfeld & Nicolson; London, 1973)

Aldiss, Brian W. and Harrison, Harry (editors). *Hell's Cartographers* (Weidenfeld & Nicolson; London, 1975)

Amis, Kingsley. *New Maps of Hell* (Four Square edition; London, 1963)

de Camp, L. Sprague. *Science-Fiction Handbook* (Hermitage House; New York, 1953)

Eshbach, Lloyd Arthur (editor). *Of Worlds Beyond* (Advent Publishers Inc; Chicago, 1971 edition)

Farmer, Philip José. *Doc Savage, His Apocalyptic Life* (Panther Books edition; St Albans, 1975)

Goulart, Ron. *An Informal History of the Pulp Magazine* (Ace Books; New York, 1973 edition)

Harbottle, Philip. *The Multi-Man* (published privately; Wallsend, 1968)

Jones, Robert Kenneth. *The Shudder Pulps* (Fax Collectors Editions; Oregon, 1975)

Moskowitz, Sam. *Explorers of the Infinite* (World Publishing Co; Cleveland, 1963)

Moskowitz, Sam. *Seekers of Tomorrow* (World Publishing Co; Cleveland, 1966)

Nolan, William F. (editor) *3 to the Highest Power* (Avon Books; New York, 1968)

Rogers, Alva. *A Requiem for Astounding* (Advent Publishers Inc; Chicago, 1973 edition)

Tuck, Donald H. *The Encyclopedia of Science Fiction and Fantasy: Volume 1* (Advent Publishers Inc; Chicago, 1974 edition)

Versins, Pierre. *Encyclopédie de L'Utopie des Voyages Extraordinaires et de la Science Fiction* (Editions L'Age d'Homme; Lausanne, 1972)

Warner, Harry, Jr. *All Our Yesterdays* (Advent Publishers Inc; Chicago, 1969)

INDICES

Cockcroft, T. G. L. *Index to the Weird Fiction Magazines* (published privately; New Zealand, 1964)

Cole, W. R. *A Checklist of Science Fiction Anthologies* (privately published; New York, 1964)

Day, Brad M. *The Complete Checklist of Science Fiction Magazines* (Wehman Bros; New York, 1961)

Day, Donald B. *Index to the Science Fiction Magazines: 1926–1950* (Perri Press; Portland, 1952)

Evans, Bill and Pavlat, Bob. *Fanzine Index* (reprinted by H. P. Piser; New York, 1965)

Metcalf, Norm. *The Index of Science Fiction Magazines: 1951–1965* (J. Ben Stark; California, 1968)

Strauss, Erwin S. *Index to the S-F Magazines: 1951–1965* (MIT SF Society; Massachusetts, 1966)

MAGAZINE ARTICLES

Amazing Stories
June 1947. Special Shaver issue with articles by Richard Shaver, Ray Palmer and others

November 1970. 'Dianetics: The Evolution of a Science' by Barry N. Malzberg

March 1971. 'What is Scientology' by Rev. Robert H. Thomas

Fantastic Stories

August 1975. 'El-Ron of the City of Brass' by L. Sprague de Camp

The Magazine of Fantasy & Science Fiction

September 1962. Special Theodore Sturgeon issue with articles by James Blish, Judith Merril and Sam Moskowitz

May 1963. Special Ray Bradbury issue with articles by William F. Nolan

April 1971. Special Poul Anderson issue with articles by James Blish and Gordon R. Dickson

April 1972. Special James Blish issue with articles by Lester Del Rey, Robert A. W. Lowndes and Mark Owings

Other Worlds

June 1952. Special 'Editors' issue with articles, 'The Story of Science-Fiction's Editors' by James V. Taurasi and 'An Open Letter to Paul Fairman' by Raymond Palmer

Vision of Tomorrow

July 1970. 'Topless in Utopia' by Walter Gillings

August 1970. 'Pages in Waiting' by Walter Gillings

September 1970. 'The Birth of New Worlds' by John Carnell